WOMAN'S WEEK[LY]
TREASURY
FOR 1983

We hope that this first edition of Woman's Weekly in book form will keep you entertained and interested throughout the year. With that in mind, we have divided the contents into four sections — Spring, Summer, Autumn and Winter — and in these sections you will find romantic encounters in our short stories, beauty and fashion hints, gardening and travel advice, useful cookery, craft ideas and classic knitting. And many more of the features that you enjoy week by week in your favourite magazine. Do turn the pages and discover the delights of this little book for yourself.

SBN 85037-527-4

' IPC Magazines Ltd., 1982

£1·95

WOMAN'S WEEKLY
TREASURY

CONTENTS

COLOUR SECTIONS

SPRING BEGINS

And in green underwood and cover
Blossom by blossom the spring begins.

A. C. Swinburne

The sweet wind caressing
My cheek like a blessing
Murmurs a message so clear!
The trees in their sprouting,
All Nature is shouting
The words I am longing to hear!
And the birds in their flying
Come joyously crying,
"Oh glory, the Springtime is near!"

Miriam Eker

6

Colour photo on page 20

Quilted for Comfort

Revive the age-old craft of quilting to stitch soft furnishings for a bedroom.

Our headboard and quilt are designed to fit a single divan 190 cm long, 91 cm wide and 47 cm high (75 x 36 x 18½ in.). Adjust the measurements to fit your bed, if necessary.

The headboard

You will need: *For the board –* a piece of 12 mm (½ in.) chipboard 9700 x 740 mm (38 x 29 in.); two pieces of 76 x 25 mm (3 x 1 in.) prepared softwood 510 mm (20 in.) long; four 32 mm (1¼ in.) No. 8 countersunk screws; wood adhesive; metric graph paper. *For the cover –* 80 cm (⅞ yd.) of patterned furnishing fabric 122 cm (48 in.) wide and the same amount of unbleached calico 180 cm (72 in.) wide; 1.60 m (1¾ yd.) of heavyweight Terylene wadding.

To make the headboard: To scale up the pattern, copy it square by square on to a large sheet of metric graph paper (join pieces if necessary). Cut out pattern. Tape it to piece of chipboard and draw round the outline with a pencil. Cut the headboard to shape using a coping saw or powered jigsaw.

Prepare the two supports to length and form a slot in each one (see diagram). Glue, then screw them to the back of the board, with slots spaced to match fixing bolts on bed.

To make the cover: Pin headboard pattern to right side of furnishing fabric. If your fabric has large motifs, centre one of them in the middle of the cover as we have done. Cut out, adding 5 cm (2 in.) all round the edge, then cut two pieces of wadding to the same size. Place fabric, right side up, on top of wadding,

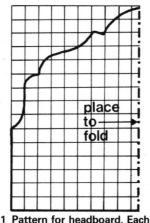

1 **Pattern for headboard. Each square = 5 cm. Place to fold to complete other half.**

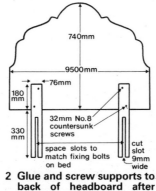

2 **Glue and screw supports to back of headboard after cutting it to shape.**

matching edges. Pin, then tack layers firmly together, round edge and across fabric.

Machine round the prominent motifs in the design to quilt, keeping the lines as simple as possible. Centre pattern on quilted fabric, pin, then trim fabric to within 3 cm (1¼ in.) of edge of pattern. Remove pattern. Use pattern to cut a backing piece from calico, adding 3 cm (1¼ in.) all

round for seams.

Pin quilted fabric and calico together, right sides facing. Tack, then machine round top and side edges taking a 2.5 cm (1 in.) seam. Trim seams and clip curves. Trim wadding on lower edge by 3 cm (1¼ in.), then turn up and machine a double hem all round lower edge. Turn cover right side out and slip over bedhead.

The quilt

You will need: (for a bed the size of ours) 5.60 m (6⅛ yd.) of furnishing fabric 122 cm (48 in.) wide (plus an allowance for matching the pattern); 5.60 m (6⅛ yd.) of heavyweight Terylene wadding and the same amount of backing fabric 122 cm (48 in.) wide — curtain lining is ideal.

To make the quilt: Cut two 278 cm (109 in.) lengths of furnishing fabric. Cut one in half lengthways. Tack, then machine one piece down each side of the main piece, matching the pattern. Trim fabric to 196 cm (77 in.) wide, an equal amount off each side.

Cut two pieces of wadding each 278 cm (109 in.) long. Lay them side by side and join by tacking together loosely with zig-zag stitches down the length. Tack fabric to wadding and quilt as for bedhead cover. Trim quilted fabric to 271 x 189 cm (106 x 74½ in.)

Join pieces of backing fabric as for main fabric to make a piece the same size. Place quilted fabric and backing together, right sides facing, and taking 2 cm (¾ in.) seams, machine round three sides and four corners. Trim seams, clip corners, turn through to right side and slipstitch short edge.

LALLA

I wasn't like Lalla. I wanted to make friends,
and it would be nice to know the Royston boys. But
Lalla was different, even then, in that far
off green spring; she was a figure of some
mystery and special magic . . .

THERE was a Before and an After. Before was before our father died, when we lived in London, in a tall narrow house with a little garden at the back. When we went on family ski-ing holidays every winter and attended suitable — and probably very expensive — day schools.

Our father was a big man, outgoing and immensely active. We thought he was immortal, but then most children think that about their father. The worst thing was that Mother thought he was immortal too, and when he died, keeling over on the pavement between the insurance offices where he worked, and the company car into which he was just about to climb, there followed a period of ghastly limbo. Bereft, uncertain, lost, none of us knew what to do next. But after the funeral and a little talk with the family lawyer, Mother quietly pulled herself together and told us.

At first we were horrified. "Leave London? Leave school?" Lalla could not believe it. "But I'm starting 'O' levels next year."

"There are other schools," Mother told her.

"And what about Jane's music lessons?"

"We'll find another teacher."

"I don't mind about leaving school," said Barney. "I don't much like my school anyway."

Mother gave him a smile, but Lalla persisted in her inquisition. "But where are we going to *live*?"

"We're going to Cornwall."

AND so it was After. Mother sold the lease of the London house and a removals firm came and packed up all the furniture and we travelled, each silently thoughtful, by car to Cornwall. It was spring, and because Mother had not realised how long the journey would take, it was dark by the time we found the village and, finally, the house. It stood just inside a pair of large gates, backed by tall trees. When we got out of the car, stiff and tired, we could smell the sea and feel the cold wind.

"There's a light in the window," observed Lalla.

"That'll be Mrs. Bristow," said Mother, and I knew she was making a big effort to keep her voice cheerful. She went up the little path and knocked at the door, and then, perhaps realising it was ludicrous to be knocking at her own door, opened it. We saw someone coming down the narrow hallway towards us — a fat and bustling lady with grey hair and a hectically flowered pinafore.

"Well, my dear life," she said, "what a journey you must have had. I'm all ready for you. There's a kettle on the hob and a pie in the oven."

The house was tiny compared to the one we had left in London, but we all had rooms to ourselves, as well as an attic for the dolls' house, the books, bricks, model cars and paint-boxes we had refused to abandon, and a ramshackle shed alongside the garage where we could keep our bicycles. The garden was even smaller than the London garden, but this didn't matter because now we were living in the country and there were no boundaries to our new territory.

We explored, finding a wooded lane which led down to a huge inland estuary where it was possible to fish for flounder from the old sea wall. In the other direction, a sandy right-of-way led past the church and over the golf links and the dunes to another beach — a wide and empty shore where the ebb tide took the ocean out half a mile or more.

The Roystons, father, mother and two sons, lived in the big house and were our landlords. We hadn't seen them yet, though Mother had walked, in some trepidation, up the drive to make the acquaintance of Mrs. Royston, and to thank her for letting us have the house. But Mrs. Royston hadn't been in, and poor Mother had had to walk all the way down the drive again with nothing accomplished.

Continued overleaf

"How old are the Royston boys?" Barney asked Mrs. Bristow.

"I suppose David's thirteen and Paul's about eleven." She looked at us. "I don't know how old you lot are."

"I'm seven," said Barney, "and Jane's twelve and Lalla's fourteen."

"Well," said Mrs. Bristow. "That's nice. Fit in nicely, you would."

"They're far too young for me," said Lalla. "Anyway, I've seen them. I was hanging out the washing for Mother and they came down the drive and out of the gate on their bicycles. They didn't even look my way."

"Come now," said Mrs. Bristow, "they're probably shy as you are."

"We don't particularly want to know them," said Lalla.

"But ..." I started, and then stopped. I wasn't like Lalla. I wanted to make friends. It would be nice to know the Royston boys. They had a tennis court; I had caught a glimpse of it through the trees. I wouldn't mind being asked to play tennis.

But for Lalla, of course, it was different. Fourteen was a funny age, neither one thing nor the other. And as for the way that Lalla looked! Sometimes I thought that if I didn't love her, and she wasn't my sister, I should hate her for her long, cloudy brown hair, the tilt of her nose, the amazing blue of her eyes, the curve of her pale mouth. During the last six months she seemed to have grown six inches.

I was short and square and my hair was too curly and horribly tangly. The awful bit was, I couldn't remember Lalla ever looking the way I looked, which made it fairly unlikely that I should end up looking like her.

A FEW days later Mother came back from shopping in the village to say that she had met Mrs. Royston in the grocer's and we had all been asked for tea.

Lalla said, "I don't want to go."

"Why not?" asked Mother.

"They're just little boys. Let Jane and Barney go."

"It's just for tea," pleaded Mother.

She looked so anxious that Lalla gave in. She shrugged and sighed, her face closed in resignation.

We went, and it was a failure. The boys didn't want to meet us any more than Lalla wanted to meet them. Lalla was at her coolest, her most remote. I knocked over my teacup, and Barney, who usually

---

A proverb is a short sentence based on long experience.

Cervantes

---

chatted to everybody, was silenced by the superiority of his hosts. When tea was over Lalla stayed with the grown-ups, but Barney and I were sent off with the boys.

"Show Jane and Barney your tree-house," Mrs. Royston told them as we trailed out of the door.

They took us out into the garden and showed us the tree-house. It was a marvellous piece of construction, strong and roomy. Barney's face was filled with longing. "Who built it?" he asked.

"Our cousin Godfrey. He's eighteen. He can build anything. It's our club, and you're not members."

They whispered together and went off, leaving us standing beneath the forbidden tree-house.

W HEN the summer holidays came, Mother appeared to have forgotten about our social debt to the Royston boys and we were careful not to remind her. So their names were never raised, and we never saw them except at a distance, cycling off to the village or down to the beach. Sometimes on Sunday afternoons they had guests and played tennis on their court. I longed to be included, but Lalla, deep in a book, behaved as though the Roystons didn't exist. Barney had taken up gardening, and, with his usual single-mindedness, was concentrating on digging himself a vegetable patch. He said he was going to sell lettuces, and Mother said that maybe he was the one who was going to make our fortune.

It was a hot summer, made for swimming. Lalla had grown out of her old swimsuit, so Mother made her a cotton bikini out of scraps. It was pale blue, just right for her tan and her long, pale hair. She looked beautiful in it, and I longed to look just like her. We went to the beach most days, and often saw the Royston boys there. But the beach was so vast that there was no necessity for social contact, and we all avoided each other.

Until one Sunday. The tide came in during the afternoon that day, and Mother packed us a picnic so we could set off after lunch. When we got to the beach, Lalla said she was going to swim right away, but Barney and I decided we would wait. We took our spades and went down to where the outgoing tide had left shallow pools in the sand. There we started the construction of a large and complicated harbour. Absorbed in our task, we lost track of time, and never noticed the stranger approaching. Suddenly a long shadow fell across the sparkling water.

I looked up, shading my eyes against the sun. He said "Hello", and squatted down to our level.

"Who are you?" I asked.

"I'm Godfrey Howard, the Roystons' cousin. I'm staying with them."

Barney suddenly found his tongue. "Did you build the tree-house?"

"That's right."

"How *did* you do it?"

Godfrey began to tell him. I listened and wondered how any person apparently so nice could have anything to do with those hateful Royston boys. It wasn't that he was particularly good-looking. His hair was mousey, his nose too big and he wore spectacles. He wasn't even very tall. But there was something warm and friendly about his deep voice and his smile.

"Did you go up and look at it?"

Barney went back to his digging. Godfrey looked at me. I said, "They wouldn't let us. They said it was a club. They didn't like us."

"They think you don't like them. They think you come from London and that you're very grand."

This was astonishing. "Grand? *Us*?" I said indignantly. "We never even pretended to be grand." And then I remembered Lalla's coolness, her pale, unsmiling lips. "I mean — Lalla's older – it's different for her." His silence at this was encouraging. "I wanted to make friends," I admitted.

He was sympathetic. "It's difficult sometimes. People are shy." All at once he stopped, and looked over my shoulder. I turned to see what had caught his attention, and saw Lalla coming towards us across the sand. Her hair lay like wet silk over her shoulders, and she had knotted her red towel around her hips like a sarong. As she approached, Godfrey stood up. I said, introducing them the way Mother introduced people, "This is Lalla."

"Hello, Lalla," said Godfrey.

"He's the Roystons' cousin," I went on quickly. "He's staying with them."

"Hello," said Lalla.

Godfrey said, "David and Paul are wanting to play cricket. It's not much good playing cricket with just three people and I wondered if you'd come and join us?"

'Lalla won't want to play cricket,' I told myself. 'She'll snub him and then we'll never be asked again.'

But she didn't snub him. She said, uncertainly, "I don't think I'm much good at cricket."

"But you could always try?"

"Yes." She began to smile. "I suppose I could always try."

A ND so we all finally got together. We played a strange form of beach cricket invented by Godfrey, which involved much lashing out at the ball and hysterical running. When we were too hot to play any longer, we swam. The Roystons had a couple of wooden surf boards and they let us have turns, riding in on our stomachs on the long, warm breakers of the flood tide. By five o'clock we were ready for tea, and we collected our various baskets and haversacks and sat around in a circle on the sand. Other people's picnics are always much nicer than one's own, so we ate the Royston sandwiches and chocolate biscuits, and they ate mother's scones with loganberry jam in the middle.

We had a last swim before the tide turned, and then gathered up our belongings and walked slowly home together. Barney and the two Roystons led the way, planning the next day's activities, and I walked with Godfrey and Lalla. But gradually, in the natural manner of events, they fell behind me. Plodding up and over the springy turf of the golf course, I listened to their voices.

"Do you like living here?"

"It's different from London."

"That's where you lived before?"

"Yes, but my father died and we couldn't afford to live there any more."

"I'm sorry, I didn't know. Of course, I envy your living here. I'd rather be at Carwheal than anywhere else in the world."

"Where do you live?"

"In Bristol."

"Are you at school there?"

"I've finished with school. I'm starting college in September. I'm going to be a vet."

"A vet?" Lalla considered this. "I've never met a vet before."

He laughed. "You haven't actually met one yet."

I smiled to myself in satisfaction. They sounded like two grown-ups talking. Perhaps a grown-up friend of her own was all that Lalla had needed. I had a feeling that we had crossed another watershed. After today, things would be different.

Continued overleaf

THE Roystons were now our friends. Our relieved mothers — for Mrs. Royston, faced with our unrelenting enmity, had been just as concerned and conscience-stricken as Mother — took advantage of the truce, and after that Sunday we were never out of each other's houses. Through the good offices of the Roystons, our social life widened, and Mother found herself driving us all over the county to attend various beach picnics, barbecues, sailing parties and teenage dances. By the end of the summer we had been accepted. We had dug ourselves in. Carwheal was home. And Lalla grew up.

She and Godfrey wrote to each other. I knew this because I would see his letters to her lying on the table in the hall. She would take them upstairs to read them in secret in her room, and we were all too great respecters of privacy ever to mention them. When he came to Carwheal, which he did every holiday, to stay with the Roystons, he was always around first thing in the morning on the first day. He said it was to see us all, but we knew it was Lalla he had come to see.

He now owned a battered second-hand car. A lesser man might have scooped Lalla up and taken her off on her own, but Godfrey was far too kind, and he would drive for miles, to distant coves and hill-tops, with the whole lot of us packed into his long-suffering car, and the boot filled with food and towels and snorkels and other assorted clobber.

But he was only human, and often they would drift off on their own, and walk away from us. We would watch their progress and let them go, knowing that in an hour or two they would be back — Lalla with a bunch of wild flowers or some shells in her hand, Godfrey sunburned and tousled — both of them smiling and content in a way that we found reassuring and yet did not wholly understand.

L ALLA had always been such a certain person, so positive, so unveering from a chosen course, that we were all taken by surprise by her vacillating indecision as to what she was going to do with her life. She was nearly eighteen, with her final exams over and her future spread before her like a new country observed from the peak of some painfully climbed hill.

Mother wanted her to go to university.

"Isn't it rather a waste of time if I don't know what I'm going to do at the end of it? How can I decide now what I'm going to do with the rest of my life? It's inhuman. Impossible."

"But darling, what do you want to do?"

"I don't know. Travel, I suppose. Of course, I could be really original and take a typing course."

"It might at least give you time to think things over."

This conversation took place at breakfast. It might have continued forever, reaching no satisfactory conclusion, but the post arrived as we sat there over our empty coffee cups. There was the usual dull bundle of envelopes, but, as well, a large square envelope for Lalla. She opened it idly, read the card inside and made a face. "Goodness, how grand, a proper invitation to a proper dance."

"How nice," said Mother, trying to decipher the butcher's bill. "Who from?"

"Mrs. Menheniot," said Lalla.

We were all instantly agog, grabbing at the invitation in order to gloat over it. We had once been to lunch with Mrs. Menheniot, who lived with Mr. Menheniot and a tribe of junior Menheniots in a beautiful house on the Fal. For some unspecified reason they were very rich, and their house was vast and white with a pillared portico and green lawns which sloped down to the tidal inlets of the river.

"Are you going to go?" I asked.

Lalla shrugged. "I don't know."

"It's in August. Perhaps Godfrey will be here and you can go with him."

"He's not coming down this summer. He has to earn money to pay his way through college."

She would not make up her mind whether or not she would go to Mrs. Menheniot's party, and probably never would have come to any decision if it had not been for the fact that, before very long, I had been invited too. I was really too young, as Mrs. Menheniot's booming voice pointed out over the telephone when she rang Mother, but they were short of girls and it would be a blessing if I could be there to swell the numbers. When Lalla knew that I had been asked as well, she said of course we would go. She had passed her driving test and we would borrow Mother's car.

We were then faced with the problem of what we should wear, as Mother could not begin to afford to buy us the sort of evening dresses we wanted. In the end she sent away to Liberty's for yards of material, and she made them for us, beautifully, on her sewing machine. Lalla's was pale blue lawn and in it she looked like a goddess — Diana the Huntress perhaps. Mine was a sort of tawny-gold and I looked quite presentable in it, but of course not a patch on Lalla.

When the night of the dance came, we put on our dresses and set off together in Mother's Mini, giggling slightly with nerves. But when we reached the Menheniots' house, we stopped giggling because the whole affair was so grand as to be awesome. There were floodlights and car parks and hundreds of sophisticated-looking people all making their way towards the front door.

Indoors, we stood at the foot of the crowded staircase and I was filled with panic. We knew nobody. There was not a single familiar face. Lalla whisked a couple of glasses of champagne from a passing tray and gave me one, I took a sip, and at that very moment a voice rang out above the hubbub. "Lalla!" A girl was coming down the stairs, a dark girl in a strapless satin dress that had very obviously not been made on her mother's sewing machine.

Lalla looked up. "Rosemary!"

She was Rosemary Sutton from London. She and Lalla had been at school together in the old days. They fell into each other's arms and embraced as though this was all either of them had been waiting for. "What are you doing? I never thought I'd see you here. How marvellous. Come and meet Allan. You remember my brother Allan, don't you? Oh, this is exciting."

Allan was so good-looking as to be almost unreal. Fair as his sister was dark, impeccably turned out. Lalla was tall but he was taller. He looked down at her, and his rather wooden features were filled with both surprise and obvious pleasure. He said, "But of course I remember." He smiled and laid down his glass. "How could I forget? Come and dance."

I SCARCELY saw her again all evening. He took her away from me and I was bereft, as though I had lost my sister for ever. At one point I was rescued by Mrs. Menheniot herself, who dragooned some young man into taking me to supper, but after supper even he melted away. I found an empty sofa in a deserted sitting-out room, and collapsed into it. It was half-past-twelve and I longed for my bed. I wondered what people would think if I put up my feet and had a little snooze.

Somebody came into the room, and then withdrew again. I looked up and saw his retreating back view. I said, "Godfrey." He turned back. I got up off the sofa, back on to my aching feet.

"What are you doing here? Lalla said you were working."

"I am, but I wanted to come. I drove down from Bristol. That's why I'm so late." I knew why he had wanted to come. To see Lalla. "I didn't expect to see you."

"They were short of girls, so I got included."

We gazed glumly at each other, and my heart felt very heavy. Godfrey's dinner jacket looked as though he had borrowed it from some larger person, and his bow tie was crooked. I said, "I think Lalla's dancing."

"Why don't you come and dance with me, and we'll see."

I thought this a rotten idea, but didn't like to say so. Together we made our way towards the ballroom. The ceiling lights had been turned off and the disco lights now flashed red and green and blue across the smoky darkness. Music thumped and rocked an assault on our ears, and the floor seemed to be filled with an unidentifiable confusion of people, of flying hair and arms and legs. Godfrey and I joined in at the edge, but I could tell that his heart wasn't in it. I wished that he had never come. I prayed that he would not find Lalla.

But of course, he saw her, because it was impossible not to. It was impossible to miss Allan Sutton as well. They were both so tall, so beautiful. Godfrey's face seemed to close up.

"Who's she with?" he asked.

"Allan Sutton. He and his sister have come down from London. Lalla used to know them."

I couldn't say any more. I couldn't tell Godfrey to go and claim her for himself. I wasn't even certain by then what sort of a reception she would have given him. And anyway, as we watched them, Allan stopped dancing and put his arm around Lalla, drawing her towards him, whispering something into her ear. She slipped her hand into his, and they moved away towards the open french window. The next moment they were lost to view, swallowed into the darkness of the garden beyond.

At four o'clock in the morning Lalla and I drove home in silence. We were not giggling now. I wondered sadly if we would ever giggle together again. I ached with exhaustion and I was out of sympathy with her. Godfrey had never even spoken to her. Soon after our dance he had said goodbye and disappeared, presumably to make the long, lonely journey back to Bristol.

She, on the other hand, had an aura of happiness about her that was almost tangible. I glanced at her and saw her peaceful, smiling profile. It was hard to think of anything to say.

It was Lalla who finally broke the silence. "I know what I'm going to do. I mean, I know what I'm going to do with my life. I'm going back to London. Rosemary says I can live with her. I'll take a secretarial course or something, then get a job."

"Mother will be disappointed."

"She'll understand. It's what I've always wanted. We're buried down here. And there's another thing; I'm tired of being poor. I'm tired of home-made dresses and never having a new car. We've always talked about making our fortunes, and as I'm the eldest I might as well make a start. If I don't do it now, I never will."

I said, "Godfrey was there this evening."

"Godfrey?"

"He drove down from Bristol."

Continued overleaf

She did not say anything and I was angry. I wanted to hurt her and make her feel as bad as I felt. "He came because he wanted to see you. But you didn't even notice him."

"You can scarcely blame me," said Lalla, "for that."

AND so she went back to London, lived with Rosemary, and took a secretarial course, just as she said she would. Later, she got a job on the editorial staff of a fashionable magazine, but it was not long before one of the photographers spied her potential, seduced her from her typewriter, and started taking pictures of her. Soon her lovely face smiled at us from the cover of the magazine.

"How does it feel to have a famous daughter?" people asked Mother, but she never quite accepted Lalla's success, just as she never quite accepted Allan Sutton. Allan's devotion to Lalla had proved unswerving and he was her constant companion.

"Let's hope he doesn't marry her," said Barney, but of course eventually, inevitably, they decided to do just that. "We're engaged!" Lalla rang up from London to tell us. Her voice sounded, unnervingly, as though she was calling from the next room.

"Darling!" said Mother, faintly.

"Oh, do be pleased. Please be pleased. I'm so happy and I couldn't bear it if you weren't happy, too."

So of course Mother said that she was pleased, but the truth was that none of us really liked Allan very much. He was — well — spoilt. He was conceited. He was too rich. I said as much to Mother, but Mother was loyal to Lalla. She said, "*Things* mean a lot to Lalla. I think they always have. I mean, possessions and security. And perhaps someone who truly loves her."

I said, "Godfrey truly loved her."

"But that was when they were young. And perhaps Godfrey couldn't give her love."

"He could make her laugh. Allan never makes her laugh."

"Perhaps," said Mother sadly, "she's grown out of laughter."

AND then it was Easter. We hadn't heard from Lalla for a bit, and didn't expect her to come to Carwheal for the spring holiday. But she rang up, out of the blue, and said that she hadn't been well and was taking a couple of weeks off. Mother was delighted, of course, but concerned about her health.

By now we were all more or less grown-up. David was studying to be a doctor, and Paul had a job on the local newspaper. I had achieved a place at the Guildhall School of Music, and Barney was no longer a little boy but a gangling teenager with an insatiable appetite. Still, however, we gathered for the holidays, and that Easter Godfrey abandoned his sick dogs and ailing cows to the ministrations of his partner and joined us.

It was lovely weather, almost as warm as summer. The sort of weather that makes one feel young again — a child. There was scented thyme on the golf links and the cliff walks were starred with primroses and wild violets. In the Roystons' garden the daffodils blew in the long grass beneath the tree-house, and Mrs. Royston put up the tennis net and swept the cobwebs out of the summer house.

It was during one of these sessions that Godfrey and I talked about Lalla. We were in the summer house together, sitting out while the others played a set.

"Tell me about Lalla."

"She's engaged."

"I know. I saw it in the paper." I could think of nothing to say. "Do you like him, Allan Sutton, I mean."

I said "Yes", but I was never much good at lying.

Godfrey turned his head and looked at me. He was wearing old jeans and a white shirt, and I thought that he had grown older in a subtle way. He was more sure of himself, and somehow more attractive.

He said, "That night of the Menheniots' dance, I was going to ask her to marry me."

"Oh, Godfrey."

"I hadn't even finished my training, but I thought perhaps we'd manage. And when I saw her, I knew that I had lost her. I'd left it too late."

ON the day that Lalla was due to arrive, I took Mother's old car into the neighbouring town to do some shopping. When the time came to return home, the engine refused to start. After struggling for bit, I walked to the nearest garage and persuaded a kindly, oily man to come and help me. But he told me that it was hopeless.

We walked back to the garage and I telephoned home. But it wasn't Mother who answered the call, t was Godfrey.

I explained what had happened. "Lalla's train is due at the junction in about half-an-hour and we said someone would meet her."

There was a momentary hesitation, then Godfrey said, "I'll go. I'll take my car."

When I finally reached home, exhausted from carrying the laden grocery bags from the bus stop, Godfrey's car was nowhere to be seen.

A short time later the telephone rang. But it wasn't Lalla, explaining where they were, it was a call from London and it was Allan Sutton.

"I have to speak to Lalla."

His voice sounded frantic. I said cautiously, "Is anything wrong?"

"She's broken off our engagement. I got back from the office and found a letter from her and my ring. She said she was coming home. She doesn't want to get married."

I found it in my heart to be very sorry for him. "But Allan, you must have had *some* idea."

"None. Absolutely none. It's just a bolt from the blue. I know she's been a bit off-colour lately, but I thought she was just tired."

"She must have her reasons, Allan," I told him, as gently as I could.

"Talk to her, Jane. Try to make her see sense."

He rang off at last. I put the receiver back on the hook and stood for a moment, gathering my wits about me and assessing this new and startling turn of events. I found myself caught up in a tangle of

---

If you have a contented mind, you have enough to enjoy life with.

Plautus

---

conflicting emotions. Enormous sympathy for Allan; a reluctant admiration for Lalla who had had the courage to take this shattering decision; but, as well, a sort of rising excitement.

Godfrey. Godfrey and Lalla. Where were they? I knew then that I could not face Mother and Barney before I had found out what was going on. Quietly, I opened the door and went out of the house, through the gates, down the lane. As soon as I turned the corner at the end of the lane, I saw Godfrey's car parked on the patch of grass outside the church.

It was a marvellously warm, benign sort of evening. I took the path that led past the church and towards the beach. Before I had gone very far, I saw them, walking up over the golf links towards me. The wind blew Lalla's hair over her face. She was wearing her London high-heeled boots so was taller than Godfrey. They should have appeared ill-assorted, but there was something about them that was totally right. They were a couple, holding hands, walking up from the beach as they had walked innumerable times, together.

I stopped, suddenly reluctant to disturb their intimacy. But Lalla had seen me. She waved, and then let go of Godfrey's hand and began to run towards me, her arms flailing like windmills. "Jane!" I had never seen her so exuberant. "Oh, Jane." I ran to meet her. We hugged each other, and for some stupid reason my eyes were full of tears.

"Oh, darling Jane . . ."

"I had to come and find you."

"Did you wonder where we were? We went for a walk. I had to talk to Godfrey. He was the one person I could talk to."

"Lalla, Allan's been on the phone."

"I had to do it. It was all a ghastly mistake."

"But you found out in time. That's all that matters."

"I thought I was going after what I wanted. I thought I had what I wanted, and then I found out that I didn't want it at all. Oh, I've missed you all so much. There wasn't anybody I could talk to."

Over her shoulder I saw Godfrey coming, tranquilly, to join us. I let go of Lalla and went to give him a kiss. I didn't know what they had been discussing as they paced the lonely beach, and I knew that I never would. But still, I had the feeling that the outcome could be nothing but good for all of us.

I said, "We must go back. Mother and Barney don't know about anything. They'll be thinking that I've dissolved into thin air, as well as the pair of you."

"In that case," said Godfrey, and he took Lalla's hand in his own once more, "perhaps we'd better go and tell them."

And so we walked home; the three of us. In the warm evening, in the sunshine, in the fresh wind.

THE END

Rosamunde Pilcher, 1982

The Holiday Gourmet

**Eating and drinking away from home
is all part of the holiday fun**

FRESH pawpaw and mangoes for breakfast beside the gentle Caribbean that laps the western shores of Barbados ... a high summer lunch of the spinach and runny egg-filled triangular pastries called briks and a succulent couscous in a Tunisian desert oasis ... moules marinières and baby turbot in an inspired light sauce in an unpretentious find of a restaurant in the back streets of Boulogne ... a surfeit of lampreys somewhere in the heart of the Bordeaux country ... sheep's eyes in one of Morocco's Imperial Cities, cods' tongues in Trondheim, wild boar in the mountains of Sardinia, flying fish in the West Indies ... such culinary experiences are certainly part of the stuff that holiday memories are made on.

Eating and drinking away from home can be a source of enormous pleasure as well as a physical necessity. But in order to ensure maximum pleasure combined with maximum value for money — and maximum prospects of holiday health, provided you use commonsense over such things as drinking-water in places of obviously dubious hygiene, unwashed fruit and salads and dust-covered offerings from roadside purveyors — the best advice you can take is to live as much as possible on the freshest of the local produce.

Every region of every country has its specialities and these are the goodies to look out for. Think of superb seafood and salt meadow lamb in Brittany; fresh sardines, simply grilled over charcoal and served with generous quarters of lemon and hunks of crusty bread on the Algarve coast of Portugal; giant prawns cooked with garlic and herbs to delight visitors to Spain who order *gambas a la plancha;* roast sucking-pig in Majorca; scampi in its home town of Venice; fresh cod, halibut, sea-trout and ptarmigan in Norway as alternatives to the special temptation of the famous Cold Table; the fun of a fondue in Switzerland, with time-honoured forfeits to be paid by those rash enough to let a piece of steak or bread drop off its long-handled fork into the pot; swordfish steaks in Malta or Turkey or Madeira; oak-smoked kippers on the Isle of Man; giant T-bone steaks in Texas. All will do you a lot more good than the local attempt at 'English' food or the proudly advertised 'Tea like Mother makes'.

Seek out the places where you can see the local working community or families happily ensconced — armed, if in a country whose language is totally unfamiliar, with a food and drink dictionary. The food in such places i likely to be authentic, typical of the best of th region and, because local produce is used in preference to ingredients imported to cater fo an 'international' menu, more realisticall priced.

The national drinks of a country, similarly are often a better bargain than any importe liquors — and often, indeed, than coffees, tea or soft drinks. So don't always decline the ouz or the jug of local vino in favour of some mor familiar refreshment, thinking that you ar being economical. Quite possibly you are not!

Cafés and bars in the immediate vicinity of al tourist high-spots are inevitably more expensiv than those tucked away in the back streets. Bu the sheer pleasure of sitting in such famou settings as St. Mark's Square in Venice, th Champs-Elysées, the Via Veneto in Rome o Cannes' Croisette is worth every extra penny.

An agreeable ambience can be very much par of the pleasure of eating and drinking and certai places in the world can be guaranteed to provid that elusive quality which heightens the sense and makes the occasion something special, lon to linger in the memory. Florian's, the red plus and mahogany café in St. Mark's Square whic has been a favourite meeting-place since the 18t century ... the fish restaurants that line th waterfront at Piraeus, the port of Athens, or th shores of the Bosphorus on the outskirts of Istanbul ... the Heurigen restaurants in th wine-growing village of Grinzing, on the edge the Vienna Woods, with good wine flowing and Schrammelquartett playing Viennese songs . the floating restaurants of Hong Kong Aberdeen Harbour ... the Windows on th World restaurant on the 107th floor of the Worl Trade Center in New York ... the pavemer cafés of Rome's Via Veneto, Paris's Champ Elysées or Cannes' Croisette ... the brown ba and liqueur and gin tasting shops of Amsterda ... the *tapas* bars of Spain ... the *kellers* of th Austrian alpine resorts where you can enjo lively music with your gulaschsuppe and jug o wine ... and, for the sophisticated epitome dining out as a pleasurable experience, Maxim in Paris, its waiters past-masters at makin customers feel special, its decor unique, its foo sublime... in all these places the ambience is pleasing as the food or drink, satisfying bot aesthetic and physical appetites.

Right: Pavement café, Champs-Elysées.

SPRING BEGINS

*E*at well, eat wisely with Smoked Fish Cakes, Choice Chicken Loaf,
Egg Hubble Bubble and pennywise Monday's Pie' recipes start page 30.
Right: Two's company — instructions for this pretty twin-set with lacy panel down
the front are on page 27.

18

*M*aking the most of an attic bedroom means choosing a fabric and matching soft furnishings throughout. See page 7.
Right: Dreamy days . . . do you spend them wishing for the perfect figure? Turn to page 51 and we'll try to help make your dreams come true . . .

*S*titch in time. Embroider a flower-bedecked face to fit into a wooden case. Directions start on page 33.
Right: This delightful top-to-toe layette makes the perfect basis for baby's first wardrobe. Instructions on page 44.

22

*F*resh home-grown vegetables, unsurpassed for flavour, delight the eye as well as the palate — and are money-savers, too.

VEGETABLES
for a small garden

With crop rotation and planning for succession, an average-sized garden can give you fresh produce for most of the year, explains JOY SIMMONS

YOU can grow quite a few vegetables in a plot only 12 ft. by 12 ft., or almost enough to supply a family of four in a plot 30 ft. by 50 ft. Even a paved yard can be utilised; several saladings — *tomatoes, lettuces, radishes* — as well as *dwarf beans* and *spinach* — grow well in containers.

If possible, reduce attacks from pest and disease by crop rotation. This simply means swapping the crops round each year. Where there's sufficient room, divide the plot into three: (a) *roots*, (b) *brassicas*, (c) *beans, peas, tomatoes, lettuces*, etc. In a mini-plot, divide it into two, switching *roots* with *brassicas* each year.

Normally, vegetables are grown in oblong or square beds, but they can be grown in borders with curving edges, or even among the flowers, if it fits in better with your particular garden design. Those of you who have seen intensive culture in France and Austria will know how much use can be made of a limited space when the need arises.

The majority of vegetables thrive in loamy soil, though not all require the same manurial treatment. Root vegetables — *carrots, parsnips, long-rooted beets, turnips* — should not be grown in freshly manured ground if you want well-shaped roots. Brassicas — *cabbages, sprouts, kale and broccoli* — do best in firm ground manured for a previous crop. *Peas, beans, tomatoes, courgettes* and *lettuces* enjoy soil enriched with well rotted manure or compost.

Digging should be carried out in late winter, if possible, ready for spring sowing. Choose a dry day for the operation. Where manure is to be incorporated, spread it over the surface, turning it in as you work. You can leave the soil in biggish clods at this stage, raking it down to a fine tilth in spring. If you can afford it, work in plenty of peat.

A balanced fertiliser, applied about ten days before sowing or planting, will help produce good crops. If the soil is acid, apply a dressing of hydrated lime (½ lb. to the square yard) during winter, but not within two months of manuring or fertilising.

How about soil for containers? John Innes Potting Compost No. 3 or Levington Potting Compost will suit most kinds of vegetables.

Where plants are sown direct in the container, scatter two or three inches of *seed compost* over the surface. *Tomatoes* can also be grown in peat bags (growing bags) and the bag can be re-used for *lettuces* and *carrots* in the second year.

Some crops are more worth while than others in a small garden. Personally, in those circumstances, I would go for *runner* and *dwarf French beans, early dwarf peas, lettuces, carrots, turnips, beetroots, perpetual spinach, cabbages, sprouting broccoli, dwarf sprouts, curly kale* and *tomatoes.*

I choose *turnips* and *beetroots* rather than *parsnips* because the latter occupy valuable space for as much as 33 weeks, compared with turnips 7-12 weeks and beetroots 16 weeks. *Peas* could be replaced by *broad beans*, if you wished.

With the exception of the brassicas, the vegetables mentioned are sown in drills where the plants are to remain. *Brassicas* are sown in a seed bed in drills 6 in. apart for transplanting in June or July in rows 18-24 in. apart, allowing 2 ft. between the plants. This leaves the ground vacant from April onwards, when a quick-growing crop such as *lettuces, radishes* or *summer spinach* could be grown.

Runner beans are sown 2 in. deep, 4-6 in. apart, in double rows 9 in apart, in mid-May, supporting the plants with bean poles, trellis or a wigwam of canes.

Dwarf beans can be sown 2 in. deep, 6 in. apart, in rows 12 in. apart. *Broad beans* are sown 3 in. deep as early as February, given suitable weather, spacing the seed 9 in. apart, in rows 18 in. apart.

In a large or medium-sized plot, the spacing between the rows would be greater, but we are assuming the plot is small.

Leave 1 ft. between the rows of most other vegetables (6-9 in. between *lettuce* rows). Sow *dwarf peas* in flat-bottomed drills 2-3 in. deep and 2-3 in. apart, from early March until June.

Perpetual spinach and *beetroots* may be sown from mid-April onwards; *carrots, turnips, parsnips, lettuces* and *sprouts* in March; *kale, broccoli* and *summer* and *autumn cabbages* in April.

Sow *tomatoes* in a suitable compost in a temperature of 15-18°C (60-65°F) in March, pricking off the seedlings into small pots of

Continued overleaf

potting compost when one pair of true leaves — that is, not the *first* leaves — have formed. These half-hardy plants cannot be planted in the open until after frosts. The bush variety *Pixie* does extremely well in tubs.

I am often asked whether any vegetables can be grown in a semi-shady border. These conditions are not ideal, but *cabbages, spinach, runner beans* and *lettuces* should give reasonable results provided that the soil is properly prepared.

Don't overlook the fact that early sowings of *dwarf peas* and *broad beans* will be cleared in time for a sowing of *winter spinach* or *lettuce*, thus making full use of the plot throughout the year.

BEST OF THE BERRIES

You do not need a large garden to grow some of the more expensive soft fruits. For instance, *strawberries* can be grown in plastic Tower Pots, special strawberry tubs or even in large flower pots, on a patio or paved area, while cordon-trained *red* and *white currants* (single, double or triple cordons) and cordon or fan-trained *gooseberries* occupy little space if they are grown against a north wall or fence.

Strawberries do well in a barrel.

Loganberries and *blackberries* (choose thornless varieties) also thrive planted against a north wall or fence, the long shoots providing an attractive feature if trained fanwise or in other more complicated designs.

The *raspberry* is another fruit that can be grown against a fence or on wires as a dividing "hedge" between flower and vegetable borders. But this fruit does best in a sunny position, although you can grow canes reasonably well in semi-shade.

Blackcurrants require more room, as they should always be grown in bush form. Like raspberries they prefer sun but will tolerate little shade.

Gooseberries hardly come into the category of "luxury" fruits, but the fact that they can be grown against a north wall and in a wide range of soils makes them an ideal fruit for the small suburban garden.

TIPS FOR TOP FRUIT

When buying "top fruit" trees — *apples, pears, plums* and so on — ask for bushes or trees on dwarf or semi-dwarf stock rather than the old-fashioned large-type trees. These will come into bearing sooner and are easier to manage than the latter, quite apart from the fact that they take up less room.

Where only one or two trees are to be grown make sure that the varieties are compatible to

Three ways of training — fan shape, espalier (horizontal branches) and cordon (short spurs on single stem).

cross-pollinate one another. Although some apples will produce a crop with their own pollen all of them bear better with a cross-pollinator.

Choose varieties that crop at different times where possible, so that you have fruit for several months or more.

If you've room for only one tree, plant a *Family Fruit Tree*. These are trees which have been grafted with three or more compatible varieties of apples or pears for the purpose of pollination. You can, for instance, have two early and one late dessert apple on the same tree thus spreading the cropping season.

The form of tree you grow will depend on the space available and individual choice. They can be trained as pyramids, cordons and espaliers, but a bush variety on dwarf or semi-dwarfing stock is normally most suitable for the amateur unless one undertakes regular pruning.

Pears can also be grown in these forms. An espalier pear is a popular choice for growing in good loam against a sheltered, sunny wall.

Plums and *gages* are not really satisfactory for growing in restricted form, but fan-trained, bush, half-standard and pyramid-trained trees will yield well. The semi-dwarfing stock *St Julien A* is the most suitable for small gardens.

TWO'S COMPANY

A long-sleeved sweater with lacy centre panel together with a matching sleeveless jacket makes an attractive duo to set off skirts and trousers

Instructions in 5 sizes. Colour photo on page 19.

MATERIALS: *Allow the following quantities in 25 g balls of Jaeger 3-ply: Sweater: 9 for 81 cm, 86 cm and 91 cm sizes; 10 for 97 and 102 cm sizes. Sleeveless Jacket: 7 for 81 cm and 86 cm sizes; 8 for 91 cm, 97 cm and 102 cm sizes. For any one size of either garment: A pair each of No. 11 (3 mm) and No. 13 (2¼ mm) knitting needles; 5 buttons for jacket.*

TENSION: *Work at a tension of 34 stitches and 45 rows to measure 10 x 10 cm, over the stocking stitch, using No. 11 (3 mm) needles, to obtain measurements given below.*

ABBREVIATIONS: To be read before working: *K., knit plain; p., purl; st., stitch; tog., together; s.s., stocking st. (k. on right side and p. on wrong side); inc., increase (by working twice into text st.); dec., decrease (by taking 2 sts. tog.); up 1, pick up loop lying between needles and k. or p. into back of it); y. fwd., yarn forward to make a st.; .k.p.o. (slip 1, k. 1, pass slipped st. over); single rib s k. 1 and p. 1 alternately.*

NOTE: *The instructions are given for the 81 cm (32 inch) bust size. Where they vary, work figures within first brackets for 86 cm (34 inch) size; work figures within second brackets for 91 cm (36 inch) size, and so on.*

THE SWEATER

THE BACK: With No. 13 (2¼ mm) needles cast on 144 (152) (160) (168) (176) sts. and work 4 rows in single rib.

Change to No. 11 (3 mm) needles and beginning with a k. row, s.s. 152 rows.

To shape armholes: Cast off 4 sts. at beginning of next 2 rows, then dec. 1 st. each end of next row and the 11 (13) (15) (17) (19) following alternate rows — 112 (116) (120) (124) (128) sts.

S.s. 51 (47) (47) (43) (43) rows.

To slope shoulders: Cast off 11 (12) (11) (12) (13) sts. at beginning of next 2 rows, then 11 (11) (12) (12) (12) sts. on the following 4 rows.

Break yarn and leave 46 (48) (50) (52) (54) sts. on a spare needle.

THE FRONT: With No. 13 (2¼ mm) needles cast on 144 (152) (160) (168) (176) sts. and work 13 rows in single rib.

Dec. row: Rib 47 (51) (55) (59) (63), work 2 tog., * rib 10, work 2 tog.; repeat from * 3 times, rib 47 (51) (55) (59) (63) — 139 (147) (155) (163) (171) sts.

Change to No. 11 (3 mm) needles.

1st pattern row: K. 37 (41) (45) (49) (53), for panel ** s.k.p.o., y.fwd, k. 1, y.fwd., k. 2 tog., *k. 5, k. 2 tog., y.fwd., k. 1, y.fwd., s.k.p.o., k. 5, s.k.p.o., y.fwd., k. 1, y.fwd., k. 2 tog. **; repeat from * to ** twice more, k. 37 (41) (45) (49) (53).

2nd and every alternate row: P. to end.

3rd row: K. 37 (41) (45) (49) (53), ** s.k.p.o., y.fwd., k. 1, y.fwd., k. 2 tog., * k. 4, k. 2 tog., y.fwd., k. 3, y.fwd., s.k.p.o., k. 4, s.k.p.o., y.fwd., k.1, y.fwd., k. 2 tog. **; repeat from * to ** twice more, k. to end.

5th row: K. to panel, ** s.k.p.o., y.fwd., k. 1, y.fwd., k. 2 tog., * k. 3, k. 2 tog., y.fwd., k. 5, y.fwd., s.k.p.o., k. 3, s.k.p.o., y.fwd., k. 1, y.fwd., k. 2 tog **; repeat from * to ** twice more, k. to end.

Continued overleaf

MEASUREMENTS

in centimetres (and inches, in brackets)

			91	(36)	97	(38)	102	(40)
83·5	(32¾)	88·5	(34¾)	93	(36½)	97·5	(38½)	102·5	(40¼)
36	(14¼)	36	(14¼)	36	(14¼)	36	(14¼)	36	(14¼)
54·5	(21½)	54·5	(21½)	55·5	(21¾)	55·5	(21¾)	56	(22)
37·5	(14¾)	37·5	(14¾)	37·5	(14¾)	37·5	(14¾)	37·5	(14¾)
91	(36)	95·5	(37½)	100·5	(39½)	105	(41¼)	109·5	(43)
36·5	(14¼)	36·5	(14¼)	36·5	(14¼)	36·5	(14¼)	36·5	(14¼)
57·5	(22½)	57·5	(22½)	58·5	(23)	58·5	(23)	59·5	(23½)

TWO'S COMPANY *Continued*

7th row: K. to panel, ** s.k.p.o., y.fwd., k. 1, y.fwd., k. 2 tog., * k. 2, k. 2 tog., y.fwd., k. 2 tog., y.fwd., k. 3, y.fwd., s.k.p.o., y.fwd., s.k.p.o., k. 2, s.k.p.o., y.fwd., k. 1, y.fwd., k. 2 tog. **; repeat from * to ** twice more, k. to end.

9th row: K. to panel, ** s.k.p.o., y.fwd., k. 1, y.fwd., k. 2 tog., * k. 3, y.fwd., k. 2 tog., y.fwd., s.k.p.o., k. 1, k. 2 tog., y.fwd., s.k.p.o., y.fwd., k. 3, s.k.p.o., y.fwd., k. 1, y.fwd., k. 2 tog. **; repeat from * to ** twice more, k. to end.

10th row: P. to end.

11th to 18th rows: Repeat 9th and 10th rows, 4 times.

19th row: K. to panel, ** s.k.p.o., y.fwd., k. 1, y.fwd., k. 2 tog., * k. 1, k. 2 tog., y.fwd., k. 9, y.fwd., s.k.p.o., k. 1, s.k.p.o., y.fwd., k. 1, y.fwd., k . 2 tog **; repeat from * to ** twice more, k. to end.

20th row: P. to end.

These 20 rows form the pattern panel. Repeat them a further 6 times, then the 1st to 12th rows again.

To shape armholes: Keeping continuity of the panel, cast off 4 sts. at beginning of next 2 rows, then dec. 1st. each end of next row and the 11 (13) (15) (17) (19) following alternate rows — 107 (111) (115) (119) (123) sts.

Pattern 30 (26) (26) (22) (22) rows.

To divide for neck: Next row: P. 42 (43) (44) (45) (46) and leave these sts. on a spare needle for right front neck, p. 23 (25) (27) (29) (31) and leave on a st. holder, p. to end and work on these last 42 (43) (44) (45) (46) sts. for left front neck.

The left front neck: Dec. 1 st. at neck edge on each of the next 10 rows — 32 (33) (34) (35) (36) sts.

Pattern 10 rows — pattern 11 rows here when working right front neck.

To slope shoulder: Cast off 11 (12) (11) (12) (13) sts. at beginning of next row, and 11 (11) (12) (12) (12) sts. on the following alternate row.

Work 1 row, then cast off 10 (10) (11) (11) (11) sts.

The right front neck: With right side facing, rejoin yarn to inner end of sts. on spare needle and work as left front neck, noting variation.

THE SLEEVES (2 alike): With No. 13 (2¼ mm) needles cast on 64 (64) (68) (68) (72) sts. and work 13 rows in single rib.

Increase row: Rib 5 (5) (6) (6) (3), up 1, * rib 6 (6) (5) (5) (5), up 1; repeat from * until 5 (5) (7) (7) (4) sts. remain, rib to end — 74 (74) (80) (80) (86) sts.

Change to No. 11 (3 mm) needles and, beginning with a k. row, s.s. 2 rows, then inc. 1 st. each end of next row and the 17 following 8th rows — 110 (110) (116) (116) (122) sts.

S.s. 19 rows.

To shape sleeve top: Cast off 4 sts. at

beginning of next 2 rows, then dec. 1 st. each end of next row and the 8 (8) (9) (9) (10) following alternate rows — 84 (84) (88) (88) (92) sts.

P. 1 row, then dec. 1 st. each end of the next 3 (30) (32) (32) (34) rows. Cast off 24 sts.

THE NECK RIBBING: First join right shoulder seam.

With right side facing, rejoin yarn and using No. 13 (2¼ mm) needles, pick up and k. 28 sts from left front neck edge, increasing 3 sts. evenly, k. across front neck sts., pick up and k. 28 sts from right front neck edge, and finally increasing 2 sts. evenly k. across back neck sts — 130 (134) (138) (142) (146) sts.

Work 28 rows in single rib. Cast off in rib.

TO MAKE UP THE SWEATER: Press lightly on wrong side with a warm iron over a damp cloth. Join remaining shoulder seam continuing with a flat seam across neck ribbing. Set in sleeves; join side and sleeve seams. Fold neck ribbing in half and catch down on wrong side.

THE SLEEVELESS JACKET

THE BACK: With No. 13 (2¼ mm) needles cast on 152 (160) (168) (176) (184) sts. and work 14 rows in single rib.

Change to No. 11 (3 mm) needles and beginning with a k. row, s.s. 156 rows.

To shape armholes: Cast off 8 sts. at beginning of next 2 rows, then dec. 1 st. each end of next row and the 14 (16) (18) (20) (22) following alternate rows — 106 (110) (114) (118) (122) sts.

S.s. 55 (51) (51) (47) (47) rows.

To slope shoulders: Cast off 9 (10) (11) (10) (11) sts. at beginning of next 2 rows, then 10 (10) (10) (11) (11) sts. on the following 4 rows.

Cast off remaining 48 (50) (52) (54) (56) sts.

THE POCKET BACKS (2 alike): With No. 11 (3 mm) needles cast on 39 sts. and s.s. 40 rows. Break yarn and leave on a st. holder.

THE LEFT FRONT: With No. 13 (2¼ mm) needles cast on 73 (77) (81) (85) (89) sts.

Beginning odd-numbered rows with k. 1 and even-numbered rows with p. 1, work 14 rows in single rib.

Change to No. 11 (3 mm) needles and beginning with a k. row, s.s. 40 rows.

Pocket row: K. 17 (19) (21) (23) (25), slip next 39 sts. onto a st. holder and leave at front of work, and in their place, k. across 39 sts. of one pocket back, then k. remaining 17 (19) (21) (2 (25) sts. of row — 73 (77) (81) (85) (89) sts.

P. 1 row.

1st pattern row: K. 24 (26) (28) (30) (32 work from ** to ** on 1st pattern row of sweat front, k. 24 (26) (28) (30) (32).

2nd and every alternate row: P. to end.

**** Dec. 1 st. at armhole edge on next row and the 14 (16) (18) (20) (22) following alternate rows, *at the same time*, dec. 1 st. at front edge as before on the 4th row from previous front dec., and the 8 (9) (10) (12) (13) following 4th rows — 35 (36) (37) (40) (41) sts.

Pattern 5 rows, then dec. 1 st. at front edge as before on next row and the 6 (6) (6) (5) (5) following 6th rows — 28 (29) (30) (31) (32) sts.

Pattern 7 (3) (3) (1) (1) row(s) — pattern 8 (4) (4) (2) (2) rows here when working right front.

To slope shoulder: Cast off 10 (9) (10) (11) (10) sts. at beginning of next row and 9 (10) (10) (10) (11) sts. on the following alternate row.

Work 1 row. Cast off remaining 9 (10) (10) (10) (11) sts.

THE RIGHT FRONT: Work as left front to *******

To shape front edge: 1st row: K. 2, k. 2 tog., pattern to end.

2nd to 4th rows: Pattern 3 rows

Repeat last 4 rows, 4 times, then 1st row again — 67 (71) (75) (79) (83) sts.

To shape armhole and continue shaping front edge: 1st row: Cast off 8 sts., p. to end.

Work as given for left front from ******** to end.

THE FRONT BORDER: Join shoulder seams. With No. 13 (2¼ mm) needles cast on 15 sts.

1st rib row: K. 2, * p. 1, k. 1; repeat from * until 1 st. remains., k. 1 more.

2nd rib row: K. 1, * p. 1, k. 1; repeat from * to end. Repeat last 2 rows, 3 times.

1st buttonhole row: Rib 6, cast off 3, rib to end. **2nd buttonhole row:** Rib 6, turn, cast on 3, turn, rib to end. Rib 30 rows.

Repeat the last 32 rows, 3 times, then the 2 buttonhole rows again.

Continue in rib until border fits up right front, round neck and down left front, casting off when correct length is assured.

THE ARMHOLE BORDERS (2 alike): With right side facing, rejoin yarn and using No. 13 (3¼ mm) needles, pick up and k. 178 (178) (186) (186) (194) sts. all round armhole edge and work 9 rows in single rib. Cast of in rib.

THE POCKET TOPS (2 alike): With right side facing, rejoin yarn and using No. 13 (2¼ mm) needles work across sts. as follows: K. 7, * inc., k. 8; repeat from * to end — 43 sts.

Beginning with a 2nd row, work 9 rows in rib as given on front border. Cast off in rib.

TO MAKE UP THE SLEEVELESS JACKET: Press as for sweater. Join side seams including armhole borders. Sew front border into place, setting top buttonhole level with first front shaping. Sew down pocket backs to wrong side and row ends of pocket tops to right side. Add buttons.

3rd row: K. 24 (26) (28) (30) (32), work from ** to ** on 3rd pattern row of sweater front, k. to end.

Continue in this way repeating from ** to ** on adjacent sweater front rows across centre 25 sts., for a further 91 rows finishing with a wrong side row. *******

To shape front edge: 1st row: Pattern until 4 sts. remain, s.k.p.o., k. 2.

2nd to 4th rows: Pattern 3 rows.

Repeat last 4 rows, 4 times more — 68 (72) 76) (80) (84) sts.

To shape armhole and continue shaping front edge: 1st row: Cast off 8 sts., pattern until sts. remain, s.k.p.o., k. 2.

2nd row: P. to end.

Simple Economical Meals

Here are some varied and tasty recipes for every day, which won't strain the family housekeeping budget too much!

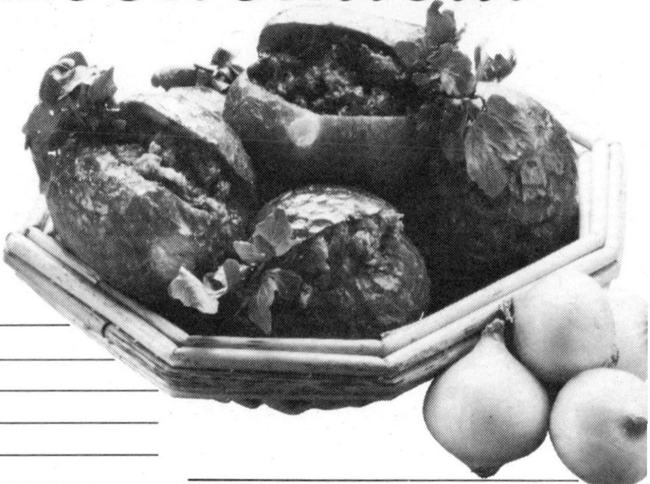

CORNED BEEF BUNDLES

Serves 4

4 bread rolls
2 oz. margarine, melted

For the Filling

7 oz. can corned beef
1 medium onion, chopped
8 oz. can tomatoes
1 teaspoon vinegar
¼ level teaspoon mixed herbs
Salt and pepper
1 tablespoon chopped parsley, optional

Set the oven to gas mark 6 or 400°F/200°C.

Cut off the tops of the rolls and remove the crumb from the centre of each, reserving 2 oz. for the filling. Brush the rolls inside and out with the margarine, and brush the lids as well.

In the pan used to melt the margarine, fry the onion gently until soft. Add the tomatoes and simmer for 5 minutes to evaporate some of the liquid. Remove the pan from the heat and mix in the vinegar, herbs, parsley if used, plenty of salt and pepper, 2 oz. of breadcrumbs and the chopped corned beef.

Divide the mixture equally between the rolls and wrap each in a square of foil. Stand the rolls on a baking sheet and bake in the oven for 15 minutes. Open foil and return rolls to oven for 15 minutes.

SMOKED FISH CAKES

Makes 8

½ lb. smoked mackerel
1 lb. potatoes
4 oz. onion
2 eggs, size 2-3
3 level tablespoons flour
½ level teaspoon baking powder
1 level teaspoon salt
½ teaspoon pepper
Oil for frying

Peel the potatoes and onion and grate them into bowl. Leave for 10 minutes then squeeze ou excess liquid.

Skin the fish and break it into small pieces Mix the fish and potato with the eggs, flour baking powder and seasoning, stirring togethe well.

Mark the mixture into eight, spoon eacl portion into the hot oil and fry for about minutes on each side or until cooked and golde brown. Garnish with watercress.

Serve the fish cakes with lemon.

HINTS TO HELP CUT THE HIGH COST OF FEEDING YOURSELF AND THE FAMILY

- All the usual advice such as thinking ahead and planning meals for a few days really does save hard cash, saves time too as cooking becomes more efficient.
- Don't buy on impulse unless you knock something else off your shopping list.
- Things are cheapest wher supplies are plentiful; so mak the most of fresh vegetable and find new ways o preparing them.
- And when fruit is in seaso buy ingredients for jams jellies, preserves, or fruit fo freezing.

MONDAY'S PIE

Serves 4

oz. cooked meat such as chicken, sausages, tc.

oz. margarine

level tablespoons flour

pint milk

pint water

chicken stock cube

bay leaf

lb. cooked vegetables or a packet of mixed frozen vegetables

alt and pepper

-6 slices buttered bread

Pint pie dish

et the oven to moderately hot, Mark 5, 375°F/ 90°C.

Cut the cooked meats into neat pieces. Melt he margarine, stir in the flour then the milk and ater. Bring to the boil, stirring. Reduce the eat and add the stock cube, bay leaf, egetables, meat and salt and pepper to taste. Turn the mixture into the pie dish.

Cut the crusts off the bread if liked and cut ach slice into 4 triangles. Arrange on the top of he pie and bake in the oven for 30 minutes until he mixture is heated through and the topping is olden brown and crisp.

EGG HUBBLE BUBBLE

Serves 4

rashers bacon, rinded and chopped

tablespoon oil

oz. can baked beans

-2 tablespoons tomato ketchup

good pinch mixed herbs

teaspoon chopped capers, optional

lb. cooked potatoes, cubed

alt and pepper

eggs

½-2 pint shallow ovenproof dish

Set the oven to moderately hot, Mark 5, 375°F/ 190°C.

Cook the bacon in the oil until crisp then remove from the heat and stir in the baked beans, ketchup, herbs, capers, cubed potatoes and salt and pepper to taste. Spoon the mixture into the dish and make 4 hollows with the back of a spoon.

Break an egg into each hollow. Sprinkle with salt and pepper.

Bake towards the top of the oven for 35-40 minutes or until the eggs are cooked and the mixture heated through.

CHOICE CHICKEN LOAF

Serves 4-6

1 lb. cooked chicken meat

1 can 'Soup for One' condensed celery soup

2 oz. spring onions, trimmed and finely sliced

2 large eggs (size 2), beaten

2 tablespoons single cream, milk or plain yoghurt

¼ level teaspoon salt

Pepper

A 1 lb. loaf tin, greased and base-lined

Set the oven to very moderate, gas mark 3 or 325°F/160°C.

Cut a few large pieces of chicken into ½ inch wide strips and roughly chop the rest of the meat. Mix all the chicken, soup, spring onions, eggs, cream, salt and pepper together. Spoon the mixture into the loaf tin, level the top with the back of a spoon and cover with a piece of buttered foil. Bake just above the centre of the oven for 1¼ to 1½ hours or until firm.

Remove the chicken loaf from the oven and press overnight.

Note: You will need to cook a 2½ to 3 lb. chicken — either by roasting or boiling — to get 1lb. of cooked chicken meat.

Continued overleaf

Colour photographs
are on page 18

Buy in the right quantities – there's no economy if half he stuff goes stale before you an use it.

Try other cheaper brand ames — after two or three mes, you may come to like hem better — tastes can be hanged.

● Make your own — home-made mixes, etc. usually cost less and taste much better.

● Keep a stock of basic foods in the cupboard or freezer. Skimmed milk is cheaper than fresh and has fewer calories. Some canned fish and meat is very cheap for simple meals.

● Keep food properly and avoid waste. A fridge is an asset only if the food keeps in first class condition, so wrap properly.

● Mark all cans and packets with the dates on which you bought them; use them in rotation.

GOOD THRIFT TIPS

Here are some more ideas for saving a few pence. Perhaps they will encourage you to find other ways of cost-cutting.

Home Made Yoghurt

At a pot per person yoghurt can be expensive when catering for a family. But it can be made easily at home at a fraction of the cost.

Ordinary bottled fruit juices are perfect for flavouring, and chopped fresh fruit can be used to top the yoghurt, or be stirred in just before serving.

Home-made yoghurt is also a boon to slimmers as the amount of sugar intake can be controlled.

YOGHURT

Makes 4-5 pots

1 pint sterilised or U.H.T. milk

2 tablespoons natural yoghurt

Clean empty yoghurt or cream cartons

Vacuum flasks or home-made incubator

Make the incubator: Insulate the sides and base of a cake storage tin with thick layers of pages from old magazines or with cotton wool, etc. Fold up some extra pages to place between the cartons and on top.

Heat the milk to 110°F/43°C. If a thermometer is not available, use your little finger as a guide and heat the milk until it feels comfortably warm for 10 seconds. (The temperature is critical; if it is too hot the yoghurt will be killed; if too cool the yoghurt will not be activated and will not set the milk.)

When the milk is at the right temperature, stir in the yoghurt and mix well. Either pour into the flask and cover or pour into the pots, cover with lid or foil and place in the insulated cake tin. Cover with a thick layer of magazine pages or cotton wool and place cake tin lid in place. For extra insulation, wrap a towel over and around the tin. Leave overnight.

Note: You should be able to use some of the home-made yoghurt to start your next batch. A further 3 or so batches can be made like this, after which a fresh yoghurt should be bought and used.

Soup

Is ideal budget food. Small amounts of meat, chicken and vegetables can quickly be made into soup by adding them to a well flavoured stock or thin white sauce:

It can be made into a nourishing meal by topping with grated cheese or pouring over toasted cheese on French bread.

Home-made stock is the basis of all goo[d] soups. It is so easy to make and you'll find it add[s] lots of extra flavour to your soups

Bone Stock

This can be made from both raw and cooke[d] chicken and other poultry carcasses, meat or fis[h] bones and trimmings.

Place the bones in a large saucepan and cov[er] with cold water. Add clean vegetable trimming[s] and peelings or 2 carrots, a slice of turnip and a[n] onion. Add a bay leaf, parsley stalks, etc. (if yo[u] want a well coloured stock leave the skin on th[e] onion) and a tablespoon of tomato purée can b[e] added for extra colour.

Bring the stock slowly to the boil so that th[e] flavour and goodness is extracted. Skim an[d] simmer for 1 - 2 hours depending on the quanti[ty] and size of the bones.

Strain the stock into a large bowl and leave [to] cool.

When cold remove any fat and use for sauce[s] etc.

Stock can be kept for up to 4 days in the fridg[e] but if any leafy vegetables have been used th[e] stock should be boiled every day to preve[nt] sourness.

To freeze: After removing the solidified f[at] the stock can be poured into 1 pint containers [or] ice cube trays and frozen.

Note: A pressure cooker can be used to make th[e] stock.

Bacon

Keep an eye open for bargains in bacon join[ts] such as collar, forehock and knuckle. The[y] make marvellous main meals and are cheap[er] than fresh meats.

Bony, lean boiled forehock served with parsley sauce gives a great hot meal one day, an[d] can be served cold with potato and green salad [or] pickles on the following day.

Small fat end pieces can be bought whole [and] cut into rashers economically and it's surprisin[g] how they can flavour soups, potato and onio[n] hotpots and chicken casseroles. The fat rashe[rs] can be fried until crisp and used as garnish f[or] soups or salads or vegetables; added to filling[s] for omelettes; as a flavouring or topping f[or] scrambled eggs or cheese dishes or mixed in[to] pasta dishes.

An ideal way of using the pieces of meat fro[m] bacon hock is to make it into spiced bacon pâté[.]

Put 6 - 8 oz. cooked bacon, 1 hard-boiled eg[g] and 2 tablespoons chutney through the minc[er] or into the food processor.

Blend the ingredients together then mix [in] enough ketchup or mayonnaise to flavour an[d] bind the ingredients together.

Serve with salad or as a sandwich filling.

STITCH IN TIME

Create an ornamental
wall clock with
flower-embroidered face
set in stylish
carpentered case
(shown in colour on page 22)

THE CARPENTRY

You need: one piece of prepared softwood 1170 x 32 x 9 mm (46 x 1¼ x ³/₈ in.); one piece of prepared softwood 380 x 95 x 9 mm (15 x 3¾ x ³/₈ in.); one piece of ogee architrave moulding 1470 x 45 x 16 mm (58 x 1¾ x ⁵/₈ in.); one piece of 3 mm (¹/₈ in.) hardboard 273 mm (10¾ in.) square.
You will also need: 12 and 32 mm (½ and 1¼ in.) panel pins; 16 mm (⁵/₈ in.) cut brads (glazing sprigs); wood glue; glasspaper; varnish; one battery clock movement with black hands.
Note: the measurements shown above for timber widths and thicknesses are nett. The lengths allow for cutting to size.
To make: Cut four pieces of architrave moulding and three pieces of 32 mm (1¼ in.) wide softwood, 355 mm (14 in.) long. Take three

mouldings and glue and pin a length of softwood to the back of each piece, flush with the outside (thicker) long edge of the moulding, to form a rebate (see diagram below). Mitre the ends of these three pieces plus the unbacked moulding to a finished overall length of 340 mm (13³/₈ in.).

Now make a card template for shaping the clock top. To do this, mark 10mm squares on thin card then draw in the outline, square by square (see squared section of the diagram). Cut the template to shape with scissors.

From 95 x 9 mm (3¾ x ³/₈ in.) softwood cut one piece 340 mm (13³/₈ in.) long. Mark a pencil line centrally across the width and mark a second line along the length, 32 mm (1¼ in.) up from the
Continued overleaf

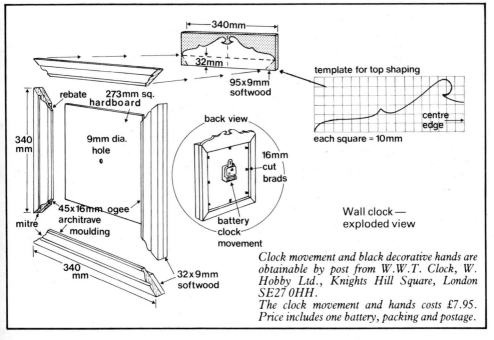

template for top shaping

each square = 10mm

340mm

32mm

95x9mm softwood

rebate   273mm sq. hardboard

340 mm

9mm dia. hole

45x16mm ogee architrave moulding

mitre

340 mm

back view

16mm cut brads

battery clock movement

32x9mm softwood

centre edge

Wall clock — exploded view

Clock movement and black decorative hands are obtainable by post from W.W.T. Clock, W. Hobby Ltd., Knights Hill Square, London SE27 0HH.
The clock movement and hands costs £7.95. Price includes one battery, packing and postage.

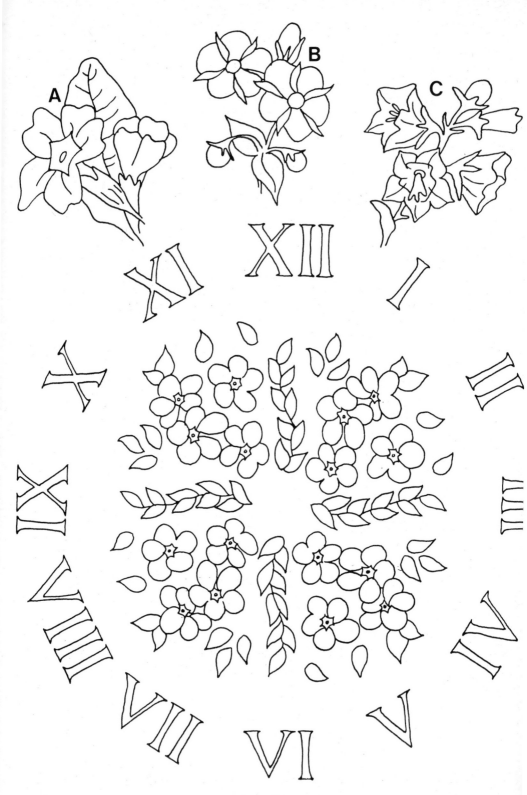

A

B

C

XI XII I

X II

IX III

VIII IV

VII VI V

bottom edge (see dotted lines on diagram). Place the template on the board with the centre and bottom edges of the template against the appropriate marked lines on the board. Run a pencil around the template to mark the shaping on the board. Reverse and re-position the template and mark the other half.

Cut the board to shape using a fretsaw, then glue and pin it to the back of the spare piece of ogee moulding. Position the top edge of the moulding against the pencil mark running along the board and ensure that the ends of both pieces are flush. Remove the bottom corners of the board, flush with the mitres on the moulding.

Glue and pin the four sides of the clock frame together, using one 32 mm (1¼ in.) panel pin for each join.

For the clock face cut one piece of hardboard 273 mm (10¾ in.) square and drill a 9 mm (³/₈ in.) diameter hole through centre.

FINISHING

Recess visible panel pin heads with a pin punch and fill holes with a suitably coloured wood stopping. When dry, smooth surfaces with fine grade glasspaper and remove dust.

Finish the clock frame with Ronseal walnut coloured polyurethane varnish, carefully following the directions on the tin.

To complete the clock, place the finished embroidery centrally on the hardboard face, stretch it to remove creases and glue the fabric edges to the back of the face. Make small snips in the centre of the canvas to clear the hole in the hardboard, using pointed scissors.

Fix the clock face in the frame using cut brads (see inset central diagram on previous page). Attach the clock movement to the back of the clock face, fit hands and insert battery. Fix a screw into the wall for hanging.

THE EMBROIDERED FACE

You will need: a 46 cm (18 in.) sqare of white or cream, closely-woven cotton or linen; Anchor Stranded Cotton as follows — two skeins each of green 0255 and 0258; one skein each of black 0403, lilac 0104, purple 0107, mid blue 0131, dark blue 0139, red 047, coral 011, orange 0316, yellow 0302, pale yellow 0300; needle; tracing paper; dressmaker's carbon paper.

To copy the design: Rule a 23 cm (9 in.) square on tracing paper and draw diagonal lines from corner to corner to find the centre point. Place tracing paper centrally over pattern opposite and trace off the numerals and the flower designs inside them. To complete the floral pattern that borders the numerals, trace off flower groups A, B and C four times (using colour picture on page 22 for positioning); then repeat one of the central flower designs at each corner.

To transfer the design to the fabric, centre your tracing right side up on the fabric, slip a piece of dressmaker's carbon between the fabric and the tracing and pin all the layers together. Use a knitting needle to draw over the outline of the design and mark it on to the fabric.

To embroider: Use only three strands of thread throughout. Follow our colour picture on page 22 as a guide.

Embroider the numerals in black satin stitch, and all leaves in green satin stitch.

Work all flower groups A, B and C in satin stitch, colouring flowers as follows —

A — Purple, lilac, mid blue, dark blue; yellow centres.

B — Red, coral; yellow centres.

C — Pale yellow, yellow, orange; light green centres. Work pale yellow straight stitches for veins on leaves and red straight stitches near stalk.

For the small flower outlines inside the numerals and at each corner, use back stitch in mid blue, lilac or red. Work a French knot in black at each flower centre and outline it with yellow back stitch.

SATIN STITCH

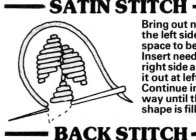

Bring out needle at the left side of the space to be filled. Insert needle at the right side and bring it out at left. Continue in this way until the shape is filled.

BACK STITCH

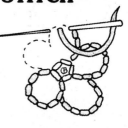

Bring out needle on right side of work, insert it 3 mm (¹/₈ in.) further along the line and bring it out 5 mm (¼ in.) back. Insert needle at end of previous stitch and continue.

FRENCH KNOT

Bring out needle and twist thread two or three times round needle. Holding twists on needle with your thumb, insert the needle where it first came out (see arrow) and draw thread through.

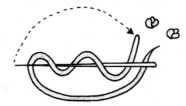

DON'T SAY IT WITH FLOWERS

So much for the first day of the rest of my life! I had a rotten cold, felt thoroughly dejected and utterly alone and unloved. Surely things *had* to get better now!

THERE was definitely something lunatic about the spectacle of that gang of oilskinned flower-pickers, progressing in a Quasimodo-like shuffle through the slanting sheets of Cornish rain. Pausing to straighten up and extract a rubber band from the sodden canvas pouch at my waist, I wondered how it was I had ever come to be amongst that bent-backed number, gathering and bunching with sheer, mechanical absorption. On and on before us stretched the regimented rows of daffodils. I viewed the awesome sight with aptly jaundiced eyes.

"Cheer up, Abby! I always say:'When things seem so bad that you think they can't possibly get any worse — then they generally do'!" teased a masculine voice alongside me.

I suppose it was my preoccupied expression which had attracted Toby Gallagher's well intentioned comment, but, just for once, his ability to joke at adversity fell on stony ground.

Yesterday's unheralded and unexplained departure by Lorraine, my flatmate, had precipitated me into a monetary crisis. My finances rested precariously on her paying her share of the rent. It was due at the end of the week, a whole month in advance. My prospects of paying the lump sum on my own were as bleak as the rain-drenched landscape in which I stood.

"I didn't need those words of cold comfort, thank you very much," I replied stiffly, as I peered up at Toby's kindly face from beneath the dripping brim of my sou'wester.

My response must have emerged even more sharply than I had intended it to, because his lop-sided grin instantly straightened and the twinkle in his clear hazel eyes faded away.

"Do pardon me for speaking, ma'am," he commented drily.

"I'm sorry, Toby. It's just I've got a very bad case of the blue glooms today," I apologised abjectly.

"Hardly surprising," Toby granted graciously. "What with the foul weather and these wretched Ice Follies conspiring to make picking difficult, it's enough to give a saint the pip! Still, better not let the grass grow under our feet. As Daniel Kitto says, every idle word is one less flower in the bunch."

Toby gave me a broad wink and staggered on into the full blast of the force-seven gale, his arms protectively encircling his 'lots' of Ice Follies as he took them down to the trailers for boxing.

I TURNED my attention back to my row, feeling more cheerful. Toby always had a tonic effect on me. In fact, I had long since realised that, if it hadn't been for him, my acquaintance with the flower fields would have begun and ended that thin-aired afternoon in early March when I had attacked my first row of daffodils.

I had been togged out then unbecomingly in bright yellow oilskins, the pouch for rubber bands tied round my middle almost giving the impression I possessed a waist. Even so, I hardly recognised myself as Abigail Meacham. It was not so much the protective clothing that made me feel I had forfeited my identity, so much as the number thirty-nine marked on the back of my yellow jacket. Its overtones of penal servitude made it hard to believe I had volunteered to work for the flower farm.

Continued overleaf

Daniel Kitto, the despot of Gwarra Point Farm, had done nothing to dispel this impression. He had a voice as harsh as the lines on his weathered face, and his grey eyes glittered and snapped beneath ferocious, beetling brows as he roamed up and down, licking his new crop of flower-pickers into shape.

"Just pick them — don't sabotage them!" he had addressed me, with a humourless glower. "I want good bunches, picked the full length of the stem. If you can't do the job properly by the end of the week, you'll be given your cards. You'd better work up your speed, too. Twenty-eight lots a day is the minimum I expect when you've had a few days' practice. I can't afford to subsidise slackers. I take it you have understood what a 'lot' is?"

Contrary to Daniel Kitto's belief, I was not a complete numbskull. "There's ten flowers to a bunch, twenty bunches to a lot," I had recited with a thin edge to my voice.

"And I suppose you think twenty-eight lots a day seems a great deal. Well, it's not," Daniel Kitto had informed me flatly. "My experienced workers can easily double that number at the height of the season. So, I don't want to hear you complaining that the basic quota is too high. And heaven help you if you try to cheat by saying you've picked more than you have, when you bring in your lots. If I catch you or anyone else playing that trick, you'll be straight off the field — instant dismissal. Have I made myself clear?"

"Abundantly," I'd answered, through gritted teeth.

"Right then, Thirty-Nine. It's up to you whether you're kept on or not, isn't it?"

Daniel Kitto had not waited for my reply, which was probably just as well. I'd been sorely tempted to tell him that he could keep his precious job. I had not been made to feel so small since I was an ink-stained schoolgirl, and the aspersions cast on my honesty had cut me to the quick.

"Just who does he think he is?" I demanded under my breath.

There was an amused chuckle from just behind me and a rich-timbred voice commented: "Personally, I've just reached the conclusion that Simon Legree is alive and well and ruling at Gwarra Point Farm!"

Spontaneous laughter burst from my lips as I turned to the speaker. Hazel eyes twinkled at me from a lean, intelligent face.

"I'm Toby Gallagher," the stranger had introduced himself with a comic bow. "Or, if you want to be formal, you may call me Twenty-Seven."

"I much prefer Toby."

"So do I. And, since informality is to be the keynote, you are .. ?"

"Abigail." I welcomed the opportunity to remind myself of the fact. "My name is Abigail Meacham."

"Spoken like a born survivor." Toby grinned. "I'll make a wager that you'll be here to the bitter end."

"What will you bet?" I queried promptly.

"Let's be reckless, Abby. You don't mind my calling you Abby, do you? It rolls off the tongue more easily. Let's see, if you last till the picking's over, I'll treat you to an evening out. Restaurant of your choice, candlelit dinner, wine and liqueurs. I'll put on my best suit and you can wear something frivolously feminine. How does that grab you?"

"It sounds like an offer I can't refuse," I answered, with a slight twinge of conscience over my boy friend, Gordon, in faraway Ardcote.

"Great!" exclaimed Toby. "The prospect will sustain me through the weary weeks ahead."

W HETHER it was the incentive of dinner with Toby, or sheer coincidence, I'll never know but, shortly after our conversation, my daffodil-picking began to click.

What was even more amazing was that, after a few days, I was bringing in my twenty-eight lots and more. I was never a speed merchant but I was consistent and conscientious, which was maybe why, as the flower season passed its peak on Mothering Sunday and the inevitable lay-offs began, I was still amongst the hard core regulars, plodding along at my own practised pace.

Now, as William the foreman stomped between the rows, bellowing "Crib time! Stop picking. Get your crib!", I gladly unbent my back and trudged with the other pickers to the spot in the hedge where we had left our crib bags. Crib, Toby's definition, was our rustic tea-break and provided a welcome interlude from the mechanical routine of flower-picking.

Toby was sheltering from the lashing rain beneath an overhang of gorse, his back pressed against the solid, Cornish bank. He was a short distance from everyone else and I joined him.

I peeled off my slimy, household gloves and took out my flask. I poured my coffee and got as much comfort from wrapping my numb fingers around the hot beaker as I did from sipping its scalding contents.

A DAY ON THE RIVER

The four little Robins thoroughly enjoy themselves in the Captain's rowing boat.

"I don't think you ought to play on the beach today," said Captain Rock-Pipit to his little guests on the morning after the big storm. "The sea is still rather cross!"

The four little Robins looked disappointed, but they soon cheered up when the Captain suggested that they took his rowing-boat and spent a day on the tiny river that wound its way through Sand Hopper Bay down to the sea.

So directly after breakfast, Captain Rock-Pipit and the two Robin fathers launched the rowing-boat, and then everyone stood on the river bank, watching as the four little Robins sailed upstream between the tall reeds and rushes.

Rosemary had promised that she would look after Rowena most carefully, and so, as Richard and Roley took an oar each, she sat in the stern of the boat with her baby cousin.

They saw several of Captain Rock-Pipit's river friends—the Water Rats and the Herons—and then, when they were sitting on the grassy bank eating the delicious picnic lunch that Mrs. Rock-Pipit had prepared for them, who should come sailing along but Mrs. Duck and her two ducklings—Desmond and Doris. She knew the little Robins were spending the day on the river, and had promised to keep an eye on them.

Mrs. Duck and her jolly little ducklings spent the afternoon with Roley and Rosemary and their cousins, and how pleased the little Robins were, when, as a special treat, she gave them all a ride on her back, before it was time to row back to The Old Boat House!

"The joys in my life are becoming very basic," I remarked to Toby.

He nodded understandingly. "I know what you mean. Like not wearing a leaky set of oilskins on a day like this, or getting a row of daffs that are all at the right stage for picking, or discovering that the itch on your hand isn't flower rash. Best of all, hosing off the mud at the end of the day and feeling civilised because you've got clean wellies."

"I was thinking about Wordsworth's poem earlier," I mused. "There's not much of the 'beside the lake, beneath the trees, fluttering and dancing in the breeze' in this job, is there?"

"Regrettably, no," Toby agreed, eyeing the lines of greenery that whirled like dervishes in the buffeting wind. "And 'I gazed and gazed but little thought what wealth the show to me had brought,' has somehow gained a mercenary significance. Though I don't suppose Wordsworth ever visualised brown wage packets when he wrote about 'wealth'."

TOBY'S innocent mention of money brought back my pressing worry. He noticed my frown and asked: "What's the matter, Abby? You're very down today. Is there anything I can do to help?"

I shook my head. "Not unless you'd care to donate a few of your lots to increase my piecework."

"Are you that short of cash?"

"I'm that short of Lorraine," I said, managing a wry smile. "She cleared off yesterday whilst I was at work. Didn't even leave me a note, but the fact that she's taken all her belongings makes it look like a permanent move. I simply can't afford to live in the flat by myself and, even if I leave, I've got to give Mrs. Pascoe, our landlady, a month's notice. So I've got to find four weeks' rent from somewhere."

"It won't be so easy to get another flat either," said Toby, stating the unpleasant obvious. "Not with the tourist season approaching. Most property is let to visitors at sky-high rates. I've been lucky myself, being able to winter in my brother Ken's holiday home, otherwise I wouldn't be here now. Mind you," he added ruefully, "there might be something to be said for that."

I sighed deeply. "It's beginning to look as though I shall have to go home to Ardcote."

"Would that be so bad?" Toby queried gently. "After all, haven't you got a Prince Charming languishing away for you there?"

Continued overleaf

39

I thought guiltily of my long-suffering Gordon. I couldn't expect him to put his future in limbo for ever, on my behalf. Huskily handsome, utterly dependable (if somewhat conservative in his attitudes), Gordon offered me marriage and a ready-made home in one of Ardcote's superior suburbs. I was, as my mother kept telling me, an extremely lucky girl to have such an attractive and persistent suitor.

And I *was* very fond of Gordon, who at thirty-three was ten years my senior. Only, sometimes, he seemed more like a father-figure than a potential husband. Perhaps that was why I had resisted his proposals of marriage so doggedly. I felt I needed a breathing-space, away from Ardcote, before making such a serious commitment.

At around the same time, my friend Lorraine had decided to pursue her artistic ambitions down in Cornwall, where she had contacts in a craft centre in the small harbour town of Tredhu. So, we had thrown in our lots together. Lorraine concentrated on her gift for quilting and embroidery, whilst I divided my time between serving in the craft centre's shop and helping with the secretarial side of things there, until they closed down for the winter and I was made redundant.

"Well?" said Toby, bringing me back to the present. "It is a sensible solution, isn't it?"

"I'm not so sure that Gordon is languishing as wholeheartedly as he once did," I confessed. "It's all my fault. I know he's exasperated with me. You see, he thought I'd come back to Ardcote when I finished at the craft centre, but I decided to stay on. He's absolutely furious that I got this job flower-picking as well. He says I'm lowering myself." I bit my lip. "He was right about Lorraine, too. He always said she was irresponsible and self-centred, and that one day she would let me down. He did promise he would bale me out if that ever happened but . . ."

"But it's not easy to have to swallow humble pie," Toby finished for me, with his unnerving ability to read my mind. "I should know. I once thought I was going to set the world of science fiction alight with my literary genius. I even went so far as to chuck in a safe career in computers, so as to concentrate on my writing.

A poor Indian chief . . . made a wiser reply than any philosopher to someone complaining that he had not enough time. "Well," said Red Jacket, "I suppose you have all there is."

Emerson

"It seemed like Providence was with me when Ken bought the cottage at Boskay and let me live in it rent-free, in return for doing some renovations. Chiefly, though, it was to give me a base where I could scribble undisturbed. Ken's got faith in me, you see. Which is, apparently, more than the publishers have."

Toby paused, shook the dregs out of his beaker and screwed it back on his flask with a resigned shrug. "Take the advice of a qualified failure, Abby. Close this chapter in your life and start afresh. If you believe that means going back to your Gordon, do so as quickly as you can."

I STORED Toby's homily under the pro's for returning to Ardcote, acutely aware that he had revealed more about himself in the space of a few minutes than in the whole of the five weeks I'd known him.

"Why didn't you tell me before that you're a writer?" I asked, as we began to pack up and go back to work.

"Aspiring writer," Toby corrected me firmly. "There's a subtle difference. Well, I don't talk about it much because it's a very private corner of my life. Does that make me sound rather an odd person?"

"Actually, I think you're an extremely nice person," I reassured him. "I'm going to miss you when the flower-picking's over."

Toby gave me a long, searching look before favouring me with a warm smile. "You know something, love? I'm going to miss your funny little face, too."

Toby's words and, most especially, his 'love', stayed with me as he turned up his collar against the weather and walked away along a row of flowers. I began to wonder if Lorraine had been correct when, just a few days ago, she had asserted: "You may try to convince yourself with clichés like 'strictly platonic' and 'just good friends', but I'd say your Toby is quite smitten with you." She had arched her shapely brows conspiratorially. "He's also, in a rather underfed way, a devastatingly attractive man. And if you can't see that, you want your eyes examining, and probably your head as well! I wonder how your Gordon would react if he were to find out about Toby?"

"There's nothing to find out. I hardly think being taken to the pictures a couple of times and having the occasional drink together constitutes a passionate affair!"

"It seems to me, Abigail Meacham, that you protest too much. You want to be careful. Two strings to your bow! Aren't you getting a little ambitious?"

"There speaks the violin section of the Hallé Orchestra, I suppose?"

"Miaow and touché," Lorraine acknowledged, with a toss of her rippling black hair. We had both begun to laugh.

Now I wondered if, even then, she had made her plans to leave, although she had always boasted that she was a creature of impulse. In any case, no matter where she had gone I guessed that, with her carefree sophistication and bohemian beauty, she would land on her pretty feet, with a strong, good-looking male rushing to support her.

O F course, she might have had second thoughts, I told myself in a burst of optimism as I turned the key in the latch. But the flat received me, cold and still Lorraine-less. Only the golden silks and some sequins from her latest creation, still sparkling on the carpet, betrayed the fact she had ever lived in Flat D.

However, on a more cheerful note, there was a letter from Gordon, postmarked yesterday evening, which I picked up with a surge of tenderness. I wondered if he had received my distress signals via telepathy — a concept he pooh-poohed, along with womanly intuition. He wasn't normally a great letter-writer but, judging by the bulk of the envelope, this time he had done himself proud.

As Gordon had made such a special effort, I decided his letter deserved to be treated with respect. And so I got out of my grubby work clothes, had a good wash and changed into a clean jumper and jeans. I combed and fluffed up my hair, put on some make-up and surveyed the results in the mirror. It was not quite up to Gordon standards, but was a distinct improvement on the uncultivated, weather-beaten look.

Then I went into the kitchen, put a pastie in the oven to heat, brewed myself a pot of tea and, finally, sat down at the breakfast bar to give Gordon my undivided attention.

His letter began 'My dear Abigail' and ended 'Still with affection, Gordon'. In between reading salutation and valediction, my world turned an agonisingly slow 180 degrees, then ground to a complete standstill.

I ploughed from one well-formed, broad-nibbed word to the next, from one expensive parchment sheet to another. The oddest part was that the words seemed so familiar. Familiar, that is, from books, films and plays but never, till now, real life. They were heavily clichéd. I imagined the effort it must have taken Gordon to write them. But he had too much integrity for them not to be the truth.

If Gordon said he had met Joanne quite innocently, I knew this must be so. If he said she had merely come to his insurance company for professional advice after her home was broken into, that must have been the way it began.

If Gordon said she was charming, sensitive and kind, then I knew she was. That she had come to rely on him and needed him in a way I never had, I did not doubt for a second. And who was I to argue the point that I was the one who had always been doubtful about our getting married?

E VERYTHING he said made such calm, concise sense. Yet, for a while, my brain refused to assimilate the information it had received. I sat there, not crying, just stunned. I thought, inconsequentially, of Toby and wondered if one of his computers would be better qualified for the task of unravelling the mess I had made of my life.

"What you need," advised an eminently sensible voice in my head, "is to get that hot pastie inside you. You can't think straight on an empty stomach."

Apparently, thinking on a full one wasn't much use either. I pushed the empty plate away and aimlessly sipped another mug of tea.

From the breakfast bar, I gazed out of the kitchen window over the lichened rooftops below, to where the grey-green sea swell rolled and thundered against Tredhu's harbour wall. I wistfully recalled the brave day when Lorraine and I had arrived in Tredhu, full of boundless enthusiasm for our Cornish adventure.

The sea was calm then and Mediterranean-blue. Brightly-sailed yachts dotted the bay and busy-engined fishing boats cut their way homeward, with their wheeling escorts of shrieking gulls. The beauty of that evening had seemed such a propitious omen. It had inspired optimism and, at Lorraine's suggestion, a cider toast to "Tomorrow, the first day of the rest of our lives!"

Yes, tomorrow, I reassured myself. Things won't seem so disastrous then. I studiously ignored Toby's dismal saying which flapped about in my subconscious — after all, this time, things really could not get any worse!

Continued overleaf

I COUGHED, blew my nose for the hundredth time, and looked at the flat face of my digital alarm clock. Its fluorescent green figures told five past seven, post meridian.

So much for the first day of the rest of my life! It had been spent most inauspiciously in bed, full of cold, thoroughly dejected, and feeling utterly alone and unloved. I vowed that, henceforth, I would never look for another silver lining. Nor would I rise from my comfortable, warm bed to answer the ring of the doorbell.

It was becoming, however, a very persistent ring. Someone clearly felt a desperate need to communicate with me. Muttering to myself, I reluctantly forsook the blankets.

"Hello! You were a long time answering," Toby accused me, his finger still poised over the bellpush. Then he noticed my dressing gown. "I'm sorry, did I get you out of your bath?"

"No," I sniffed miserably. "You got me out of my bed."

"Poor Abby. There was I, thinking you had skived a day off work and gone out on the razzle, and all the time you were laid up in bed, nursing a cold."

"Do you have to sound so pleased about my misfortune?" I huffed.

"But I am. Pleased that I've found you in that is," Toby amended, then his brow furrowed disappointedly. "I was going to suggest that we might go out for a drink and chicken-in-the-basket at the Clipper. But I can see you're not up to it. We'll make it another night, when you're feeling better."

In my idiotically maudlin state of mind, I felt my bottom lip begin to tremble, like a child who's been deprived of a promised treat.

"Poor shrimpling. You are in the dumps," he sympathised, draping a conciliatory arm around my shoulders. "Tell you what, how would it be if I buzzed off and got us some fish and chips whilst you heat the plates, butter some bread and put the kettle on for a pot of tea?"

"It sounds just what the doctor ordered." I brightened up considerably. "So long as you don't mind risking my germs."

"I'm sure your germs are extremely well-bred and know their place," Toby soothed me. "Now get cracking: I'll be back before you can say 'Jack Robinson'."

I had recited several hundred 'Jack Robinson's' before Toby returned. But by then the flat's tiny sitting-room was warmed through and, with its cottage-style furniture and electric fire's flickering-coals-effect, gave a passable illusion of homeliness.

"This is very cosy," Toby approved, expertly waitering the fish and chips, whilst I carried in the tea-tray. "I wonder who invented this admirable British custom?"

"I don't know, but it was a smashing idea to uphold it. Thank you, Toby."

"My pleasure. It was for a smashing lady."

"There are some who might argue that point. Me included," I observed ruefully.

"Things not going too well with your Gordon?" Toby queried astutely.

"Come to a jarring halt, actually. He's not *my* Gordon any more." I astonished myself with the ease with which that sad little phrase slipped out. "He informed me via a 'Dear Abigail' letter. It was waiting for me when I got home yesterday."

"You do seem to get insults added to your injuries, don't you?" Toby commiserated. "But try and put your worries aside for ten minutes. Concentrate on the pressing problem of despatching those fish and chips before they get cold."

I took Toby's advice and, quarantining myself at the opposite end of the sofa, applied myself diligently to the fish and chips. There was a conversational lull as we munched. I suspected that this was the first square meal Toby had had all day, judging by the relish with which he cleared his plate.

"Well done, Abby," Toby praised, as my last chip vanished, too. "Feel any better?"

"At least a couple of pounds," I smiled at him. "Anyway, let's not raise the boring subject of me again. Tell me what's been happening in the great world outside."

‸

TOBY stretched out his legs and clasped his hands behind his head. He looked completely at home, and the thought that he seemed settled for the evening heartened me immensely.

"Oh, this and that," he answered rather cryptically. "For a start, you were very conspicuous by your absence. Fact is, it made me realise how important you've become to me. There! That's a confession you wouldn't have heard if you hadn't received Gordon's letter. It also helps considerably not to have your friend Lorraine around. An exceptionally beautiful girl, Lorraine. But rather like a praying mantis in butterfly's clothing. She always gave me the impression she was about to put me on her evening menu. I take it her whereabouts are still a mystery?"

"As unexplained as the Bermuda Triangle."

"So, you're still in financial straits and, not to put too fine a point on it, your Gordon won't be bailing you out."

"Look here, Toby Gallagher," I tackled him firmly. "All of a sudden you're wearing a very smug expression. I don't like smug expressions. They make me feel I'm missing out on something."

"You are, and it's high time I told you." His self-possession disintegrated into pure, little-boy excitement as he broke his news in a low and vibrant voice, as though he hardly believed what he was saying. "Abby, I heard from a publisher today. I've had my first book accepted!"

"Oh Toby! That's fantastic news. But why on earth didn't you tell me before? How could you sit there like the Sphinx, listening to my silly chatter, whilst all the time . . ."

"It wasn't easy," Toby confessed, with his endearing, lop-sided smile. He scrutinised my animated face. "Are you really as pleased as you look?"

"I'm on cloud nine for you! I feel like laughing and crying all at once."

"I'm glad. I wanted you to be the first to know. Even before Ken or the rest of my family." He paused and gazed at me fondly. "Don't you think that in itself is rather revealing?"

He moved up the sofa, took my hand, and pressed it gently between his own warm palms. "Hey! Don't look so dismayed."

My cheeks crimsoned. "Toby, I've probably got it all wrong, but I'm scared that, very soon, you're going to say something which'll mean I have to make the leap from broken to budding romance. I can't do that in the space of twenty-four hours. Not even for you," I told him softly.

"Listen to me," counselled Toby firmly. "I shall mention the dreaded four-letter word just once. I love you, Abby. And all the symptoms tell me that it's an incurable condition. But I can understand your being uncertain of your feelings for me and, the way things are, it would not be fair on you to test them at this moment. So, any proposal I might make to you this evening is going to be of a strictly business nature. Okay?"

"Okay."

Toby examined my fingers thoughtfully. The joints, swollen from concentrated flower-picking, did not make them a particularly attractive sight but he did not seem to mind.

"These can type, can't they?" he asked at last.

"Yes. Quite rapidly."

"Good." Toby beamed. "The fact is, I had quite a long talk over the phone with the publisher. Not only are they prepared to accept one book, but they'd like to see more of my work. Unfortunately, most of that is either in longhand or typed manuscripts which have been so much revised that I'm the only person who can make any sense of them. I desperately need them re-copied."

"Are you offering me the job?"

"I'd pay you the proper rate. Don't worry, I'm not as penurious as I appear. I was a very thrifty lad for several years before I took my wholehearted plunge into writing."

"Then whatever possessed you to go flower-picking?" I enquired incredulously.

"Perhaps it was to give myself a short, sharp shock of reality," Toby suggested, amused. "It also gave me you. So let's not decry it too vehemently."

HE put his arm around my shoulders and gently drew me closer to him. I snuggled my head against his chest. The steady rhythm of his breathing and his hand absent-mindedly caressing my hair helped to reassure me that the world was not such a hard, comfortless place after all.

"Mind you," Toby chuckled, "you realise that my offer of employment now claims precedence over your loyalty to Daniel Kitto?"

"You mean, no more flower-picking?" I queried blissfully.

"In a bunch of Ice Follies, yes!" Toby confirmed, and then went on to comment blandly: "I take it, however, that your motive for casting in your lot with me is not one of pure escapism. May I go even further to predict that, once the mists have cleared from your mind, you'll be able to appreciate my vision of a mutually satisfying partnership together, from both its commercial and romantic aspects!"

"Just promise me one thing, Toby." I looked up at him shyly. "Just in case a certain four-letter word should be raised again. I know it sounds silly, but what with Daniel Kitto, and working through all sorts of ghastly weather, and seeing those horrid daffodils row upon row nearly every day, I have become — florally speaking — terribly jaded. So, if you should want to say, you know . . ."

Toby gave me a squeeze and kissed my cheek lightly. "I get the message, shrimpling. Cross my heart and hope to die. To you, Abby, I hereby solemnly vow and promise that the next time I mention a certain word, I shall do so without the aid of a single, solitary flower!"

THE END

Josephine Preston, 1982

43

TOP TO TOE LAYETTE

Shawl, crossover vest, matinee jacket, angel top, dress, leggings, bootees, bonnet and helmet

In one size only. Colour photo on page 23

MATERIALS: *Allow the following quantities in 20 g balls of Robin Bambino Courtelle and Nylon in 3-ply and 4-ply:*
SHAWL: *12 balls of 3-ply; a pair each of No. 6 (5 mm) and No. 8 (4 mm) knitting needles.*
MATINEE JACKET, DRESS AND ANGEL TOP: *4 balls of 4-ply for each garment; a pair of No. 10 (3¼ mm) knitting needles; a No. 10 (3¼ mm) circular needle; 3 buttons; 1 metre of narrow lace.* **BOOTEES:** *1 ball of 4-ply; a pair of No. 10 (3¼ mm) knitting needles; ¾ metre of narrow ribbon* **THE BONNET:** *1 ball of 4-ply; a pair each of No. 10 (3¼ mm) and No. 11 (3 mm) knitting needles; 1 metre of 2·5 cm (1 inch) wide ribbon.* **THE VEST:** *2 balls of 3-ply; a pair of No. 10 (3¼ mm) needles; 1 metre of narrow ribbon.* **THE LEGGINGS:** *4 balls of 4-ply; a pair of No. 10 (3¼ mm) knitting needles; 41 cm (16 inches) of narrow ribbon; a waist length of elastic.*
THE HELMET: *1 ball of 4-ply; a pair of No. 10 (3¼ mm) knitting needles; 1 button.*
TENSION AND MEASUREMENTS: *Worked at a tension of 28 stitches and 34 rows to measure 10 × 10 cm over the stocking stitch, using No. 10 (3¼ mm) needles and 4-ply, and 30 stitches and 38 rows to measure 10× 10 cm over the stocking stitch, using No. 10 (3¼ mm) needles and 3-ply and 24 stitches and 30 rows to measure 10 × 10 cm, over the pattern, using No. 10 (3¼ mm) needles and 4-ply, the layette will be suitable for a 46 cm (18 inch) chest size.* **SHAWL:** *106 cm (41¾ inches) × 106 cm (41¾ inches).* **MATINEE JACKET:** *Side seam, 15 cm (6 inches); length, 25 cm (9¾ inches); sleeve seam, 16 cm (6¼ inches).* **DRESS:** *Side seam, 19·5 cm (7¾ inches); length, 29·5 cm (11½ inches); sleeve seam, 3 cm (1¼ inches).* **ANGEL TOP:** *Side seam, 15 cm (6 inches); length, 25 cm (10 inches); sleeve seam, 16 cm (6¼ inches).* **BOOTEES:** *Foot length, 8·5 cm (3¼ inches).* **BONNET:** *All round face edge, 34 cm (13½ inches); depth, 13 cm (5 inches).* **VEST:** *Side seam, 16 cm (6¼inches); length, 26 cm (10¼ inches); sleeve seam, 4 cm (1½ inches).* **LEGGINGS:** *All round at widest part, 66 cm (26 inches).* **HELMET:** *All round face edge, 37 cm (14½ inches).*

ABBREVIATIONS: To be read before working: *K., knit plain; p., purl; st., stitch; tog., together; inc., increase (by working twice into next st.); dec., decrease (by taking 2 sts. tog.); s.s., stocking st. (k. on the right side and p. on the wrong side); single rib is k. 1 and p. 1 alternately; g.st., garter st. (k. plain on every row); y.r.n., yarn round needle to make a st.; y.o.n., yarn over needle to make a st.; sl.; slip; p.s.s.o., pass sl. st. over; s.k.p.o., sl. 1, k. 1, p.s.s.o.; y. fwd., yarn forward to make a st.; m.st., moss st.*

NOTE: *Instructions in brackets are worked the number of times stated after the last bracket.*

THE SHAWL

TO MAKE THE CENTRE: With No. 8 (4 mm) needles and 3-ply yarn cast on 217 sts. and work in pattern as follows:

1st row: P. 1, * k. 3, p. 1; repeat from * to end.

2nd row: K. 1, * p. 3, k. 1; repeat from * to end.

3rd row: P. 1, * y.o.n., sl. 1, k. 2 tog., p.s.s.o., y.r.n., p. 1; repeat from * to end.

4th row: As 2nd row.

5th row: K. 2, * p. 1, k. 3; repeat from * ending last repeat with k. 2.

6th row: P. 2, * k. 1, p. 3; repeat from * ending last repeat with p. 2.

7th row: K. 2 tog., y.r.n., * p. 1, y.o.n., sl. 1, k. 2 tog., p.s.s.o., y.r.n.; repeat from * until 3 sts. remain, p. 1, y.o.n., s.k.p.o.

8th row: As 6th row.

Repeat the last 8 rows, 35 times more. Cast off.

THE BORDER (4 pieces alike): With long No. 6 (5 mm) needles cast on 227 sts.

1st row: K. 1, p. until 1 st. remains, k. 1.

Change to No. 8 (4 mm) needles.

1st row: K. 2, * y.fwd., k.6, sl. 1, k. 2 tog., p.s.s.o., k.6, y.fwd., k. 1; repeat from * until 1 st. remains, k. 1.

2nd and every alternate row: K. 2 tog., p. until 2 sts. remain, k. 2 tog.

3rd row: K. 2, * y.fwd., k. 5, sl. 1, k. 2 tog., p.s.s.o., k. 5, y.fwd., k. 1, y.fwd., k. 2 tog.; repeat from * ending last repeat with k. 2 instead of k. 1, y.fwd., k. 2 tog.

5th row: K. 2, * y.fwd., k. 4, sl. 1, k. 2 tog.,

p.s.s.o., k. 4, y.fwd., k. 1, (y.fwd., k. 2 tog.) twice; repeat from * until 13 sts. remain, y.fwd., k. 4, sl. 1, k. 2 tog., p.s.s.o., k. 4, y.fwd., k. 2.

7th row: K. 2, * y.fwd., k. 3, sl. 1, k. 2 tog., p.s.s.o., k. 3, y.fwd., k. 1, (y.fwd., k. 2 tog.) 3 times; repeat from * until 11 sts. remain, y.fwd., k. 3, sl. 1, k. 2 tog., p.s.s.o, k. 3, y.fwd., k. 2.

9th row: K. 2, * y.fwd., k. 2, sl. 1, k. 2 tog., p.s.s.o., k. 2, y.fwd., k. 1, (y.fwd., k. 2 tog.) 4 times; repeat from * until 9 sts remain, y.fwd., k. 2, sl. 1, k. 2 tog., p.s.s.o., k. 2, y.fwd., k. 2.

11th row: K. 2, * y.fwd., k. 1, sl. 1, k. 2 tog., p.s.s.o., k. 1, y.fwd., k. 1, (y.fwd., k. 2 tog.) 5 times; repeat from * until 7 sts. remain, y.fwd., k. 1, sl. 1, k. 2 tog., p.s.s.o., k. 1, y.fwd., k. 2.

13th row: K. 2, * y.fwd., sl. 1, k. 2 tog., p.s.s.o., y.fwd., k. 1, (y.fwd., k. 2 tog.) 6 times; repeat from * until 5 sts. remain, y.fwd., sl. 1, k. 2 tog., p.s.s.o., y.fwd., k. 2.

15th row: K. 2, * y.fwd., k. 2 tog.; repeat from * until 5 sts. remain, y.fwd., sl. 1, k. 2 tog., p.s.s.o., y.fwd., k.2.

16th row: As 2nd row.

17th to 20th rows: Repeat 15th and 16th rows, twice — 207 sts. Cast off.

TO MAKE UP THE SHAWL: Press work very lightly on the wrong side, using a cool iron over a dry cloth. Join cast-off edges of borders to sides of centre piece, then join corner seams.

———THE MATINEE JACKET———

THE BACK: With No. 10 (3¼ mm) needles and 4-ply yarn cast on 97 sts.

M.st. row: K. 1, * p. 1, k. 1; repeat from * to end.

M.st. 3 more rows.

Repeat the 8 pattern rows given for shawl centre, 7 times.

To shape the armholes: Cast off 3 sts. at the beginning of each of the next 2 rows, then dec. 1 st. at each end of the following 5 right side rows — 81 sts. **

Next (dec.) row: * P. 2 tog., p. 1; repeat from * to end — 54 sts.

Break off yarn and leave sts. on a spare needle for yoke.

THE LEFT FRONT: With No. 10 (3¼ mm) needles cast on 54 sts.

1st m.st. row: * K. 1, p. 1; repeat from * to end.

2nd row: * P. 1, k. 1; repeat from * to end. M.st. 1 more row.

Next row: M.st. 5 and leave on a safety pin for front border, m.st. to end — 49 sts.

*** Work 56 rows in pattern as given for shawl centre — work 57 rows here when working right front.

To shape the armhole: Cast off 3 sts. at the beginning of the next row, then 1 st. at the same edge on the 5 following right side rows — 41 sts.

Next (dec.) row: P. 2 tog., * p. 1, p. 2 tog.;

repeat from * to end — 27 sts.

Break off yarn and leave sts. on a spare needle.

THE RIGHT FRONT: With No. 10 (3¼ mm) needles cast on 54 sts.

Beginning with a 2nd row, m.st. 3 rows as given for left front.

Next row: M.st. until 5 sts. remain, turn and leave these sts. on a safety pin for front border — 49 sts.

Work as given for left front from *** to end, noting variation.

THE SLEEVES (both alike): With No. 10 (3¼ mm) needles cast on 37 sts. and work 6 rows in m.st. as given for back.

Next (inc.) row: * K. 3, inc.; repeat from * until 5 sts. remain, k. to end — 45 sts.

Beginning with the second pattern row as given for shawl, pattern 15 rows.

Maintaining continuity of the pattern and taking extra sts. into the pattern as they occur, inc. 1 st. at each end of the next row and the 3 following 8th rows — 53 sts.

Pattern 15 rows.

To shape the sleeve top: Work as given for armhole shaping on back to ** when 37 sts. will remain.

Next (dec.) row: P.7, * p.2 tog., p.8; repeat from * to end — 34 sts. Break off yarn and leave sts. on a spare needle.

THE YOKE: With right side of work facing, sl. the 27 sts. of left front, 34 sts. of left sleeve, 54 sts. of back, 34 sts. of right sleeve, then the 27 sts. of right front on to a No. 10 (3¼ mm) circular needle — 176 sts.

Working backwards and forwards in rows, beginning with a k. row, s.s. 2 rows.

1st (dec.) row: K. 8, * s.k.p.o., k. 2 tog., k. 8; repeat from * to end.

Beginning with a p. row, s.s. 5 rows.

Continued overleaf

2nd (dec.) row: K. 7, * s.k.p.o., k. 2 tog., k. 6; repeat from * until 1 st. remains, k. 1.

S.s. 5 rows.

3rd (dec.) row: K. 6, * s.k.p.o., k. 2 tog., k. 4; repeat from * until 2 sts. remain, k. 2.

S.s. 5 rows.

4th (dec.) row: K. 5, * s.k.p.o., k. 2 tog., k. 2; repeat from * until 3 sts. remain, k. 3.

S.s. 3 rows.

5th (dec.) row: Sl. 1, k. 2 tog., p.s.s.o., * k. 2, s.k.p.o.; repeat from * until 1 st. remains, k. 1 — 47 sts.

Break off yarn and leave sts. on a spare needle.

THE RIGHT FRONT BORDER: With wrong side of work facing, sl. the 5 sts. on safety pin at right front on to a No. 10 (3¼ mm) needle and work 71 rows in m.st.

Next (buttonhole) row: P. 1, k. 1, y.fwd., k. 2 tog., p. 1.

M.st. 13 rows, then repeat the buttonhole row. .

M.st. 12 rows. Break off yarn and leave sts. on a safety pin.

Sew on border.

THE LEFT FRONT BORDER: With right side of work facing, sl. the 5 sts. on safety pin at left front on to a No. 10 (3¼ mm) needle and work 97 rows in m.st.

Do not break off yarn.

Sew on border.

THE NECK BORDER: With wrong side of work facing, m.st. across 5 sts. of left front border, the 47 sts. of yoke and the 5 sts. of right front border — 57 sts.

Next (buttonhole) row: P. 1, k. 1, y.fwd., k. 2 tog., m.st. to end.

M.st. a further 2 rows. Cast off.

TO MAKE UP THE MATINEE JACKET: Press work lightly on the wrong side, using a cool iron over a dry cloth. Join tiny underarm seams, then join sleeve and side seams. Sew on buttons. Sew lace trimming to bottom of yoke.

————————THE DRESS————————

THE BACK: With No. 10 (3¼ mm) needles cast on 93 sts. M.st. 4 rows, and work 72 rows in pattern as shawl centre — work 56 rows here when working angel top.

To shape the armhole and divide for back opening: Next row: Cast off 3, pattern to end.

Next row: Cast off 3, pattern a further 41 sts. and leave these 42 sts. on a spare needle for left half back, p. 3 and leave these sts. on a safety pin for border, pattern to end work on these 42 sts. for right half back.

The right half back: Dec. 1 st. at armhole edge on the next row and the 4 following right side rows — 37 sts.

Dec. row: P. 2, * p. 2 tog., p. 1, p. 2 tog., p. 2; repeat from * to end — 27 sts.

Break of yarn and leave sts. on a spare needle for yoke.

The left half back: With right side of work facing, rejoin yarn to inner end of sts. on spare needle and work as given for right half back to end.

THE FRONT: With No. 10 (3¼ mm) needles cast on 93 sts.

Work as back until armhole shaping is reached.

To shape the armholes: Cast off 3 sts. at the beginning of each of the next 2 rows, then dec. 1 st. at each end of the next row and the 4 following right side rows — 77 sts.

Next (dec.) row: * P. 2 tog., p. 1, p. 2 tog., p. 2; repeat from * ending last repeat with p. 2 tog. instead of p. 2 — 54 sts.

THE SLEEVES (both alike): With No. 10 (3¼ mm) needles cast on 41 sts. and work 4 rows in m.st. as given for back of matinee jacket.

Next (inc.) row: K. 3, * inc., k. 2; repeat from * until 2 sts. remain, k. 2 — 53 sts.

Beginning with the 2nd pattern row as given for shawl, pattern 7 rows.

To shape the sleeve top: Work as given for armhole shaping on back of matinee jacket, when 37 sts. will remain.

Next (dec.) row: P. 7, * p. 2 tog., p. 8; repeat from * to end — 34 sts.

Break off yarn and leave sts. on a spare needle for yoke.

THE YOKE: With right side of work facing, sl. the 27 sts. of right half back, 34 sts. of right sleeve, 54 sts. from front, 34 sts. from left sleeve and 27 sts. of left half back on to a No. 10 (3¼ mm) circular needle — 176 sts.

Work as given for yoke on matinee jacket to end.

Break off yarn and leave sts. on a spare needle.

THE LEFT BACK BORDER: With No. 10 (3¼ mm) needles cast on 4 sts. and repeat the m.st. row given for the right front on matinee jacket, 39 times.

Break off yarn and leave sts. on a safety pin. Sew on border.

THE RIGHT BACK BORDER: With right side of work facing, sl. the 3 sts. on safety pin on to a No. 10 (3¼ mm) needle.

1st row: Inc., k. 1, p. 1 — 4 sts.

M.st. 11 rows.

Next (buttonhole) row: K. 1, y.fwd., k. 2 tog., p. 1.

M.st. 13 rows.

Repeat the buttonhole row again.

M.st. a further 12 rows.

Do not break off yarn. Sew on border.

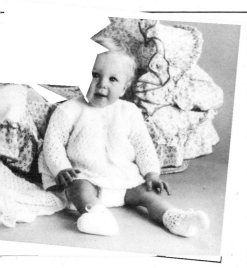

7, k. 2 tog., pick up and k. 10 sts. down other side of instep and finally, k. 11 sts. from safety pin — 51 sts.

S.s. 7 rows.

To shape for foot: 1st (dec.) row: K. 1, s.k.p.o., k. 18, s.k.p.o., k. 5, k. 2 tog., k. 18, k. 2 tog., k. 1.

K. 1 row.

2nd (dec.) row: K. 1, s.k.p.o., k. 17, s.k.p.o., k. 3, k. 2 tog., k. 17, k. 2 tog., k. 1.

K. 1 row.

3rd (dec.) row: K. 1, s.k.p.o., k. 16, s.k.p.o., k. 1, k. 2 tog., k. 16, k. 2 tog., k. 1.

K. 1 row.

4th (dec.) row: K. 1, s.k.p.o., k. 15, sl. 1, k. 2 tog., p.s.s.o., k. 15, k. 2 tog., k. 1 — 35 sts. Cast off k.wise.

TO MAKE UP THE BOOTEES: Press as given for matinee jacket. Join back and underfoot seam. Thread ribbon through slot row to tie at front.

THE BONNET

TO MAKE: With No. 10 (3¼ mm) needles and 4-ply, cast on 93 sts. and work 2 rows in m.st. as for back of matinee jacket.

Work 19 rows in pattern as given for shawl centre.

Dec. row: * P. 14, p. 2 tog.; repeat from * until 13 sts. remain, p. to end — 88 sts.

Change to No. 11 (3 mm) needles and work 5 rows in single rib.

Change back to No. 10 (3¼ mm) needles and, beginning with a k. row to reverse brim, s.s. 24 rows.

To shape the crown: 1st row: * K. 9, k. 2 tog.; repeat from * to end.

2nd and every alternate row: All p.

3rd row: * K. 8, k. 2 tog.; repeat from * to end — 72 sts.

Continue in this way, decreasing 8 sts. on every alternate row working 1 st. less between the decreases on each successive repeat of the dec. row for a further 7 dec. rows — 16 sts.

P. 1 row.

Next row: * K. 2 tog.; repeat from * to end — 8 sts.

Break off yarn leaving a long end, thread this through remaining sts., draw up tightly and fasten off securely. Join back seam for 5 cm (2 inches). Fold back brim.

THE EDGING: With right side of work facing and using No. 10 (3¼ mm) needles, pick up and k. 50 sts. around back neck edge, working through both thicknesses of brim.

Cast off p.wise.

TO COMPLETE THE BONNET: Press as for matinee jacket. Sew a length of ribbon to each side of brim.

Continued overleaf

THE NECK BORDER: With righ side of work facing, and using No. 10 (3¼ mm) needles, m.st. across 4 sts. of right back border, 47 sts. of yoke and 4 sts. of left back border — 55 sts.

Next (buttonhole) row: K. 1, y.fwd., k. 2 tog., m.st. to end. M.st. 2 rows. Cast off.

TO MAKE UP THE DRESS: Press as for matinee jacket. Join tiny underarm seams, then join sleeve and side seams. Catch down cast on edge of left back border, behind right border. Sew on buttons. Sew lace trimming to bottom of yoke.

THE ANGEL TOP

TO MAKE: Work back, front and yoke as given for dress, noting variations, then work sleeves as given for matinee jacket. Press and make up as given for dress.

THE BOOTEES

TO MAKE (both alike): With No. 10 (3¼ mm) needles and 4-ply, cast on 37 sts. and work 2 rows in m.st. as given for back of matinee jacket.

Work 16 rows in pattern as given for shawl centre.

Next (dec.) row: * K. 1, (p. 1, k. 1) 3 times, p. 2 tog.; repeat from * 3 times, k. 1 — 33 sts.

Next row: P. 1, * k. 1, p. 1; repeat from * to end. **Next (slot) row:** K. 1, * y.fwd., k. 2 tog.; repeat from * to end.

Rib 2 rows, then p. 1 row.

To divide for instep: Next row: K. 22, turn, leaving 11 sts. on a safety pin.

Next row: P. 11, turn, leaving remaining 11 sts. on a safety pin.

The instep: On centre 11 sts., s.s. 12 rows. Break off yarn.

With right side of work facing, sl. 11 sts. at right side on to a No. 10 (3¼ mm) needle with point to inner end, pick up and k. 10 sts. from row ends of instep, across instep sts., k. 2 tog., k.

47

THE VEST

THE BACK: With No. 10 (3¼ mm) needles and 3 ply cast on 68 sts. and k. 5 rows.

Beginning with a k. row, s.s. 58 rows.

To shape the armholes: Cast off 3 sts. at the beginning of each of the next 2 rows, then dec. 1 st. at each end of the next row and the 4 following right side rows — 52 sts.

S.s. 19 rows.

To slope the shoulders: Cast off 7 sts. at the beginning of each of the next 4 rows — 24 sts. Cast off.

THE LEFT FRONT: With No. 10 (3¼ mm) needles cast on 48 sts. and k. 4 rows.

Next row (wrong side): K. 4 and leave these sts. on a safety pin for border, k. to end — 44 sts.

Beginning with a k. row, s.s. 50 rows.

To slope the front edge: Dec. 1 st. at front edge on each of the next 2 rows.

Work 1 row.

Repeat the last 3 rows, once more, then the first 2 rows again — 38 sts.

To shape the armhole and continue sloping front edge: 1st row: Cast off 3 sts., k. to end.

2nd row: Dec., p. to end.

3rd row: Dec., k. until 2 sts. remain, dec.

4th row: P. to end

5th row: As 3rd row.

6th row: As 2nd row.

7th row: Dec., k. to end.

8th row: As 2nd row.

9th row: As 3rd row.

10th row: As 4th row.

11th row: As 3rd row.

12th row: As 2nd row.

13th row: K. to end.

Dec. 1 st. at front edge on each of the next 2 rows.

Work 1 row.

Repeat the last 3 rows, twice more, then the 1st 2 rows again — 14 sts.

**** S.s. 6 rows — s.s. 7 rows here when working right front.

To slope the shoulder: Cast off 7 sts. at the beginning of the next row — 7 sts.

Work 1 row, then cast off.

THE RIGHT FRONT: With No. 10 (3¼ mm) needles cast on 48 sts. and k. 4 rows.

Next row (wrong side): K. until 4 sts. remain, turn, leaving these 4 sts. on a safety pin for border — 44 sts.

Beginning with a k. row, s.s. 50 rows.

To slope the front edge: Dec. 1 st. at front edge on each of the next 2 rows.

Work 1 row.

Repeat the last 3 rows, twice — 38 sts.

To shape the armhole and continue sloping front edge: 1st row: Cast off 3, p. until 2 sts. remain, dec. **2nd row:** Dec., k. until 2 sts. remain, dec.

3rd row: All p.

4th row: As 2nd row.

5th row: P. until 2 sts. remain, dec.

6th row: K. until 2 sts. remain, dec.

7th row: As 5th row.

8th row: As 2nd row.

9th row: As 3rd row.

10th row: As 2nd row.

11th row: As 5th row.

12th row: All k.

Dec. 1 st. at front edge on each of the next 2 rows.

Work 1 row.

Repeat the last 3 rows, twice, then the 1st 2 rows again — 14 sts.

Work as given for left front from ******** to end, noting variation.

THE SLEEVES (both alike): With No. 10 (3¼ mm) needles cast on 42 sts. and k. 5 rows.

Beginning with a k. row, s.s. 2 rows.

Continuing in s.s., inc. 1 st. at each end of next row and following 4th row — 46 sts.

S.s. 5 rows.

To shape the sleeve top: Cast off 3 sts. at the beginning of each of the next 2 rows, then dec. 1 st. at each end of the next 12 rows — 16 sts. Cast off.

THE LEFT FRONT BORDER: First join shoulder seams. With right side of work facing and using No. 10 (3¼ mm) needles, work in g.st. until border is long enough when slightly stretched, to fit up left front to centre back neck, casting off when correct length is assured. Sew on border.

THE RIGHT FRONT BORDER: With wrong side of work facing and using No. 10 (3¼ mm) needles, work as given for left front border. Sew on border, joining cast-off edges together at centre back neck.

TO MAKE UP THE VEST: Press as for matinee jacket. Set in sleeves, then join sleeve and side seams, leaving a small opening in right seam, 2.5 cm (1 inch) below armhole. Sew narrow ribbon to each front border just below 1st front dec.

THE LEGGINGS

THE RIGHT LEG: With No. 10 (3¼ mm) needles and 4 ply cast on 74 sts. for waist and work 4 rows in single rib.

Next (slot) row: K. 1, * y.fwd., k. 2 tog., p. 1, k. 1; repeat from * until 1 st. remains, p. 1.

Rib 7 rows.

K. 1 row here when working left leg.

Work in s.s., shape for extra length on back as follows: **1st row:** K. 10, turn.

2nd and every alternate row: Sl. 1, p. to end.

3rd row: K. 20, turn.

Continue in this way, working 10 sts. more on each alternate row until 10 turning rows have been completed.

S.s. 2 rows — s.s. 1 row here when working left leg.

Continuing in s.s., inc. 1 st. at each end of the next row and the 8 following 6th rows — 92 sts.

S.s. 3 rows.

To shape the leg: Dec. 1 st. at each end of the next 9 rows and then on each end of the following 16 right side rows — 42 sts.

S.s. 21 rows, decreasing 1 st. at end of the last row — 41 sts.

Next (slot) row: K. 1, * y.fwd., k. 2 tog.; repeat from * to end.

S.s 3 rows. *****

To divide for instep: Next row: K. 33, turn, leaving remaining 8 sts. on a safety-pin.

Next row: P. 13, turn, leaving remaining 20 sts. on a safety-pin.

On these 13 sts., s.s. 14 rows. Break off yarn.

With right side of work facing, sl. the 20 sts. at right side on to a No. 10 (3¼ mm) needle, with point to inner end, pick up and k. 10 sts. from row ends of instep, across instep sts., k. 2 tog., k. 9, k. 2 tog., pick up and k. 10 sts. from other side of instep and, finally, k. 8 sts. from safety-pin — 59 sts.

S.s. 7 rows.

To shape for foot: 1st dec. row: K. 4, k. 2 tog., s.k.p.o., k. 22, s.k.p.o., k. 7, k. 2 tog., k. to end.

Next and every alternate row: All k.

2nd dec. row: K. 3, k. 2 tog., s.k.p.o., k. 21, s.k.p.o., k. 5, k. 2 tog., k. to end.

3rd dec. row: K. 2, k. 2 tog., s.k.p.o., k. 20, s.k.p.o., k. 3, k. 2 tog., k. to end.

4th dec. row: K. 1, k. 2 tog., s.k.p.o., k. 19, s.k.p.o., k. 1, k. 2 tog., k. to end.

5th dec. row: K. 2 tog., s.k.p.o., k. 18, sl. 1, k. 2 tog., p.s.s.o., k. to end — 39 sts.

Cast off k. wise.

THE LEFT LEG: Work as given for right leg to *****, noting the extra row to be worked after the waist ribbing, thus reversing the shaping for extra length on back, by reading p. for k. and k. for p.

To divide for instep: K. 21, turn, leaving remaining 20 sts. on a safety-pin.

Next row: P. 13, turn, leaving remaining 8 sts. on a safety-pin.

On these 13 sts., s.s. 14 rows. Break off yarn.

With right side of work facing, sl. the 8 sts. at right side on to a No. 10 (3¼ mm) needle with point to inner end, pick up and k. 10 sts. from row ends of instep, across instep sts., k. 2 tog., k. 9, k. 2 tog., pick up and k. 10 sts. from other side of instep and, finally, k. 20 sts. from safety-pin — 59 sts.

S.s. 7 rows.

To shape for foot: 1st dec. row: K. 18, s.k.p.o., k. 7, k. 2 tog., k. 22, k. 2 tog., s.k.p.o., k. 4.

Next and every alternate row: All k.

2nd dec. row: K. 18, s.k.p.o., k. 5, k. 2 tog., k. 21, k. 2 tog., s.k.p.o., k. 3.

Continue decreasing in this way on every alternate row until the 5th dec. row has been completed — 39 sts. Cast off k. wise.

TO MAKE UP THE LEGGINGS: Press as for matinee jacket. Join front and back seams. Join under-foot seams, then join leg seams. Thread length of narrow ribbon through slot row at ankles. Thread a length of elastic through slot row at waist and sew ends tog.

THE HELMET

THE BUTTONHOLE FLAP: With No. 10 (3¼ mm) needles and 4-ply cast on 3 sts.

1st row: P. 1, k. 1, p. 1.

2nd row: Inc., inc., p. 1.

3rd row: (P. 1, k. 1) twice, p. 1.

4th row: Inc., k. 1, p. 1, inc., k. 1 — 7 sts.

5th and 6th rows: K. 1, * p. 1, k. 1; repeat from * to end.

Buttonhole row: M.st. 3, y.fwd., k. 2 tog., p. 1, k. 1. M.st. 21 rows.

Inc. 1 st. at each end of the next row.

M.st. 3 rows.

Repeat the last 4 rows, 5 times more — 19 sts.

M.st. 4 rows. Break off yarn and leave sts. on a spare needle.

THE BUTTON FLAP: Work as for buttonhole flap, omitting buttonhole.

THE MAIN PART: With No. 10 (3¼ mm) needles cast on 8 sts., then on to this needle and with wrong side of work facing, m.st. 19 sts. of button flap, turn, cast on 43 sts., turn and with wrong side of work facing, m.st. 19 sts. of buttonhole flap, turn, cast on 8 sts. — 97 sts.

M.st. 6 rows. Work 32 rows of pattern as given for shawl centre.

To shape the crown: 1st dec. row: P. 1, * sl. 1, k. 2 tog., p.s.s.o., p. 1, (k. 1, p. 1) 4 times; repeat from * to end.

M.st. 3 rows. **2nd dec. row:** P. 1, * sl. 1, k. 2 tog., p.s.s.o., p. 1, (k. 1, p. 1) 3 times; repeat from * to end.

M.st. 3 rows. **3rd dec. row:** P. 1, * sl. 1, k. 2 tog., p.s.s.o., p. 1, (k. 1, p. 1) twice; repeat from * to end.

M.st. 3 rows. **4th dec. row:** P. 1, * sl. 1, k. 2 tog., p.s.s.o., p. 1, k. 1, p. 1; repeat from * to end. M.st. 3 rows.

5th dec. row: P. 1, * sl. 1, k. 2 tog., p.s.s.o., p. 1; repeat from * to end — 17 sts. M.st. 1 row.

6th dec. row: As 5th dec. row — 9 sts.

Break off yarn, leaving a long end, thread this through remaining sts., draw up tightly and fasten off securely.

TO MAKE UP THE HELMET: Press. Join back seam. Sew on button to correspond with buttonhole.

Slimming - the Nutritious Way

*This way of slimming will help you to lose weight
without undue cost, using health-giving, everyday foods which will
also benefit the rest of the family, says Diana de Quin*

Anne is a fully qualified dietician and is a member of the British Dietetic Association. Her working day is spent advising people how to re-design their eating patterns and most of the men and women she helps have the same problem — how best to lose weight.

When they meet her for the first time, it may occur to them that she is her own best advertisement. Her figure is slim, her skin good and her hair thick and shiny.

Her first step in interviewing a slimmer is to take the dietary history. She makes a careful list of the day's intake of food, and it helps her a great deal if the would-be slimmer is completely honest. It's very usual, she says, to be told "I eat hardly anything — no breakfast, a small snack at lunchtime and a meal in the evening". Yet the fact remains that the slimmer is already several stone overweight. It is her job to get at the truth, to help re-plan the entire eating pattern and get it onto a more balanced and sensible basis, at the same time reducing the calorific intake so that the patient does lose weight.

Her questions gradually build up the picture. "Do you take sugar?" "Do you drink alcohol?" "Do you eat sweets, chocolates, cakes, biscuits or any other extras?" Over-eaters, once they can be persuaded to admit the truth, are comparatively simple to treat but there are those who are genuinely low-intake eaters whose extra poundage was added years ago and who have stuck at the same weight ever since. These, explains Anne, do constitute more of a problem. Sometimes she asks a slimmer to write down everything she eats for a complete week and if she forgets to bring the telltale piece of paper with her, Anne reckons she's got the message!

Anne preaches the value of exercise — not so much to lose weight, as to tone the body and give a healthier attitude. A feeling of increased vitality is in itself an encouragement.

The latest ideas in diet aim at balance — cutting out a certain category of food, such as the carbohydrates, is not, in Anne's view, acceptable and could lead to trouble. She thinks it important to eat a reasonable quantity of some of the more bulky foods in order to provide roughage and the correct nourishment. Bulky foods are digested more slowly and foods high in dietary fibre — whole grain cereals, brown rice, brown pasta, vegetables and fruit — provide added bulk without many calories and are also the source of useful vitamins.

The overall plan then is to aim at giving yourself as much variety as possible while keeping the calorie intake low — 1,000 calories a day is what Anne advocates in order to lose weight. Here we should mention that the great advantage of this type of dieting is that no great extra cost is involved and that the rest of the family can eat the same foods with advantage. The emphasis is on cutting down rather than on cutting out.

Anne doesn't tell her patients exactly what to eat as she feels that personal preferences are important. You must be able to include as many as possible of your favourite foods or you won't stick to your diet. But there are limits and these are laid down in her diet suggestions. It is, however, according to her view better to cheat occasionally and stick to your diet in the main rather than try to be over-strict, lose heart and resign yourself to permanent overweight.

One of the problems of dieting which most slimmers experience is that they lose weight steadily for some weeks and then reach what Anne calls a "plateau" where their weight remains static. This is really disappointing for someone who has been trying hard. Faced with this situation she tries to talk her slimmer round, explaining the necessity for patience and suggesting that a little extra exercise just now could help. The regular pattern of weight loss will be resumed if the diet is adhered to.

HELPFUL HINTS

• On the diet advocated, the average weight loss should be two pounds per week. Don't be tempted to weigh yourself more than once a week and do it at the same time of day, on the same scales and wearing the same clothes.
• Have a weight goal and keep a record of progress.
• Drink plenty of water. Anne suggests a glass before a meal and another glass with the meal to help satisfy hunger.
• Sit down regularly, at specified times of the day and relax while eating, rather than "eat on the run".
• Use cooking methods which do not require the addition of fat. Remove as much fat from meat as possible before cooking.
• Sugar, sweet foods, soft drinks and alcohol are all to be avoided. Small amounts of artificial sweeteners as of the saccharin type are useful but try to adjust your tastes to less sweet foods. Tinned fruits should only be included if they are in natural, unsweetened juices.
• Flavour foods with herbs, spices, lemon juice, vinegar or other non-fattening seasonings. Cut out gravies and sauces as far as possible.
• Low calorie foods with a strong flavour like pickled onions add interest. Also useful are meat extract drinks, pure tomato juice and low-calorie drinks marketed for dieters.

Continued overleaf

DAILY FOOD PLAN — 1,000 CALORIES

BASIC PLAN	ALTERNATIVES (use amounts in basic plan unless otherwise stated).
Dairy Products ½ pint milk	One fluid oz. carton of plain unsweetened yoghurt to replace ¼ pint milk.
½ oz. butter 2 oz. English cheese	4 oz. cottage cheese.
Meat, Fish, Poultry 2 oz. meat, 3 oz. poultry, oily fish, 4 oz. white fish.	Beef, lamb, pork, gammon, offal, chicken, white fish, herring, mackerel, canned fish (drain off the oil) or canned meats.
Eggs 1 size 3.	
Vegetables 2 oz. serving of potato. Two 4 oz. servings of other vegetables (preferably leafy green or yellow and often eaten raw). Larger portions may be taken of vegetables which are especially low-calorie.	Peas, sweetcorn, baked beans or lentils. Carrots, cabbage, Brussels sprouts, green beans, onions, leeks, salad vegetables, tomatoes, cauliflower, swedes, spring greens, mushrooms, parsnips or turnips.
Fruit 4 oz. serving of unsweetened citrus fruit or their juices. 4 oz. serving of other fruit — unsweetened.	Orange, tangerine, grapefruit. Apple, pear, rhubarb, stone fruits or soft fruits.
Bread or cereal (Preferably wholegrain) two two-thirds oz. servings.	½ oz. crispbread (not starch reduced) to replace two-thirds oz. bread. ½ oz. unsweetened breakfast cereals, porridge, rice or pasta.

SAMPLE MENUS

(1) **Breakfast**
Bran flakes — ½ oz. — with milk from allowance.
Tea or coffee with milk from allowance.

Lunch
Sandwich:
　Bread — two-thirds oz.
　English cheese 2 oz.
　Butter from allowance.
　Lettuce, cucumber, celery, tomato.
Apple — 1 medium.
Tea or coffee with milk from allowance.

Evening Meal
Stew:
　Meat — 2 oz.　Potato — 2 oz.
　Carrots — 4 oz.　Onions — 2 oz.
Brussels sprouts — 2 oz.
Fresh fruit salad made with orange and grapefruit segments.
Tea or coffee with milk from allowance.

(2) **Breakfast**
Poached egg — 1 standard
Toast or bread two-thirds oz.
Butter from allowance.
Tea or coffee with milk from allowance.

Lunch
Salad:
　Cottage cheese — 4 oz.
　Lettuce, cucumber, celery.
　Tomato — 2 oz.
Bread — two-thirds oz.
Butter from allowance.
Orange — 1 medium.
Tea or coffee with milk from allowance.

Evening meal.
Chicken, grilled, baked or stewed — 3 oz.
Potato — 2 oz.
Runner beans — 4 oz.
Stewed or baked apple — 4 oz.
Tea or coffee with milk from allowance.

A SUMMER'S DAY

All the live murmur of a summer's day.

Matthew Arnold

Slanting like spears, the late noon shadows fall
Across the lawn where garden teas are set;
An open doorway in the moss-grown wall
Beckons me through from coolness into sun.

Where roses flaunt their skirts of pink and flame,
And marigolds stand in ranks of green and gold,
The stone archway curves sharply round to frame
Vistas of twisting paths and beckoning ways.

Behind the wall crowd Summer's sweet delights,
The scent of lime flowers heavy on the breeze;
And through the mirage of light and shimmering haze,
The blackbird calls from gnarled old orchard trees.

Soon I must go, slow walking through the gate,
Into the heat of crowded road and lane,
Look back to hold the beauty I still can see,
Knowing I may never come that way again.

Ida Walton

STONE'S THROW FROM HEAVEN

Martin said it was the best place in the
whole world, this summer meadow, deep in
swaying, feathery grass and full of the murmur of
bees. But although I was only fifteen, I knew
this perfection couldn't last ...

WE WERE all quite stunned when Aunt Harriet's letter arrived saying she had broken her left ankle, and was laid up, and wasn't it unthinkable but, after all these years, she'd have to give up the Summer Fête?

The Rothley Summer Fête is an institution in the life of the village and Aunt Harriet is its kingpin, a position which suits her very well. (She appointed herself one of life's captains at a very early age, and the passing years have only served to strengthen her belief in herself as a born leader.)

But as far as the Fête is concerned, she spares herself no effort. She makes mountains of jam, allocates orders for tablecloths, tea-cosies and sundry other articles on poor, unsuspecting newcomers to the district and, on the day itself, hands over her beloved house and garden.

Carrbrooke is the loveliest house I know. Neither too big nor in the least ostentatious, but individual, sure of itself, standing square and solid amongst a riot of rhododendrons and azaleas. My happiest times have been spent there; long, endless days of sunshine and laughter when childhood, with its certainties and uncomplicated practicalities, was a world as yet unshadowed by the harsh realities of growing up and life in general.

Even now, as I approach the awesomely mature age of twenty-five, in the quiet, private moments of approaching sleep I can still conjure up memories of Carrbrooke. I float along on a fragile fantasy of golden summers, picnics in the waist-high grass of the Long Meadow, and Aunt Harriet herself, bossy and high-flown and adorable.

We still consider her invincible, and make unfair, unmalicious jokes about germs and epidemics never daring to attack her. Certainly, at almost seventy, she had the energy and looks of a woman twenty years younger. The perfidious left ankle was hard to visualise.

Mother brought the letter up to my room and sat on the bed, reading it aloud. I was at home on an impromptu, unscheduled holiday, having left behind the grime and smog of the Midland town where I lecture in psychology at the polytechnic. I adore my job, am nicely fond of Geoff, the latest man in my life, but for ages now have felt less than sparkling. I seem to drift through my days without zest or flair, merely existing. So, as befits a psychology graduate of four years' standing, I decided that a break in the pattern was called for, and after a bit of juggling with timetables at work, and a deal of convincing Geoff that I wasn't actually eloping with an unknown Apollo, I packed a suitcase and drove home.

I was thoroughly spoiled and cosseted there. I slept late each morning and breakfasted on grapefruit and perfectly-boiled eggs, nestling in silver cups. I walked for miles on the Downs with Susie, our retriever, allowing the pure Sussex air to cleanse me, slough away my lethargy and bring colour to my cheeks. Each day found me fresher, stronger, like a patient recovering from illness. Everything seemed quite back to normal — until Aunt Harriet's letter arrived.

I SAT UP in bed, my eyes fixed on Mother's face, my voice high with concern and disapproval, as though falls and broken ankles were unthinkable as far as Aunt Harriet was concerned.

"Not hold the *Fête?*" I said, and Mother patted my hand as though she feared I might throw a

Continued overleaf

54

tantrum. "But it's impossible, unthinkable. The Fête is her *life*, her whole year revolves around it." I regarded my poor mother with a psychologist's steely eye. "You realise that the Rothley Fête has played the role of husband and family to Aunt Harriet all these years?"

Mother stopped patting my hand and picked up my breakfast tray.

"Rubbish, Fran!" she said with admirable restraint. "And what else can you expect, with Harriet rushing around as though she were still a teenager? I bet she's been climbing ladders or replacing glass in the greenhouse or something equally mad."

She stopped at the doorway and regarded me with interest.

"It is a shame about the Fête, though. Fran, you don't fancy going down and helping out? You've still got two weeks, and you say you're feeling much better. You could take over and stay until Sunday week."

I answered non-committally enough, dwelling on the complications of the whole thing, but already, deep down inside me, there was an extraordinary seed of excitement. How marvellous to be involved in the Fête again. Indeed, not just involved, but very probably running the whole thing.

I lay back against the pillows and closed my eyes, summoning up the sounds and smells of the Rothley Summer Fête. I could see the lawns dappled with the shadows of the cedar tree, hear the sonorous droning of the honey-bees bumping their way from flower to flower. And then suddenly, sharply, unbidden, it was that other summer, the last unspoilt Carrbrooke summer when I grew up. That was the year I finally realised that life wasn't just our cosy family world where feelings, however provoked, were kept under control, always settling back into place after an upset, like the world on its axis. It was ten years ago and I was just fifteen. It was the summer of Martin Fielding, the summer I fell in love.

M ARTIN had lived in Rothley for as long as I could remember. His father was the blacksmith and summer visitors used to congregate at the forge, fascinated by the fierce waves of heat, the incredible strength of Mr. Fielding.

Martin himself never took to the life. At sixteen, he was thin and handsome, and had an air of independence about him that I envied greatly. His life wasn't bound by regular mealtimes, trips to places of interest, or the writing of endless postcards home. He lived out his days in the most delightfully unfettered way. He knew every tree in the High Plantation, and he spent hours sketching. His drawings were amazingly good, and I remember my father scrutinising them one day. He went to speak to Mr. Fielding on the subject of possible art scholarships for Martin, but Mr. Fielding got cross as adults do when they feel they are being criticised, objectively or otherwise.

The village girls giggled a lot when Martin was about but he seemed not to notice. He was concerned only with his beloved countryside and his art.

My brother Dick and I sometimes went with him on his sketching trips, but Dick soon got bored and was hopeless at freezing if a squirrel or a fox appeared. So mostly it was just Martin and me, sitting quietly in a shadowed wood or astride a giant haywain, with Martin sketching fanatically while I looked on.

Our favourite place was at the top of the Long Meadow where we would lie, almost hidden in the feathery waist-high grass, counting the skylarks high above us in the vast blue sky. Martin said it was the best place in the whole world, just a stone's throw from Heaven.

One hot, still day during the summer of my sixteenth year, we lay there, feeling the warmth of the sun on our faces, our eyelids heavy, our laughter easy and uncomplicated. It seemed to me that I could never in my whole life be happier than I was at that moment, and I wished it would never end. I felt a queer sort of fear within me as though my happiness was too perfect, too fragile and vulnerable.

The next day Annabel arrived. Annabel was the great-niece of an old school friend of Aunt Harriet's, and each summer spent a week or so at Rothley. Annabel was a year older than me, and she'd grown up a lot during the last twelve months. She had silken, honey-coloured skin and wore fashionable, tight-legged jeans and casually-knotted blouses tied at her midriff, showing off a trim, tanned waist. She glided around Rothley with a film star's confidence, and next to her I felt as dowdy as an old hen. We all seemed to pale into insignificance beside Annabel, and my worst fears were confirmed as the week progressed.

Suddenly, it was Annabel who was walking next to Martin on our way to the Long Meadow, and it was she who held forth at the evening meal about his drawings, or the blackbird's nest he'd shown her that day. And as I had no natural fight in me I withdrew there and then, without a single struggle, and chose to stay at Carrbrooke, helping Aunt Harriet. She, poor soul, must have thought I was sickening for measles or worse.

I couldn't, however, withdraw from everything, and out of civility and loyalty to my aunt, had to go to the annual harvest picnic. Aunt Harriet provided the food, and everyone who cared to come was invited. The morning was a frantic, non-stop whirl of preparations. The hampers bulged with salads and sausage rolls, hard-boiled eggs and dark green bottles of fizzy ginger beer. There was the usual tagging on of the village children, and I was glad to see that Aunt Harriet had appropriated Martin. Annabel came and walked with me, and I could sense in her every step a sort of tightly-coiled restlessness.

"I shall be glad to get back home," she said, and suddenly I was appalled at the extent of my dislike for her. Even her voice sounded mean and affected, without a trace of warmth. But she wasn't finished with me yet.

"It's all a bit nurseryish, isn't it?" Her beautiful, sun-tanned hand gestured towards the picnic procession. "Like some sort of ritual. Honestly, the way we bow and scrape to your Aunt Harriet. It's a bit of a pain."

Her voice changed slightly, softening, becoming curiously deliberate.

"*This* year was slightly better because of Rothley's own home-grown artist." We both looked ahead to where Martin was helping Aunt Harriet up the steep incline of the path.

"He's very good looking, isn't he?" She laughed. "A bit of a hick, but then he would be, never having set foot outside this place. But he's made my holiday bearable. One of the last romantics, wouldn't you say?"

I ran on ahead suddenly, pretending that Dick needed a hand with the food hamper, and wishing fervently that we were going home tomorrow.

THE picnic was enjoyable, as it happened. We played rounders and charades and ate non-stop, and as the shadows began to fall Aunt Harriet went back to the house. The rest of us sat around in a circle and told ghost stories, and Ellie Richards frightened us all to death by telling us how she had once been locked in the church overnight.

There was a chill in the air as well as in our spines, so I began rolling up the car rugs and fastening the hampers. But Annabel said, "Oh, no, not yet. Don't let's go yet. It's *early*." She looked excited and beautiful, seeming somehow to sparkle in the oncoming dusk.

"I know," she said, "let's play Secrets. It's great fun. We play it often at school."

I sensed danger straightaway and went on with my tidying, but everyone else clamoured to stay on.

Annabel was all animation. The game was simple, she said. We all had to put down our innermost secret on a piece of paper, just like making a Christmas wish, and then everyone had to guess who had written what.

A well-adjusted person is one who makes the same mistake
twice without getting nervous.

Jane Heard

It was quite fun really, and Dick came into his own as he was the only one with a torch. We all laughed a lot because it didn't take much brain power to know that Dick wanted to leave school now and help Mr. Fielding in the forge, or that Martin had written the one about wishing to wake tomorrow as Van Gogh. Ellie Richards' was a bit slanderous, making strange insinuations about the postman and young Mrs. Jennings, and my curious sense of foreboding was nudged again. In the next moment I froze, as Annabel clapped her hands for silence and then began to read aloud.

"Well, this one's certainly different." Everything about her seemed tightly-sprung, eager. "It's different and *very* romantic. And you don't have to be a genius to guess whose secret it is."

I was totally paralysed, incapable of anything except hearing her voice reading the words in a sing-song way.

"*Martin and I watched skylarks today, soaring far, far above us, like our souls. And tonight, as always, we shall be together in my dreams.*"

From the first word I had known it was a page from my diary, my precious, private diary which I would have guarded with my life. And here it was being declaimed, publicly and callously, in Annabel's mocking voice. I think I could have killed her. It was more than my pride she was destroying; it was the fragility of first love, the tender, growing seed of a new dimension in my life. And I hated her for it.

I sat there amidst the silence, beyond embarrassment, beyond shame. My lips and hands and legs were trembling, and I wondered if I would ever feel warm again. I heard Ellie say something about it being a stupid game and then I was aware that Martin's hands were on my shoulders, drawing me to my feet, supporting me as he led me down towards Carrbrooke with Dick trailing behind us like a bewildered, uncomprehending puppy.

The moon was riding high so that Carrbrooke looked like some miniature, silvered fortress amidst the trees. Dick ran ahead, his short legs pumping like pistons. Martin stopped suddenly, his face white in the moonlight as he turned me to face him at the high, wrought-iron gates.

"Fran, she's a stupid, ordinary, silly girl and you're to forget all about it."

His hands were rough on my shoulders. "Do you hear? forget *her*!"

I stared up at him. I felt drained, light as air, as if the slightest breeze might carry me off. My voice

Continued overleaf

seemed to come from another world.

"It was my diary," I said. "She'd taken a page out of my diary."

The significance of my words suddenly came to me. I couldn't believe it. Here I was, baring my childish, silly thoughts yet again, showing my vulnerability no mercy.

I put my hands to my face, feeling the fire in my cheeks, and then Martin's hands were gently holding mine, drawing me towards him. There was a moment of total silence as his lips found mine. It was a brief kiss, but it was wholly sure of itself, betraying no boyish hesitancy, and for a moment I drowned in it, forgetting tonight's humiliation. And then I ran into the house where Aunt Harriet and Dick were waiting with comfort and hot cocoa.

I don't know what Dick had told my aunt or even understood, but Annabel went home the next day and, as far as I know, never again spent a holiday at Rothley. I myself departed two days later, having decided to accept an invitation from a school friend to spend a week with her.

I had lost and gained something during that awful evening. I had lost the wonderful rapport with Martin, for only while I hugged my secret to myself could I freely enjoy his company. I had gained a new caution, a shell, perhaps; call it what you will. I was facing life from behind new-grown armour, like a crab. In my more honest moments, I wasn't sure that I had gained anything of value.

We still went to Rothley and helped with the Fête, and occasionally I glimpsed Martin. He went to art college when he was eighteen and my private glimpses of him became less and less frequent. But as the years passed, and his fame as an artist increased, then at least I'd see him from time to time on television and read about him in the press. In my dreams I recalled him, greedily, yearningly. He was my Prince of Dreams, and all the good-natured, deserving young men who came in and out of my life paled beside him. Poor unfortunates like Geoff must have despaired of my mercurial moods.

I CAME to, emerging from my reverie, slipping back into the familiar world of reality. Susie was at the bedside, her tail thumping in obsequious hope that another walk might be in the offing, and I could hear Mother busying herself downstairs. I lay there for a moment, recovering from the usual effects of a nostalgia trip. I am the perfect example of one of those people with chunks of their past so compartmentalised and preserved that it is possible for them to revisit a moment in time at will.

It's a useful, often comforting, gift to have. But it also meant that my present life was incomplete,

---

A bee is never as busy as it seems; it's just
that it can't buzz any slower.

Kin Hubbard

---

haunted by a premature, unfulfilled commitment of the heart; a source of sorrow which could not be exorcised while I continued to revisit it.

I leaned out of bed and tickled Susie's left ear. Her liquid brown eyes, melting with hope, looked into mine, and I sprang out and headed for the shower. Hurrah for golden retrievers with insatiable appetites for exercise!

We held a family discussion that evening, and after an expensive succession of telephone calls to Aunt Harriet, it was decided that I should go down to Rothley and stay until the Fête. I packed a few necessities, plus a tolerably elegent outfit to wear for the actual day, and headed for the motorway and Carrbrooke.

As I drove between the high, wrought iron gates, I had the uncanny feeling of being transported back in time. Here I was, twenty-five next birthday, successful in my job, and yet I could have been fifteen again, long-legged and skinny, with ten-year-old Dick tagging along behind. I remembered that brother Richard was now at university, launching out on a very promising legal career and sighed at the relentless passing of time.

Aunt Harriet seemed well if immobile. Her ankle was strapped in yards of bandage, and she was bossier than ever. I was exhausted by bed-time, but climbed on to my high, feathered-mattressed bed with a joy which was childish in its simplicity. I lay listening to the sounds of the High Wood — the occasional hoot of a barn owl, the ghostly sighing of the tall, swaying poplars — and I'm sure I fell asleep with a smile on my face.

The next few days were chaotic. We planned our schedules over breakfast, and I saw that Aunt Harriet was as good as ever at organising lists of things for other people to do. I polished tables, got out linen for laundering, saw that the lawns were mown regularly, ordered the flowers, the cakes, the wines. The whole of the surrounding countryside seemed to have fallen under Aunt Harriet's spell. Mountains of bramble jelly and marmalade arrived daily, and large, earnest women brought their embroidered offerings. The study table was awash with tiny white garments knitted on eager, helpful needles.

I whipped up a quick lunch one day and smiled across at my aunt.

"You are just incredible. You should have been a general or a missionary or a politician." Our eyes met and sparked, and I gave thanks for this special light in my life. I waved a hand in the direction of the latest pile of deliveries. "It's amazing. No one can say no to you."

I had another mouthful of curried chicken and then said, "Heavens, I'd completely forgotten. Your guest, your special guest, your Fête opener. Who is it? The Prime Minister was too busy, was she? Or have you gone for minor Royalty this year? Do tell."

Aunt Harriet looked directly across at me.

"It's Martin, actually, Martin Fielding."

Our eyes met again and this time there was a clash of reaction: pleading from her, disbelief from me.

Aunt Harriet was almost babbling. "It's the scoop of the year, Fran. He is, after all, just about the most celebrated artist in Britain today. He took a deal of persuading but eventually he said yes. *And he promised to give one of his small sketches for the auction.*"

'Bully for him,' I thought, 'and bully for you, but what about me? What about unsuspecting me who had no idea until this moment, that in two days' time I should be meeting my Prince of Dreams?'

To be honest, I didn't know whether I could face it. I washed up and gave myself stern lectures on maturity of thought and the structure of purpose in one's life. It didn't help. I felt as scared as if I was fifteen again.

S ATURDAY lived up to the reputation of all its predecessors. It dawned like some fairy-tale day, windless and sunny, blue skies powdered with white cotton clouds.

I'd been up since dawn, and was really quite proud of my own streamlined organisation. By eleven, everything was ready. The lawn was dotted with round tables and matching sunshades. The linen was dazzling in its whiteness and the marquees were brightly striped and offered cool, welcoming shade. My task force from the village had arrived early and Aunt Harriet, holding forth from a chaise longue under a cedar tree, soon had her minions deployed in all directions.

After lunch, I took ten minutes to shower and change into my tolerably elegant dress. I brushed my hair and was glad I hadn't been tempted to have it chopped off. I looked at myself and was glad of my slimness and my shining shoulder-length hair and my reasonably pretty face. And then I was angry at myself for placing such importance on mere outer trappings.

I went downstairs and made sure I was too busy even to think about Martin. I moved from group to group, reassuring the nervous lady behind the bathroom stall that she'd be just fine, and soothing the ruffled feathers of Rothley's celebrated cake-maker, affronted because her *pièce de résistance* wasn't in pride of place.

Just before two, I heard the growing murmur of expectant voices, and knew that the guest of honour had arrived. My deliberate cool evaporated like a puff of smoke, and my fickle limbs turned coy, quite suddenly feeling as wobbly as the jellies in the refreshment tent. But I was nicely tucked away behind a crowd of flowery-hatted ladies, and I was able to listen to Martin's speech unobserved.

It was a nice speech, all about his memories of Rothley, his family, of Aunt Harriet and the Fête. He talked a little about the world in general, how art was a great communicator, and maybe if we were more passionate about canvases than nuclear arms we'd all be better off. I closed my eyes, glad of the warmth emanating from him, happy he hadn't been changed by his great success. I felt my whole being absorbing his every word and I mourned briefly for this ghost in my life and wondered if I'd ever be free of him. Just then there was a shower of applause and the Fête had begun.

My jellied limbs were called upon straightaway and by three o'clock I was exhausted. There were two faints in the refreshment tent, the bathroom stall lady collapsed into tears after ten minutes and had to be replaced, and there was an instant panic as a demented mum reported her three-year-old Samantha well and truly missing. The vicar's spaniel came to the rescue and flushed her out from where she'd gone to sleep under the white elephant stall.

And in the first five-minute lull after *that* little crisis, I sneaked off to take a quick look at the oil painting standing in pride of place in the hall, awaiting the auction.

T HE gloom of the house, after the brilliance of the afternoon sun, made me shade my eyes at first. I could feel my heartbeat quicken as the painting came into focus. It was of the Long Meadow, with its waist-high feathery grasses and the skylarks soaring high above. I read the title: "A Stone's Throw from Heaven". I felt a lump as big as an egg in my throat, and I could almost see the stillness of the larks, feel the feathery grasses brushing against my bare arms.

"I hope you approve."

I attempted to blink away my absurd, unexpected tears before I turned to where Martin Fielding was standing in the doorway, leaning against the upright.

I smiled brightly, calling upon my years of sophistication and self-containment.

"It's beautiful, Martin. I'm glad Rothley still means so much to you."

He straightened and took a step towards me, and there was an almost tangible stillness in the hall, the kind we had known when watching a vixen with her cubs or following the antics of a capering

Continued overleaf

squirrel. His face was so eloquent in its anxiety that I thought I might truly stop breathing. Then the bathroom stall lady appeared, fortified by her tea and buns, and absolutely resolute to go on selling soaps and face flannels for as long as I wished.

The silence ebbed away from us like an out-going tide. Martin reached out to touch my hands as I passed close to him, re-entering the arena of ice-cream and tea-cosies, but for the rest of the afternoon he was constantly swallowed up in a sea of well-wishing admirers, until an urgent phone call apparently summoned him to the big city and other business. I thought perhaps he'd purposely arranged a suitable get-away. I made myself scarce, hiding in Aunt Harriet's bedroom, wondering if he'd looked for me, hoping, yet hardly daring to. I glanced at myself in the mirror and scorned my pride. There *had* been a moment of special magic in the hall; the magic of old, still alive after all these years. And now, probably, gone forever.

It wasn't until exactly eight o'clock that Carrbrooke was back to its usual quiet.

Aunt Harriet regarded me from across the kitchen table.

"Fran, you were just marvellous, but you look all in. An early night is called for."

I smiled back at her. I was pleased at the day's success, but I felt a curious sadness as though a whole portion of my life was being left behind me. Suddenly the house seemed stifling and I slipped upstairs, changing into an old sweater and slacks, desperate for fresh air and solitude.

I told Aunt Harriet I wouldn't be long. Even before I'd left the garden I knew where I was going. Perhaps for the last time, I mused, as a sort of ritual, a pilgrimage, a sloughing off of the painful remnants of childhood and adolescence.

The evening was still and beautiful, and the whole countryside was alight with a harvest-gold colour. My walk up to Long Meadow was a repetition of days long gone, and I indulged in all the old rituals, vaulting the stile, crossing the stepping stones with my eyes shut.

I sat down amidst the waist-high grass and forced myself to think of Geoff and my job and future.

I don't know how long I sat there, but suddenly I heard a sound of footsteps coming along the Long Meadow path, saw the parting of the tall, feathery grasses, and watched as Martin Fielding came to find me. He sat down and regarded me levelly, saying nothing. Then he stretched out beside me, pulling a stem of grass between his teeth. It could have been ten years ago.

"Your business didn't take long," I said, at last.

"Not too long, I'm glad to say. A little matter of cancelling a flight and extending my stay. But I didn't walk all the way here to talk about business. You avoided me very skilfully all afternoon. I *did* think I'd managed a little moment of togetherness when you were looking at my painting. Until the instant sabotage by the lady of the bath."

He waved a hand, encompassing the golden-hued landscape around us.

"There's plenty of room for escape here too, Fran." His eyes were kind and gentle. "You were always a great one for escape."

He handed me a manila folder. "Secrets," he said, and smiled at me like a teacher encouraging a slow pupil. I flushed, knowing we were both remembering those other secrets. My fingers slowly opened the folder, taking the sketches out, one by one, and my hungry eyes feasted on them.

They were all of me and seemed to encompass every mood and emotion I was capable of. There were bright, lively impressions where I was laughing, my head thrown back, and solemn, quiet ones where my face was troubled, introspective.

I looked through them again carefully, and suddenly there was a feeling of hope and warmth within me. For surely the sketches were love letters: the hopes and dreams, the memories of a distant, inaccessible lover. Martin spoke again and his voice was harsh, nervous and unsure.

"My own particular secrets, Fran, and they seem to have been with me forever. And instead of fading, as they ought, they've just become stronger, more real, all the time. I think you must have bewitched me all those years ago."

I sat there, unable to speak, overwhelmed by the thing I'd dreamed of for ten years. He leaned across and held my face in his hands.

"I'm glad your Aunt Harriet is more forthcoming than you. She's been telling me about someone called Geoff, and various other young men who seem to have swum in and out of your life, leaving no trace. Is that right, Fran? There's no one special?"

I went on listening to his words. They were a carbon copy of my own thoughts and feelings during the years when new faces and new experiences skimmed the surface of my life like gnats on a pond, leaving my innermost dreams unchanged.

The dusk was heavy when we eventually came down to Carrbrooke, and the house was ablaze with lights as we reached the high, wrought iron gates. I shivered for a moment, as the painful recollection of that other night briefly touched my memory for the last time. Then Martin held me close as we went to find Aunt Harriet.

THE END

© Greta Nelson, 1982

Picnics and Parties

Summer is the time for picnics; the time when meals move out of doors. Here we've chosen simple casual fare ideal for taking into the garden, to the seaside or the country. Delectable savouries and sandwiches, a tray bake and a good, keeping, cut-and-come-again Cherry and Almond Cake.

If travelling by foot or bike you'll need easy-to-pack food in the lightest and, where possible, dispensable wrappers. So we've suggested two super sandwich ideas plus tasty tomato and sausagemeat balls and a square or two of moist orange cake. Pop a carton of yoghurt and some fresh fruit into the basket and you've a feast! You'll probably find it easiest to pick up a drink on the way.

CHEESE AND COLESLAW SANDWICHES

Makes 6 rounds

| small sliced Granary loaf |
| oz. soft magarine |
| oz. tub of coleslaw in mayonnaise |
| oz. raisins or sultanas |
| ½ lb. cheese, thinly sliced |

Spread the bread with margarine then divide the coleslaw equally between half the slices. Sprinkle a few raisins over the top of each slice then top with a layer of thinly sliced cheese.

Sandwich together with the remaining bread. Cut in half.

To carry: pack sandwiches in a small plastic bag or overwrap in foil or cling film.

PICNIC ROLLS

Makes 6

| soft-topped rolls |
| oz. butter or margarine |
| level tablespoon Marmite |
| tablespoons sandwich spread |
| few leaves of lettuce |
| tomatoes, thinly sliced |
| inch piece of cucumber, thinly sliced |

Split and butter the rolls. Spread each half with a little Marmite and a layer of sandwich spread.

Place a lettuce leaf and a few slices of tomato and cucumber on one half of each roll. Season. Sandwich with the rest of the roll halves.

To carry: wrap in cling film or foil and place in plastic bag.

CHOCOLATE AND ORANGE SQUARES

Makes 9-12

| 4 oz. soft margarine |
| 4 oz. caster sugar |
| 4 oz. self-raising flour |
| 1 level teaspoon baking powder |
| 2 large eggs, size 2 |
| Finely grated rind of 1 orange |
| 2 oz. plain chocolate Polka Dots |
| 2 tablespoons orange juice |
| 7 by 11 by 2 inch oblong cake pan, base lined and greased. |

Set the oven to moderate, Gas Mark 4 or 350 °F/ 180 °C.

Place the margarine, sugar, flour, baking powder, eggs and orange rind in a bowl. Using electric beaters, cream for about 2 minutes until smooth, light and fluffy (the mixing will take a little longer if a wooden spoon is used). Turn into the tin and level the top. Sprinkle Polka Dots over. Bake just above the centre of the oven for about 35 minutes until firm and springy to touch.

Leave in the tin to cool then sprinkle over the orange juice. Cut into 9 or 12 portions.

To carry: either leave in the tin and overwrap with foil or wrap individual squares in foil.

CHERRY AND ALMOND CAKE

| 8 oz. glacé cherries |
| 8 oz. butter or margarine |
| 8 oz. caster sugar |
| 4 large eggs, size 2 |
| ¼ teaspoon almond essence |
| 8 oz. self-raising flour |
| 3 oz. ground almonds |
| 8½ inch spring clip tin, base lined and greased |

Set the oven to moderate, Gas Mark 4, 350°F/ 180°C.

If cherries are very sticky wash in warm water, pat dry on kitchen paper. Cut in quarters.

Cream the butter with the sugar until light and fluffy. Add the eggs one at a time beating well after each addition. Beat in the almond essence. Fold in the flour and ground almonds and then fold in the cherries.

Spoon the mixture into the tin and hollow out the centre with the back of a spoon.

Bake in the centre of the oven for about 1 hour or until firm and springy to the touch.

Continued overleaf

Makes 12

1 lb. sausagemeat

2 level tablespoons tomato ketchup

Patty tin tray

Set the oven to moderate, Gas Mark 4 or 350 °F/ 180 °C.

Divide the sausagemeat into 12 even pieces and, with lightly floured hands, shape each piece into a ball. Place each one in a patty tin. Brush each ball generously with tomato ketchup. Bake in the middle of the oven for 40 minutes.

To carry: when cold, pack in foil.

DRINKS BY THE BOTTLE

Sherry and port and straight vermouths give roughly 12-15 glasses. In single nips for cocktails, vermouths and spirits give just over 30 a bottle. Reckon 16-20 drinks of spirit from bottle when serving them with soda, tonic o other minerals. Liqueurs served in prope glasses — 30 portions. A split bottle of soda o tonic gives 2-3 drinks. A 1 pint can of tomat juice gives 4-6 drinks. Dilute a bottle of frui cordial with 7 pints of water for 20-25 drinks.

PARTY FOOD QUANTITY GUIDE

Any time of the year is party time, but summer i often the time for special occasion celebration such as weddings.

To help the many people who cater for such a event here's a guide to help them calculate ho much food will be needed for how many. We'v based it on 10-12 people, but if you're caterin for more just multiply.

Do remember it is a general guide as people' appetites do vary depending on the time of da and the occasion.

QUANTITIES FOR 10-12 PEOPLE

Food	Ingredients	Practical Notes
Seafood Cocktail	1-1¼ lb. fish ½ cucumber ¼ pint mayonnaise ⅛ pint tomato ketchup 1 large lettuce	For economy use a mixture of prawns, white fish, tuna, etc., and peeled diced cucumber. Combine fish with sauce and seasoning ahead of serving. Pile on shredded lettuce near time of serving.
Assorted Cold Meats **Chicken** **Turkey** **Pâté**	2 lb. ham, tongue, salami Two 3½-4 lb. oven-ready birds. 8 lb. oven-ready bird or two 1¼ lb. turkey roasts. 1½ lb.	Slice if necessary. Arrange attractively on plates. Cover with cling film to prevent drying. Garnish just before serving. Serve with crispbread.
Coleslaw	1½ lb. white cabbage finely shredded. ½ lb. carrots, grated. ½ pint coleslaw dressing or mayonnaise.	Additional flavouring such as some grated onion, raisins.
Rice Salad	1 lb. uncooked rice, ½ lb. peas, 11 oz. can sweetcorn. ½ pint French dressing.	Cook rice and peas. Mix all ingredients together adding 3 tablespoons chopped fresh mint or 3-4 teaspoons of mint sauce or jelly.
Potato Salad	2 lb. boiled potatoes 1 bunch spring onions ¼ pint mayonnaise 3 tablespoons soured cream	Mix all ingredients together. Season well.
Fruit Salad	3 lb. mixed fresh fruits 1½ pints water 12 oz. sugar	Make syrup, cool. Add prepared fruit. Add bananas just before serving.
Cream	¾ pint single cream ½ pint double or whipped cream	For pouring. Add 2 tablespoons milk to cream. Whip and sweeten. Gives 10 whirls.

Food	Ingredients	Practical Notes
Trifle	1 pkt. sponge fingers 4 tablespoons jam 4 tablespoons sherry 1 lb. 14 oz. can fruit salad 2 pints custard	Decorate with cream, glacé cherries and angelica.
Ice Cream	2 family size blocks or ½ litre	
Sausage Rolls	½ lb. puff pastry ¾ lb. sausagemeat	Makes 10-12 medium sized rolls.
Bouchées	½ lb. puff pastry ½ pint thick sauce 4 oz. mushrooms, chicken, egg, salmon etc.	Makes 10-12. Season sauce well. Serve warm if possible.
Sandwiches	1 large (1¾ lb.) sliced loaf 4 oz. butter softened ¾ lb. of thinly sliced meat, cheese, fish, 6 eggs	Makes 10 rounds — each round cut into 4. Season filling well.
Coffee	1½ oz. instant 3 pints water 1 pint milk ½ lb. sugar	Make coffee in jugs when required. Serve milk and sugar separately.
Tea	1 oz. tea 4 pints water ¾ pint milk ½ lb. sugar	

LITTLE MISS SUNSHINE

— is as pretty as a picture in her charming

yellow V-neck cardigan. It has cable and

lacy panels and features raglan sleeves,

which makes it easy for a child to slip on

Instructions in 3 sizes. Colour photo on page 78.

MATERIALS: *Allow the following quantities in 50 g balls of Sirdar Country Style Double Knitting: 3 balls for 51 cm, 56 cm and 61 cm sizes. For any one size: a pair each of No. 7 (4½ mm) and No. 9 (3¾ mm) knitting needles; 4 buttons; a cable needle.*

TENSION: *Work at a tension of 20 stitches and 25 rows, to measure 10 x 10 cm, over the stocking stitch, using No. 7 (4½ mm) needles, to obtain the measurements given on page 66.*

ABBREVIATIONS: *To be read before working: K., knit plain; p., purl; st., stitch; tog., together; inc., increase (by working twice into same st.); dec., decrease (by taking 2 sts. tog.); s.s., stocking st. (k. on the right side and p. on the wrong side); single rib is k.1 and p.1 alternately; y.fwd., yarn forward to make a st.; s.k.p.o., (slip 1, k.1, pass slipped st. over); k.3 tog.b., k. 3 tog. through back of loops; nil meaning nothing is worked here for this size; c.4 f., cable 4 front (slip next 2 sts. onto cable needle and leave at front of work, k.2, then k.2 from cable needle).*

NOTE: *The instructions are given for the 51 cm (20 inch) size. Where they vary, work the figures within the first brackets for the 56 cm (22 inch) size; work figures within the second brackets for the 61 cm (24 inch) size.*

THE BACK: With No. 9 (3¾ mm) needles cast on 62 (68) (74) sts. and work 10 rows in single rib, decreasing 1 st. at the end of the last row – 61 (67) (73) sts. *Continued overleaf*

We used an attractive shade called banana, but others to use could be: deep lilac, delphinium, bright red, wild rose, terracotta, aqua or tartan green.

Change to No. 7 (4½ mm) needles and work the 6-row pattern as follows:

1st row: K.16 (19) (22), y.fwd., k.3 tog.b., y.fwd., k.1, p.2, k.4, p.2, k.1, y.fwd., k.3 tog.b., y.fwd., k.1, p.2, k.4, p.2, k.1, y.fwd, k.3 tog.b., y.fwd., k.16 (19) (22).

2nd row: P.20 (23) (26), k.2, p.4, k.2, p.5, k.2, p.4, k.2, p.20 (23) (26).

3rd and 4th rows: As 1st and 2nd rows.

5th row: K.16 (19) (22), y.fwd., k.3 tog.b., y.fwd., k.1, p.2, c.4f., p.2, k.1, y.fwd., k.3 tog.b., y.fwd., k.1, p.2, c.4f., p.2, k.1, y.fwd., k.3 tog.b., y.fwd., k.16 (19) (22).

6th row: As 2nd row.

Repeat the last 6 rows, 5 (6) (7) times.

To shape the raglan armholes: 1st and 2nd rows: Cast off 2 sts. at the beginning of each of the next 2 rows.

3rd row: K.1, s.k.p.o., pattern until 3 sts. remain, k.2 tog., k.1.

4th row: K.1, pattern until 1st st. remains, k.1.

Repeat 3rd and 4th rows, 17 (19) (21) times — 21 (23) (25) sts.

Cast off.

THE LEFT FRONT: With No. 9 (3¾ mm) needles cast on 30 (34) (38) sts. and work 10 rows in single rib.**

Change to No. 7 (4½ mm) needles and work in pattern as follows:

1st row: K.12 (16) (20), y.fwd., k.3 tog.b., y.fwd., k.1, p.2, k.4, p.2, k.1, y.fwd., k.3 tog.b., y.fwd., k.2.

2nd row: P.6, k.2, p.4, k.2, p.16 (20) (24).

3rd and 4th rows: As 1st and 2nd rows.

5th row: K.12 (16) (20), y.fwd., k.3 tog.b., y.fwd., k.1, p.2, c.4f., p.2, k.1, y.fwd., k.3 tog.b., y.fwd., k.2.

6th row: As 2nd row.

Repeat the last 6 rows, 5 (6) (7) times.

To shape the raglan armhole and slope front edge: 1st row: Cast off 2 sts., pattern until 3 sts. remain k.2 tog., k.1.

2nd row: P.2, pattern to end.

3rd row: K.1, s.k.p.o., pattern until 2 sts. remain, k.2.

4th row: P.2, pattern until 1 st. remains, k.1.

5th row: K.1, s.k.p.o., pattern until 3 sts. remain, k.2 tog., k.1.

6th row: As 4th row.

Repeat 3rd to 6th rows, 6 (7) (8) times – 6 (7) (8) sts.

Repeat 3rd and 4th rows, nil (once) (once) – 6 (6) (7) sts.

For the 51 cm size only: 1st row: K.1, s.k.p.o., pattern to end.

2nd row: P.2, pattern until 1 st. remains, k.1.

3rd row: K.1, s.k.p.o., k.2.

4th row: P.3, k.1.

5th row: K.1, s.k.p.o., k.1.

6th row: P.2, k.1.

7th row: K.1, s.k.p.o.

8th row: P.1, k.1.

Take remaining 2 sts. tog. and fasten off.

For the 56 cm size only: **1st row:** K.1, s.k.p.o., k.2 tog., k.1.

2nd row: P.3, k.1.

3rd row: K.1, s.k.p.o, k.1.

4th row: P.2, k.1.

5th row: K.1, s.k.p.o.

6th row: P.1, k.1.

Take remaining 2 sts. tog. and fasten off.

For the 61 cm size only: **1st row:** K.1, s.k.p.o., k.1, k.2 tog., k.1.

2nd row: P.2, pattern 2, k.1.

3rd row: K.1, s.k.p.o, k.2.

4th row: P.3, k.1.

5th row: S.k.p.o., k.2 tog.

6th row: P.2.

Take remaining 2 sts. tog. and fasten off.

THE RIGHT FRONT: Work as given for left front to **.

Change to No. 7 (4½ mm) needles.

1st row: K.2, y.fwd., k.3 tog.b., y.fwd., k.1, p.2, k.4, p.2, k.1, y.fwd., k.3 tog.b., y.fwd., k.12 (16) (20).

2nd row: P.16 (20) (24), k.2, p.4, k.2, p.6.

3rd and 4th rows: As 1st and 2nd rows.

5th row: K.2, y.fwd., k.3 tog.b., y.fwd., k.1, p.2, c.4f., p.2, k.1, y.fwd., k.3 tog.b., y.fwd., k.12 (16) (20).

6th row: As 2nd row.

Repeat the last 6 rows, 5 (6) (7) times.

To shape the raglan armhole and slope the front edge:

1st row: K.1, s.k.p.o., pattern to end.

2nd row: Cast off 2 sts. pattern until 2 sts. remain, p.2.

3rd row: K.2, pattern until 3 sts. remain, k.2 tog., k.1.

4th row: K.1, pattern until 2 sts. remain, p.2.

5th row: K.1, s.k.p.o., pattern until 3 sts. remain, k.2 tog., k.1.

6th row: As 4th row.

Repeat 3rd to 6th rows, 6 (7) (8) times – 6 (7) (8) sts.

Repeat 3rd and 4th rows, nil (once) (once) – 6 (6) (7) sts.

For the 51 cm size only: **1st row:** Pattern 3, k.2 tog., k.1.

MEASUREMENTS in centimetres (and inches, in brackets)					
Chest sizes	51	(20)	56	(22)	61	(24)
All round at under-arms, fastened	55.5	(21¾)	62.5	(24½)	69	(27¼)
Side seam	18	(7)	20.5	(8)	22.5	(8¾)
Length	33	(13)	37	(14½)	41	(16¼)
Sleeve seam	20.5	(8)	23	(9)	26	(10¼)

OFF TO SAND HOPPER BAY

The Robin Families are so looking forward to seeing their old friends.

AT LAST the Robin Family finished packing for their holiday and then they had to put all the cases in the car. Mr. Robin had made a new roof-rack for the largest case and for the big kite, packed carefully in brown paper and string.

Roley and Rosemary were very excited when the journey to Sand Hopper Bay began. On the way they stopped for a picnic lunch with Mrs. Rosabelle Robin and Dr. Robbie and Richard and little Rowena, who had been following behind in their car.

Meanwhile, down at Sand Hopper Bay, Mrs. Rock-Pipit was busy getting ready for her guests. She loved to have the Robin Families to stay and her daughter Priscilla was very excited at the thought of seeing her small friends again. She helped her mother to shake mats, dust rooms and make up the bunks in the Old Boat House.

"I think I'll go down to the rockpools and catch some shrimps for tea," said Captain Rock-Pipit, who wasn't very keen on staying indoors.

"Hurry up then, dear," said Mrs. Rock-Pipit. "Because they will be here at about four o'clock."

"I'll go and find some wild flowers to arrange in the bedrooms," said Priscilla and she ran off, singing happily, to a place she knew on the cliffs where pretty pink flowers grew by the hundred.

2nd row: K.1, pattern to end.
3rd row: K.2, k.2 tog., k.1.
4th row: K.1, pattern to end.
5th row: K.1, k.2 tog., k.1.
6th row: K.1, p.2.
7th row: K.2 tog., k.1.
8th row: K.1, p.1.
Take remaining 2 sts. tog. and fasten off.
For the 56 cm size only: **1st row:** K.1, s.k.p.o., k.2 tog., k.1.
2nd row: K.1, pattern to end.
3rd row: K.1, k.2 tog., k.1.
4th row: K.1, p.2.
5th row: K.2 tog., k.1. **6th row:** K.1, p.1.
Take remaining 2 sts. tog, and fasten off.
For the 61 cm size only: **1st row:** K.1, s.k.p.o., k.1, k.2 tog., k.1.
2nd row: K.1, pattern 2, p.2.
3rd row: K.2, k.2 tog., k.1.
4th row: K.1, pattern to end.
5th row: S.k.p.o., k.2 tog.
6th row: K.1, p.1.
Take remaining 2 sts. tog. and fasten off.

THE SLEEVES (both alike): With No. 9 (3¾ mm) needles cast on 30 (34) (38) sts. and work 14 rows in single rib.
Change to No. 7 (4½ mm) needles and work in pattern as follows:
1st row: K.7 (9) (11), y.fwd., k.3 tog.b., y.fwd., k.1, p.2, k.4, p.2, k.1 y.fwd., k.3 tog.b., y.fwd., k.7 (9) (11).
2nd row: P.11 (13) (15), k.2, p.4, k.2, p.11 (13) (15).

3rd and 4th rows: As 1st and 2nd rows.
5th row: K.7 (9) (11), y.fwd., k.3 tog.b., y.fwd., k.1, p.2, c.4f., p.2, k.1, y.fwd., k.3 tog.b., y.fwd., k.7, (9) (11).
6th row: As 2nd row.
Maintaining continuity of the pattern and working extra sts. in s.s. as they occur, inc. 1 st. at each end of the next row and the 8 following 4th rows – 48 (52) (56) sts.
Pattern a further 1 (7) (15) rows.

To shape the raglan sleeve top: Work exactly as given for raglan shaping on back when 8 sts. will remain. Cast off.

THE FRONT BORDER: First join raglan seams. With No. 9 (3¾ mm) needles cast on 6 sts. and work 2 rows in single rib.
1st (buttonhole) row: Rib 2, cast off 2, rib 1.
2nd (buttonhole) row: Rib to end, casting on 2 sts. over those cast off on previous row.
Rib a further 16 rows.
Repeat the last 18 rows, twice, then the 2 buttonhole rows again.
Continue in rib until border is long enough when slightly stretched to fit up right front, across right sleeve top, across back neck, across left sleeve top and down left front, casting off in rib when correct length is assured.

TO MAKE UP THE CARDIGAN: Press lightly on wrong side with a warm iron over a dry cloth. Join sleeve and side seams, sew on front border. Add buttons.

MAKING A SEE-SAW

Our handyman has designed a sturdy see-saw to bring the fun of the playground into your garden. Colour photo on page 76.

THE SEE-SAW BASE

Except for the pivot bar this is made entirely from 95 mm (3¾ in.) by 21 mm (7/8 in.) prepared softwood.

To make one side frame, start by preparing the top rail and triangular block to size (see diagram 1). Join the triangular block to the centre of the top rail then drill a hole for the pivot bar through both pieces (position as shown in diagram 1). Cut two legs and one bottom rail to length and assemble one side frame (see diagram 2).

Note: Pencil in the curve at the top of each leg and avoid the waste areas (shaded sections, diagram 2) when drilling the holes for the fixing screws. Make a second side frame in the same way. Remove waste pieces with a hand saw then round over top corners of each frame with a file.

Prepare two end rails and one centre rail to length and fix them to the side frames (see diagram 3). Drill and countersink a screw clearance hole in the top edge of each side frame (see diagram 2), positioned so that it meets the hole drilled for the pivot bar. Cut the dowel required for the pivot bar to length, slot through holes in side frame, allowing an equal overhang at each side. Secure with screws inserted through the clearance holes in the frame.

MATERIALS REQUIRED

OUR SEE-SAW is suitable for children from four years upwards.

For any measurements not shown in the diagram, see Materials Required list on the right. Use waterproof wood glue such as Borden's Cascamite and 30 mm (1¼ in.) countersunk wood screws to assemble the see-saw. Drill a 4.5 mm (3/16 in.) diameter clearance hole for each screw and countersink each one so that the screw heads are well below the wood surface. If you wish to partially dismantle the base for storage, omit glue when adding the end and centre rails.

A spot of oil placed on each screw thread before it is inserted will help to resist rusting.

(All measurements in mm — millimetres) Approximate imperial (in.) equivalents are shown in brackets.

L Length
W Width
T Thickness

Prepared softwood

		L	W	T
Base, top rails	2 pieces	300 (11¾)	95 (3¾)	21 (7/8)
Base, top rails	2 pieces	95 (3¾)	95 (3¾)	21 (7/8)
Base, legs	4 pieces	546 (21½)	95 (3¾)	21 (7/8)
Base, bottom rails	2 pieces	490 (19¼)	95 (3¾)	21 (7/8)
Base, end rails	2 pieces	350 (13¾)	95 (3¾)	21 (7/8)
Base, centre rail	1 piece	350 (13¾)	95 (3¾)	21 (7/8)
Rocking board	1 piece	2,400 (94)	170 (6¾)	28 (1⅛)
Seat blocks	2 pieces	170 (6¾)	45 (1¾)	21 (7/8)
Locating blocks	2 pieces	170 (6¾)	45 (1¾)	21 (7/8)
Hand grips	2 pieces	330 (13)	45 (1¾)	45 (1¾)

Hardwood dowel

Pivot bar	1 piece	400 (15¾)	25 (1) dia.

All measurements given above are nett and small allowances should be made for cutting the pieces to length.

Other materials

Sixty-two 30 mm (1¼ in.) No. 8 countersunk wood screws
Waterproof wood glue
Four 75 mm (3 in.) by 6 mm (¼ in.) dia. coach bolts
Nuts and washers to fit the coach bolts
Medium grade glasspaper
Polyurethane varnish or paint.

neath the board at the centre, and space them apart so that the board moves easily when it is placed over the pivot bar with a locating block on each side of the bar.

Fix a seat block at each end of the board (see diagram 4). This will keep the board flat and help to prevent a young rider from slipping off the end when in full flight!

Prepare timber for two hand grips to length and drill two holes through each for the coach bolts (see diagram 4), then taper and round over the ends using a sharp knife or a file followed by glasspaper.

Use each hand grip, suitably positioned on the board, as a guide to drill the holes required in the board. Fix each grip to the board with two coach bolts and place a washer over each bolt before securing it on the underside of the board with a nut. To make the hand grips adjustable, drill a series of holes in the board, spaced not less than about 50 mm (2 in.) apart.

FINISHING

Rub down thoroughly with glasspaper wrapped round a cork sanding block to remove loose splinters and to round over edges and corners. Brush off dust and apply varnish or paint including the bottom edges of the frame legs which will come into contact with damp soil or grass.

Replace the pivot bar if it becomes worn.

HE ROCKING BOARD

ut two seat blocks and two locating blocks to ngth, equal to the width of the rocking board ee diagram 4). Fix the locating blocks under-

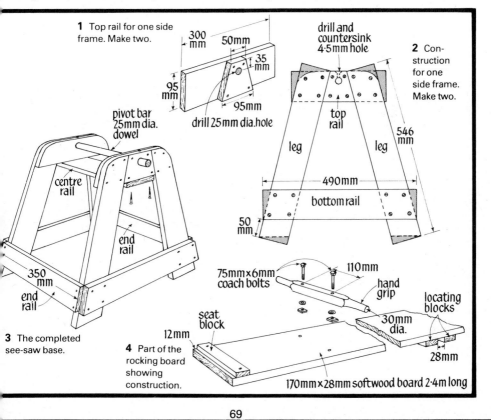

1 Top rail for one side frame. Make two.

300 mm 50mm

35 mm

95 mm

95mm

pivot bar 25mm dia. dowel

drill 25mm dia. hole

drill and countersink 4·5mm hole

2 Construction for one side frame. Make two.

top rail

leg   leg

546 mm

490mm

bottom rail

50 mm

centre rail

end rail

350 mm

end rail

3 The completed see-saw base.

75mm×6mm coach bolts

110mm

hand grip

locating blocks

30mm dia.

seat block

12mm

28mm

4 Part of the rocking board showing construction.

170mm×28mm softwood board 2·4m long

A PLACE OF ONE'S OWN

Holidays away are a joy, but there is also the bonus of making us appreciate our own home when we return, says The Man-Who-Sees

THEY had got back the day before and yes, she said, they had enjoyed every minute of their holiday. The weather had been quite good in that part of the country, and the hotel really first-class.

"But it was long enough," she said. "I think we were both ready to come home, at the end." She looked round her room as she spoke, unaware of the impression she gave of "settling" as one does into cushions, of the comfortable stretching of limbs in a well-worn garment after the slight unease of something newer and smarter. And, as her gaze came to rest on a worn part of the carpet, I could almost hear her saying to herself, as I am sure she says many times, "We really must get a new carpet for this room." Yet there was a kind of affection in that gaze.

"It's good to get away, even if for no other reason than that it makes you appreciate your own home when you get back to it," she said, proving I had read her thoughts correctly.

"There's really no place like home," I said with complete banality, because I could think of no better way of expressing what we were both feeling.

She nodded then said, "But why? What is this thing about one's own place? We grumble about it half the time...at least *I* do, and I am sure most women do — wanting this and that added or changed. I even like some of my friends' homes far better than my own. They are better appointed, more comfortable — yet, after I've been to stay with them I always find I'm more comfortable in this little place of ours.

"On holiday I was lapped in longed-for luxury, and waited on hand and foot. Our bedroom was lovely. A wonderful view from the windows, and far better beds than *we* have. So lights and all the rest. But I never felt safe a shut away in that room, or invited by that be somehow. We had lovely food, all prepared f us. For weeks before we went I was seeing it sheer heaven not to have to think of meals, cook them, or wash up after them...and envyi women who could just give orders. And I d revel in all this, at first. But somehow towar the end I was getting fidgety, wishing I could into my own kitchen and make a cup of tea.

"And of course that is just what I did, t moment we got home. And when I called ou

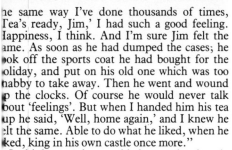

answered her own question as to why there is a special kind of happiness to be found in "one's own place".

I don't know why four particular walls, no different from millions of others, can take on this great power of sanctuary, just because they are our own, by right of rent or purchase, and we have lived in them for some time. Perhaps it is because we have given part of ourselves to them and, as with friendship, it gives something back? Our own hearth welcomes us, the ticking of our clock is not quite like any other. The furniture, possibly worn, possibly ugly, becomes so reassuring. We know all its faults, and it seems to know ours, and puts up with us as no one else's furniture will! We have to be much more on guard — guests with other people's things.

And is there any bed, however luxurious, quite so easeful as one's own bed, which one is used to? With the light beside it, just so? And the books just to hand? And the shadows in the corners of the room, beyond the radius of that lamp hiding nothing that is unfamiliar or menacing? The curtains may be old, and irritate you every time you swish them back in the morning, yet, once drawn at bedtime, they are like a portcullis to shut you in, safe for the long night.

Young people, in the exciting years of adventuring, seldom need a refuge, a sanctuary. Home is somewhere to wing away from, into a wide world. But sooner or later, one feels the need of a place of one's own in which to dwell, preferably, but not essentially, with someone loved, for long enough for the spirit of home to be born from the inanimate bricks, wood, fabrics. The time comes for most when one is a little battered, a little disillusioned, thinks a little less well of one's own powers, and has a little less trust in the benevolence of that wide world. Then one comes to know more about the real meaning of home, and to value the real gifts it can have.

NOT THE NEED

Some women never do manage to create a home, though they may live in very beautiful houses and redecorate them entirely once a year. Perhaps they have not the knack of it, or the need of it. Or the heart. Yet another woman will create it in one small room.

Some happy wanderers prefer to be footloose, though even these will talk nostalgically of their childhood home. But they have made their choice to meet their greater needs. There are others who long for home, and are deprived of it. I don't think that those of us who are fortunate fully realise the tragedy, particularly for women, in those words, so often on our lips nowadays, "The Homeless". They are deprived of something Man felt to be essential from the dawn of time when he found himself "alone and afraid, in a world he never made".

So count your blessings when that holiday or visit is ended, and you return to your warm, welcoming home.

he same way I've done thousands of times, Tea's ready, Jim,' I had such a good feeling. Happiness, I think. And I'm sure Jim felt the ame. As soon as he had dumped the cases; he ook off the sports coat he had bought for the oliday, and put on his old one which was too habby to take away. Then he went and wound p the clocks. Of course he would never talk bout 'feelings'. But when I handed him his tea up he said, 'Well, home again,' and I knew he elt the same. Able to do what he liked, when he ked, king in his own castle once more."

I think, as she rambled on, she largely

Ideas for Happy Family Outings

Royal London: Set out for Buckingham Palace to watch the pageantry of the Changing of the Guard. The ceremony starts at 11.30 daily between 1st April and 30th September (every other day in winter) and lasts about half an hour. Afterwards, walk down the Mall from the Palace. On your right is pretty St. James's Park — the view from the little bridge across its lake is enchanting and the islands are the London residence of pelicans and ducks and countless wild fowl. On your left, you will pass Clarence House (the Queen Mother's standard will be flying if she's at home), St. James's Palace (detour left past Clarence House), Marlborough House and Carlton House Terrace, before reaching Admiralty House at the end of the Mall. Go through the arch to find Trafalgar Square with Nelson's Column, Landseer's lions, St. Martin-in-the-Fields, the National Gallery, the National Portrait Gallery and many well-fed pigeons. In the afternoon, walk down Whitehall from Trafalgar Square to Parliament Square to see Westminster Abbey, Big Ben and the Houses of Parliament. On the way you will pass Admiralty House, Horse Guards, Downing Street (a turning off to the right) and the Cenotaph. See Wordsworth's favourite view of London from Westminster Bridge. Down below, from Westminster Pier and from Charing Cross Pier a little further down-river, river boats cruise to the Tower and Royal Greenwich or up-stream to Kew, Richmond and Hampton Court between April and October.

Lindisfarne, or Holy Island,

off the coast of Northumbria: Tiny island of haunting atmosphere, reached only by a narrow causeway near the village of Beal two hours before and three hours after high tide. For those who cut things fine, a hideaway on stilts, halfway across, offers safe refuge until the tide ebbs again. Cradle of Christianity under St. Aidan and the formidable St. Cuthbert, hater of all things female, even cows, who were not allowed within sight of his priory walls, the island boasts a ruined priory, Elizabethan castle, church whose yard is filled with Celtic crosses, winery where they make the Lindisfarne mead and Iron Rails Inn, whose landlord will probably tell you Holy Islanders spend their winters knitting bedsocks for seals! Fresh crab salads and sandwiches are the much-to-be-recommended speciality here. Open all year, according to tides.

Bluebell Railway, Sheffield Park Station, nr. Uckfield, East Sussex: Ride the famous Bluebell Line through the flower-splashed Sussex countryside from Sheffield Park to Horsted Keynes, your train hauled by a vintage steam locomotive. The unique Bluebell Railway, the first preserved standard gauge passenger railway, is a living museum for steam trains. Sheffield Park, built in 1882 and so celebrating its centenary, is lovingly preserved as a typical Victorian country station. Buffet and shop. Trains operate daily June to September, Wednesdays in May to October, Saturdays from March to November and Sundays throughout the year.

Llechwedd Slate Caverns,

Blaenau Ffestiniog, North Wales: Two exciting rides take visitors deep down into the heart of the Llechwedd Caverns for a glimpse of the incredible life led by the Victorian quarryman, who might have spent years working, by candlelight in the same cavern. A narrow-gauge tramway takes you to see a realistic re-creation of a cavern in operation, with appropriately dressed figures of the quarrymen and marvellous guides who bring the whole tableau to vivid life. The lower depth of the mine can be reached by a steep incline railway. Do take warm clothing. Restaurant, café and craft workshop can be found on ground level. Open daily, Easter to October, 10am - 6pm.

Tucktonia Leisure Park, Christchurch, nr. Bournemouth: Claimed to be the biggest model landscape in the world, Tucktonia's theme is the Best of Britain. The Tower of London, Concorde, QE2, Stonehenge, a typical Cornish fishing village, the Post Office Tower and Big Ben are all here, among the 200 models on show to represent 4,000 years of Britain's heritage. Trains speed along the railways, cars and lorries travel the motorways, ships sail the miniature seas and planes taxi to take off from the airport. The adjoining amusement park is the children's delight — Magic Castle Giant Slide, mini dodgems, bumper boats, roundabouts and other diversions await them. Cafeteria, public house, restaurant and gift shop. Open daily 10am to dusk.

A SUMMER'S DAY

***M**onkeying around. Directions and patterns for these two endearing fellows start on page 92.*
Right: Light and lacy, this summer sweater has flattering bloused sleeves and small Peter Pan collar. Instructions on page 90.

*F*rom our handyman — a favourite summer toy that is easy to make.
Directions and diagrams start on page 68.
Right: Lazy summer days relaxing under the sun. Sounds fantastic? Turn to page 88
for some expert advice on how to face the sun — beautifully!

...ographed in Puerto Rico for Ambre Solaire; hair by Paul Nix for L'Oreal

*F*or the small fry — always-useful child's cardigan in stocking stitch with pretty
lace stitch and cable panels. Instructions on page 64.
Right: Make the most of a lovely day and pack up a picnic of simple, easy-to-carry food
to enjoy at the seaside or in the country. See page 61.

*R*oses grown to perfection in the Royal Horticultural Society's Wisley Garden at Ripley, Surrey. A subtle blending of lovely colours — red, pink, yellow and white — is set off by green, grassy walks.

ROSES ALL THE WAY

**With so many varieties to choose from,
our national flower in some shape or form
should find a place in every garden,
says JOY SIMMONS**

SINCE civilisation began, the Rose has always held a very special place. It was known to Confucius in 500 B.C., but not ill many centuries later were the Chinese Roses rrought to Europe, to become 'ancestors' of the 'arieties we admire today.

Nowadays Rose breeding has become a skilled rt, as well as big business. There are types to uit everyone, from the dainty miniatures no nore than a few inches high to the tall climbers, lot forgetting the beautiful weeping standards o lovely for specimen planting.

For the average-sized garden, the *hybrid tea large-flowered*) type and *floribunda (cluster)* bush Roses are the most popular. The hybrid teas are insurpassed for their large and shapely individual blooms, often sweetly scented. The floribundas, on the other hand, have a longer flowering season and provide a greater splash of colour vith their trusses of blooms.

Miniature Roses are also ideal where space is estricted, both bush and standard forms being vailable.

At the other end of the scale are the *old-world* nd *modern shrub Roses*, many of which grow 7-8 t. high and almost as much across. Suitable for lanting in large shrub borders or as specimens, hese Roses, most of them richly scented, can be real joy, some of them making wonderful hedging plants. Then there are the *climbing* and ambler Roses, which can vary considerably in their vigour and eventual height.

Not all Roses are scented, of course, though a number delight us with their fragrance. It is intriguing to note that whereas a particular Rose may smell sweet to one person, it can hold little or no scent for another! That being said, the following varieties are worth noting: H.T.'s *Fragrant Cloud, Wendy Cussons, Alec's Red, Mme. Butterfly, Northern Lights, Mme. Louis Laperrière,* and the floribundas *Heaven Scent* and *Margaret Merril.*

Although Roses can be planted from October to February (or all the year round if container-grown), November is normally the best month for planting, when the soil is still warm and the roots have a chance to become established before the hard frosts.

If you are planting a new Rose bed, the ground should be dug about 18 in. deep, working in plenty of rotted farm manure, vegetable compost or peat and bonemeal. Choose an open, sunny site where possible, and preferably one sheltered from strong north winds. Set hybrid tea and floribunda bush Roses 18-24 in. apart, with the point at which the stem has been budded no more than 1 in. below the surface after treading firm.

Before planting, you should soak the roots in a bucket of water for a few hours to 'plump them up', immersing the stems as well if they appear shrivelled. *Continued overleaf*

Use a planting mixture of peat and bonemeal (a double handful of bonemeal to a three-gallon bucket of peat), scattering a little over and under the well-spread roots before filling in with soil.

Standards and climbers are planted in the same way, but when planting a standard a stake should be inserted beside the plant before the hole is filled in with soil.

All newly planted hybrid tea and floribunda bush Roses should be *hard pruned* the first spring to stimulate strong root growth. The first year after planting, the stems should be cut down to 4-6 in. in spring, immediately above an *outward-facing* bud. Aim at an open, cup-shaped bush to allow the air to circulate, bearing in mind that *the weaker the growth, the harder the pruning should be*.

In subsequent years, hybrid tea bushes required for garden display rather than exhibition blooms should be *moderately pruned;* this means reducing ripe laterals by about half the length of the previous year's wood. And on floribundas, prune one-year-old wood to roughly two thirds of its length, at the same time cutting down some of the older stems to within a few inches of the base.

The Shrub Roses need *no pruning* apart from the removal of dead wood and shortening worn-out leggy growth.

Once pruning is completed, it is advisable to spray all types of Roses with a systemic fungicide, repeating the treatment when the leaves unfold, to destroy spores of black spot. During mild spells, keep a careful watch for aphis (greenfly) and other pests, spraying with a systemic insecticide.

A Rose fertiliser can be pricked into the soil surface in April, and a mulch of peat or rotted manure applied in May.

Red and yellow bicolour H.T. Piccadilly.

ROSES AT CHRISTMAS

I am often asked if there is any way of keeping Roses fresh for Christmas decoration. If you're ready to sacrifice a number of blooms to offset losses, try cutting some half-open buds, dipping the stem ends in melted sealing wax (you can heat it over a saucepan) and wrapping each one in several thicknesses of tissue paper. After treatment, store in an airtight tin in a cool place.

The evening before the blooms are to be arranged, cut the ends off and stand the stems in warm water.

Hard Pruning *(below). Cut back stems to 4-6 in.*
Moderate Pruning *(right). Reduce stems by about half or one-third.*

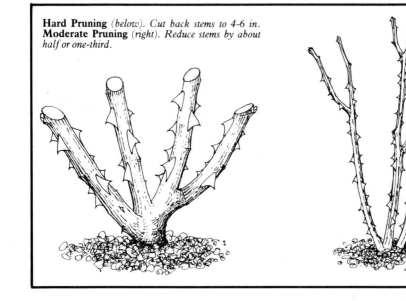

SOMETHING TO DO WITH LOVE

BY STELLA WHITELAW

Grace was a cat person, enjoying the unconditional affection so freely given by her furry friends. Hugh was not a cat person, which was a pity, for in every other way he was perfect . . .

I T ALWAYS took Grace a considerable time to walk along Oakleigh Road because she had so many friends to say hello to on the way. She would never dream of slighting an old friend, or a new one, even if it made the difference between catching the 8.15 am to Victoria Station and missing it.

First there was Mabel. Mabel was a smoky grey Persian with tabby markings, the prettiest little face and a perpetually fishy odour. She always waited on the pavement for the admiration and caresses which she considered her due.

A few houses further down was Susie, who was black, sleek, and had three legs as a result of a road accident. She was pathetically grateful for attention and would hop frantically through the flower-beds at the sound of Grace calling her name. Susie made light of her disability but she never attempted to cross a road again. She stayed on her own side, her world reduced to a few acres of garden surrounded by a border of tarmac.

Titch was also black and sleek, but with four legs and a velvet sheen to her coat that spoke volumes about her well-fed, pampered life. However, Titch came of a theatrical family and her favourite rôle was that of a homeless, starving waif thrown out on to the pavement. Her acting was pretty good, and she managed to fool a lot of people.

"Poor Titch," Grace would murmur, sympathetically stroking a forlorn ear. "Have they all gone out and left you again? And did they forget to give you your breakfast? You'll have to catch yourself a mouse."

Thomas was a thug-faced ginger tom who spent most of the day guarding cars. He sat on a car roof top, barely acknowledging Grace's friendly greeting although his timid heart yearned to respond. He was too shy even to run away. Whereas Sheba, the pale Siamese next door, spoke to no one, not even other cats, and hid in hedges perfecting her vocal imitation of a baby.

Grace never ignored any cat and this left her breathless by the time she reached the station and stumbled into a carriage. Hugh held the door open with an expression of amused tolerance on his handsome face. He helped her aboard.

"Nearly missed it again," he said. "All those darned cats, I suppose."

"Susie can't hurry," said Grace. "And I hate to miss her out. It's a miracle she's still alive."

"Ridiculous to go to all that trouble for a cat. They should have had her put down," said Hugh complacently.

"How would you like it if you had a road accident and someone decided not to bother to patch you up?" asked Grace, with a trace of anger in her low voice.

"Don't be silly," said Hugh, only half-listening. "People aren't cats."

'But cats are like people,' Grace thought. "And I'm cultivating Thomas," she said aloud. "That takes time."

Continued overleaf

She was between cats at the moment, and that meant she had a special need for the unconditional affection so generously offered by cat friends. Even the distant Thomas and the vanishing Sheba were reassuringly themselves and a challenge for Grace's incurable ailurophilia, the love of cats.

Grace sighed as she settled back into a seat and Hugh opened the *Financial Times*. She had been going out with Hugh for nearly a year. He was good company, intelligent, successful at his job as an accountant, and, for some reason totally unknown to Grace, he had singled her out.

Grace never really could understand why. There was a shortage of men in their area and Grace had felt it more acutely because of her height — her five feet eight inches immediately put off half the male population. Hugh was an easy six feet and she had been captivated the moment she fell over his feet getting on to the train one morning. His eyes seemed to radiate warmth; his hand steadying her arm had sent shivers down her spine; his dark brown voice rendered her speechless.

"Are you feeling all right?" he had enquired as he dusted off his hand-stitched brown shoes.

"Oh, yes," Grace had breathed. She had never felt better.

However, Grace soon discovered that she had a price to pay for Hugh's favours. She had to conform to the kind of behaviour Hugh expected from a young woman. She had to tone down her disco dancing from its normal wild abandon, put away her outlandish gear and wear restrained dresses and skirts. She had to go lightly with the kohl round her eyes — Hugh thought that too much make-up was vulgar.

Grace played a good game of tennis and Hugh liked having her for a partner. She had the height and reach, but Hugh soon discovered that she lacked concentration, particularly if a certain tabby kitten was around the tennis club.

"Hellow, Little Mo," said Grace, stooping to stroke the little stray who had attached herself to the club for the season. Little Mo seemed to live on bar food, crisps, and cold sausages, so Grace often brought her the odd titbit in a margarine tub.

"It's your service," Hugh hollered.

"Sorry," said Grace, throwing the ball into the air. "Little Mo feels hurt if I don't speak to her. She gets quite lonely at times."

The kitten danced across the court, bouncing after the ball, her tail a streaming banner. Hugh missed his return shot.

"You're the most impossible person I have ever come across," said Hugh, removing the kitten. "How can you tell if a cat's feelings are hurt? Tell me that."

"She looks hurt," said Grace defiantly.

"With all those stripes on her face, I fail to see how you can detect any expression. Really, Grace, it's time you grew up."

"Please stay off the court," Grace whispered to Little Mo, wrapping the kitten in her cardigan and putting her on a sunny chair. The cat's eyes blinked lovingly and she immediately went to sleep.

They played well and won the match. Hugh was pleased.

"That's my girl," he said, throwing an arm round Grace's shoulders and bending to brush the lobe of her ear with his lips. Grace almost stopped breathing. This had to be what she had been waiting for all her life. It was chemistry, magnetism, sex-appeal, any word would do — but it was still a magical something that made Grace try to change in order to please Hugh.

However, there was nothing much she could do about the cats. She had loved cats all her life, and she could not ignore them even to keep Hugh.

"For goodness' sake, come along, Grace," said Hugh, as they hurried along Oakleigh Road. "We'll miss the beginning of the film."

Grace caught him up, a little breathless. "I will not pass Susie without saying hello," she said. "She has a very uneventful life with only three legs."

"And you think your two-seconds worth makes a difference to her?" Hugh commented wryly.

"It's human contact. Without that, her life would become dry and empty."

-THE ROBIN FAMILY

RICHARD WRITES AN OPERA

His cousins like it very much but Mrs. Robin isn't so sure about the voices

ONE SATURDAY Richard went over to see Roley and Rosemary, carrying some sheets of paper under his wing and looking very pleased with himself.

He found his cousins in the kitchen watching their mother making pastry.

"Come out into the garden, I've got something to show you," said Richard excitedly and a few moments later the three little Robins were sitting in a tiny hollow at the back of Treestump House.

"I've written an opera," announced Richard. "And it's called 'The Wicked Robin of Hollow Tree Castle.' Rosemary can be the heroine. Roley can be the villain and I'll be the hero. I've written out your words, but I'll whistle the tunes for you first so you will know how they go."

Rosemary and Roley listened carefully — the opera was very exciting. The heroine was supposed to be imprisoned in Hollow Tree Castle and was leaning out of the window calling for help. When Richard gave her the signal, Rosemary began to sing in a high, frantic voice — not at all like her usual pretty chirrups.

"Louder," commanded Richard.

Mrs. Robin, hearing the shrieks rushed out into the garden. "Whatever's the matter?" she cried in alarm.

The three little Robins rolled about on the grass, laughing merrily.

"I was only rehearsing my part in Richard's opera," explained Rosemary. "I'm singing a desperate song and waiting to be rescued!"

Mrs. Robin began to laugh, too, and thought perhaps the "singing" could do with a great deal more rehearsing.

"Nonsense," said Hugh. "I've never yet met a cat that wasn't snooty and offhand."

Grace almost said that was because *he* was snooty and offhand, but she bit back the words. Sometimes she wished he was not quite so perfect for her in every other way.

It was with these sobering thoughts that Grace walked to the station the next morning. She was not sure that she wanted to change the way Hugh wanted her to. She could change herself on the surface, but beneath her lady-like exterior she would still be the girl she had always been.

Thomas, the thug-faced ginger tom, was sitting on the roof of a soft-topped sports car. She stopped and reached up to scratch his furry ear. He arched his back, embarrassed.

"Don't be shy, darling," she said gently. "I want to make friends."

"And I'd like to be your friend, too."

"How extraordinary," said Grace, recovering her composure. "I didn't know Thomas could speak."

A tousled head of unruly hair appeared from beneath the car, then a face streaked with grease grinned up at her. The young man looked at Grace with admiration in his bright blue eyes.

"We don't tell everyone," he said. "Not even the neighbours."

"I was actually talking to your cat," Grace explained formally, her hand resting lightly on Thomas's furry neck. He moved imperceptibly, half an inch forward.

"My mother's cat. I'm Pete Hardy. I'm home on leave from the army. I don't think we've met but we should have. Thomas is slipping — I rely on him for introductions."

"He's very shy," said Grace. "It's taken me months to get this far."

Pete scrambled out from under the car and brushed the dust off his jeans. "I promise I won't be so low," he grinned.

"I shall have to go," said Grace. "If I talk to people as well, I shall miss my train." She noticed they were the same height.

"Hop in. I'll give you a lift to the station." He scooped Thomas off the roof and deposited him on a flowerbed. "Do some gardening for a change," he suggested to the cat.

Grace was not late for her train that morning. Hugh noted her even breathing. There was not a strand of red-streaked hair out of place. She looked almost serious.

"No cats this morning?" he enquired.

"Only one," she said. "The shy one."

He squeezed her hand encouragingly. "That's my girl," he said. "You're showing some sense at last."

Continued overleaf

The last dance of the season was a special event in the tennis club calendar. Hugh and Grace danced together all evening. She floated in his arms, very aware of his closeness, the spicy fragrance of his aftershave, the smoothness of his cheek so close to her own. It was a wonderful evening and Grace began to think of a lifetime of such bliss. Perhaps Hugh was right when he said she was immature; perhaps it would be easy to change if she could always be so happy.

Then the music quickened to disco and Grace promptly broke a heel dancing to the latest chart success. She hobbled off the floor, the offending spike in her hand.

"You're hopeless," said Hugh, putting the heel in his pocket. They walked outside the clubhouse, their arms entwined. The music was still playing, the air full of pale blossoms swaying in the silvery moonlight. It was a perfect evening. The last of summer. Hugh took Grace into his arms and her mouth was warm and sweet as he kissed her.

As Grace soared in the heady sensation of his embrace, far away she heard a small, faint sound. At first it hardly registered, but then she heard it again and moved hesitantly away from his seeking mouth.

"Grace, what is it?" he murmured against her face. "Don't go, please."

"I thought I heard something. It came from over there."

"It was nothing. An owl, a mouse."

"No, it wasn't. I think something is hurt. I must find out." She twisted out of his arms and began to search the darkened car park, limping on her shoeless foot.

"Grace, come back. You can't do anything."

"But I can hear something crying."

Grace almost stumbled over a small dark shape stretched out on the driveway. It was Little Mo, the stray kitten. She must have been hit by a car for her back legs were stretched out behind her at an odd angle. She was quiet now, only the faint, irregular heaving of her stripy sides showing that she was still alive.

Grace crouched over the injured animal, her heart pounding.

"We must do something," she said. "It's the little tabby kitten. She's badly hurt."

"It's only a stray. She'll be dead by morning," said Hugh, strolling over. "Come back to the clubhouse. I'll buy you a drink. You look pale."

Genius begins great works; labour alone finishes them.

Joubert

Grace was aghast. "We can't just leave her, poor little thing."

"It's only a cat," said Hugh, exasperated. "You make her sound like a human being."

"I'm going to find someone who will help if you won't," said Grace fiercely. "Someone with feeling. Someone with a heart and not just a handsome face."

"You're impossible," said Hugh, his profile like granite in the moonlight. "All this fuss over a stray cat. I don't understand you."

Grace limped up the steps into the clubhouse. She knew who she was looking for. Pete was not dancing, but talking in a crowd by the bar. He looked tough and dependable, the aggressive line of his jaw softened by the humour in his eyes. He was still in jeans, a cleaner pair perhaps, with an old faded combat shirt. He saw Grace and left the group immediately.

"What's the matter?" he asked.

"It's Little Mo. She's been run over and she's very badly hurt. I don't know what to do. Perhaps we could take her to a vet, or something." Grace swallowed hard.

"Show me," said Pete.

THE WORLD shrank. Grace could not look. She hid her face in her hands as Pete bent over the small body.

"I'm sorry, Grace," he said. "She's gone. Wait here while I take her round to the shrubbery. She always liked it there."

The music was playing again and the soft, balmy air was filled with the scent of blossom. It was all unreal, the music, the dancing, the passionate kisses she had shared with Hugh.

Grace knew she could not change. She would always be this kind of person, a little awkward to live with, but not if the man really loved her. And if there were not enough men to go round, then she would make her own home and live by herself. Well, not quite by herself. There might be a cat or two.

"Would you like to walk home?" said Pete, returning at last. "I can fetch my car in the morning. You can borrow my tennis shoes."

"Yes, I would like that," said Grace, hardly audibly.

They did not talk. They walked slowly through the coolness of the night, the street lamps throwing their orange glow on to the pavements. A small grey shadow detached itself from the darkness and wound itself round Grace's ankles.

"Oh, Mabel," said Grace, with instant recognition. "You do need a bath. Hasn't your best friend told you?"

Susie leaped off a low wall and landed a little unsteadily on her three paws. She was delighted and surprised to see Grace so late, and purred loudly.

"Hello, Susie," said Grace, in a trembling voice. "You survived all right, didn't you? Not like Little Mo."

"Little Mo was too badly hurt. No one could have done anything," Pete began.

"Yes, I know," said Grace, walking on.

Titch was sitting on the top step outside her house She had only been out five minutes but she managed to make it look as though she had been there hours. Grace had to smile.

"Cheer up, beautiful," she said. "They'll let you in again soon."

They stopped outside Grace's house. She turned to Pete, wanting to say something.

"I'm between cats at the moment," she said. "I was going to bring Little Mo home for the winter."

"I know," he said.

He did not take her hand or touch her. There was no magic or chemistry. But there was something else — a tiny flame of awareness that had everything to do with love.

Thomas was sitting on top of a van. He had been trying to make up his mind all day. But here she was and she had not seen him. If he did not hurry, she would be gone and then it would be too late.

He leaped off the van and ran across the road, his heart pounding. Even now he dared not come too close, but hesitated some yards away with a little sidestep.

But Grace had seen him. She went down on one knee and held out her hand. He sniffed it cautiously. Grace did not move or speak, knowing that they had come to the moment of trust. And trust was the beginning of love.

THE END

PREPARING TO GREET THE SUN

Early summer is the time to try
on your swimsuit, says Jane Matera — a good
three or four weeks before your holiday,
when there's still time to *do* something about
the problems that confront you!

I T'S lovely to look forward to summer in general, and holidays in particular. But if past years have found you worn to a frazzle before you even set off, take some timely advice on how to greet this summer looking and feeling your best.

Don't leave all your holiday preparations to the night before you leave. Give some thought, not only to what you'll wear but how you'll want to *look* in what you'll wear. For instance:

What about your skin?

Sunbathing has a drying effect, and if your skin is on the dry side to begin with, the problem will be exacerbated. Not only that, but it's difficult, if not impossible, to achieve a really smooth, even tan if your skin is dry — all that will happen is that your skin will peel relentlessly.

Try to give your skin concentrated care for at least three or four weeks before your holiday. Switch to a creamy moisturiser, one perhaps slightly richer than you use normally on your face, and keep your body skin moisturised, too, with lavish use of body lotion, morning and evening.

Nourish your skin regularly every night with a good skinfood. You should use just the very minimum since most nourishing creams these days are feather-light and don't *need* to be plastered on one-inch thick.

Don't forget, either, to switch to a bath *oil* in preference to the more drying salts and foams; this will help soften your skin while you bathe (but do, please, remember to use a mat in the bath for safety's sake).

What about your figure?

Does that simple, guileless question elicit despairing sighs?

Don't, please, panic yourself into a mindless crash diet two or three weeks before your holiday. Cut out the unnecessary fatteners like cakes and sweets and puddings, by all means, if you feel you're not quite as sylph-like as you'd like, but don't go on a rigid starvation diet that will leave you limp, weary and cross and in no fit state for enjoying a holiday.

Instead, try some exercises to firm up your body generally. Ten minutes every morning, ten minutes every evening is all that's needed to get you back in trim.

For your waist, hips and thighs: Stand erect, with your feet apart and your hands on your hips. Now, bend *forward* from the waist as far as you can, come back up again, then bend as far *back* as you can. Maintain a steady, brisk rhythm, *and don't bend your knees!*

Do the exercise to music, if you can, to make it more tolerable. Start by bending 10 times forward, 10 times back; work gradually up to 20 times each way.

Waist-whittler: Again, stand upright, feet

apart. Again, without bending your knees, swing your left arm up in an arc and down to touch your right foot. Straighten up and swing your right arm up in an arc and down to touch your left foot. (Briskly, 10 times each side.)

Thigh reducer: Good old-fashioned knee-bends, as many as you can bear! (Keep your back straight and your hands on your hips.)

What about your legs?

If one look at your poor neglected legs sends you into a fit of despair, don't panic. All may yet be saved.

Thread veins can be covered up with a blemish stick (there's one in the Rimmel range).

Nicks and scratches from shaving do not look sightly at any time, least of all on the beach. Switch to a battery shaver or use a depilatory cream (messy, but leaves a smooth finish), and use lots and lots of handcream or body lotion on your legs to soothe and smooth them.

Consider having your legs waxed at a salon before you go on holiday. This would mean you wouldn't have to bother about defuzzing your legs for about 4-6 weeks (depending on the individual rate at which your hair grows).

Waxing is also the only really satisfactory solution to 'bikini-line' hair on the upper thighs; shaving it away will make your skin sore and depilatory creams may leave a rash. Most beauty salons offer a bikini-line waxing service and this also covers any stray hairs you may have on your tummy.

What about your feet?

Oh, dear! Forgot all about them until now, didn't you? The first thing to do is to get any problems such as corns dealt with. Make an appointment with a qualified chiropodist, if you're afflicted. However, if you prefer to try a home treatment, Scholl's medicated corn and callous pads are clinically tested and safe to use provided you follow the instructions, although they're not recommended for those prone to infections. Remember, too, that you must wear comfortable shoes.

Pamper your feet a little by giving them a weekly pedicure (preferably after a bath, when the skin is soft). Clip your toenails (straight across; don't round the edges), and deal with any hard-skin areas on your heels and soles with a pumice–stone.

Lavish *lots* of body lotion or handcream on your feet and massage it in really well.

Exercise your feet, too, to make them more supple and graceful: try (a) walking on the outer edges of your feet, to help tone up the arch muscles; (b) extending your leg and pointing your toes as far as you can, then relaxing. Try, too, to walk barefoot around the house whenever you can, if you can do so safely. Now, you should be prepared to greet the sun.

OLD-FASHIONED CHARM

Knitted in a fine, 3-ply yarn in a beautiful all-over lacy pattern, with full sleeves and flattering Peter Pan collar that add just the right touch of elegance to this pretty jersey.

Instructions in 6 sizes

Colour photo on page 75

MATERIALS: *Allow the following quantities in 25 g balls of Jaeger Botany 3-ply: 11 for the 76 cm and 81 cm sizes; 12 for the 86 cm and 91 cm sizes; 13 for the 97 cm and 102 cm sizes. For any one size: a pair each of No. 11 (3 mm) and No. 13 (2¼ mm) knitting needles.*

TENSION: *Work at a tension of 35 stitches and 42 rows to measure 10 x 10 cm over the pattern, using No. 11 (3 mm) needles, to obtain the measurements given below.*

ABBREVIATIONS: *To be read before working: K., knit plain; p., purl; st., stitch; tog., together; sl., slip; dec., decrease (by working 2 sts. tog.); y.fwd., yarn forward to make a st.; y.r.n., yarn round needle to make a st.; y.o.n., yarn over needle to make a st.; p.s.s.o., pass slipped st. over; s.k.p.o., (sl.1, k.1, p.s.s.o.); up 1, pick up loop lying between needles and p. or k. into back of it; nil, meaning nothing is worked here for this size; single rib is k.1 and p.1 alternately.*

NOTE: *The instructions are given for the 76 cm (30 inch) size. Where they vary, work the figures within the first brackets for the 81 cm (32 inch) size; work the figures within the second brackets for the 86 cm (34 inch) size, and so on.*

THE BACK: With No. 13 (2¼ mm) needles cast on 146 (154) (162) (170) (178) (186) sts. and work 52 rows in single rib.

Change to No. 11 (3 mm) needles and work the 10-row pattern as follows:

1st row: K.2, * y.fwd., K.1, s.k.p.o., p.1, k.2 tog., k.1, y.r.n., p.1, s.k.p.o., p.1, k.2 tog., y.fwd., k.1, y.fwd., k. 2 (3)(4)(5)(6)(7); repeat from * ending last repeat with k.2 instead of k.2 (3)(4)(5)(6)(7).

2nd row: P.6, * k.1, p.1, k.1, p.3, k.1, p.9 (10)(11)(12)(13)(14); repeat from * ending last repeat with p.5.

3rd row: K.2, * y.fwd., k.1, s.k.p.o., p.1, k.2 tog., k.1, p.1, sl.1, k.2 tog., p.s.s.o., y.fwd., k.3, y.fwd., k.2 (3)(4)(5)(6)(7); repeat from * ending last repeat with k.2.

4th row: P.8, * k.1, p.2, k.1, p.11 (12)(13) (14)(15)(16); repeat from * ending last repeat with p.5.

5th row: K.2, * y.fwd., k.1, y.fwd., s.k.p.o., p.1, k.2 tog., k.2 tog., y.fwd., k.5, y.fwd., k.2 (3)(4)(5)(6)(7); repeat from * ending last repeat with k.2.

6th row: P.9, * k.1, p.1, k.1, p.13 (14)(15) (16)(17)(18); repeat from * ending last repeat with p.6.

7th row: K.2, * y.fwd., k.3 y.fwd., sl.1, k.2 tog., p.s.s.o., p.1, y.o.n., k.1, s.k.p.o., p.1, k.2 tog., k.1, y.fwd., k.2 (3)(4)(5)(6)(7); repeat from * ending last repeat with k.2.

8th row: P.5, * k.1, p.3, k.1, p.11 (12)(13) (14)(15)(16); repeat from * ending last repeat with p.8.

9th row: K.2, * y.fwd., k.5, y.fwd., s.k.p.o., k.1, s.k.p.o., p.1, k.2 tog., k.1, y.fwd., k.2 (3) (4)(5)(6)(7); repeat from * ending last repeat with k.2.

10th row: P.5, * k.1, p.2, k.1, p.12 (13)(14) (15)(16)(17); repeat from * ending last repeat with p.9.

MEASUREMENTS in centimetres (and inches, in brackets)												
To fit bust sizes	76	(30)	81	(32)	86	(34)	91	(36)	97	(38)	102	(40)
All round at under-arms	83.5	(32¾)	88	(34½)	92.5	(36½)	97	(38)	101.5	(39¾)	106	(41¾)
Side seam	35	(13¾)	35	(13¾)	35	(13¾)	35	(13¾)	35	(13¾)	35	(13¾)
Length	58	(22¾)	58.5	(23)	58.5	(23)	59	(23¼)	59	(23¼)	59.5	(23½)
Sleeve seam	43.5	(17)	43.5	(17)	43.5	(17)	43.5	(17)	43.5	(17)	43.5	(17)

We chose a lovely shade called bluebell for our sweater, but other colours worth considering are mushroom, rose pink, cream or mulberry.

Pattern a further 98 rows.

Mark each end of last row to denote end of side seams. **

Pattern at further 80 (82) (84) (84) (86) rows straight.

To slope the shoulders: Cast off 6 (7) (6) (8) (7) (7) sts. at the beginning of each of the next 8 (6) (4) (2) (8) (2) rows, then 6 (6) (7) (7) (8) (8) sts.

at the beginning of each of the following 8 (10) (12) (14) (8) (14) rows – 50(52) (54) (56) (58) (60) sts.

Cast off.

THE FRONT: Work as given for back to **.

Pattern a further 61 (63) (63) (65) (65) (67) rows.

Continued overleaf

91

To divide for neck: Next row: Pattern 60 (63) (66) (69) (72) (75) and leave these sts. on a spare needle for right half neck cast off the next 26 (28) (30) (32) (34) (36) sts., pattern to end and work on these 60 (63) (66) (69) (72) (75) sts. for left half neck.

The left half neck: Keeping continuity of the pattern where possible dec. 1 st. at neck edge on each of the next 12 rows – 48 (51) (54) (57) (60) (63) sts.

Pattern a further 6 rows – pattern 7 rows here when working right half neck.

To slope the shoulder: Cast off 6 (7) (6) (8) (7) (7) sts. at the beginning of the next row and the 3 (2) (1) (nil) (3) (nil) following alternate row(s).

Work 1 row, then cast off 6 (6) (7) (7) (8) (8) sts. at the beginning of the next row and the 2 (3) (4) (5) (2) (5) following alternate rows – 6 (6) (7) (7) (8) (8) sts.

Work 1 row.

Cast off.

The right half neck: With right side of work facing, rejoin yarn to the 60 (63) (66) (69) (72) (75) sts. left on spare needle and work as given for left half neck, noting variation.

THE SLEEVES (both alike): With No. 13 (2¼ mm) needles cast on 66 (70) (70) (74) (74) (78) sts. and work 39 rows in single rib.

Next (increase) row: Rib 1 (2) (2) (3) (3) (3), up 1, * rib 1, up 1; repeat from * until 2 (2) (2) (2) (2) (3) sts. remain, rib to end – 130 (137) (137) (144) (144) (151) sts.

Change to No. 11 (3 mm) needles and work 150 rows in pattern as given on back for the 76 cm (81 cm) (81 cm) (86 cm) (86 cm) (91 cm) sizes.

Cast off.

THE COLLAR: With No. 13 (2¼ mm) needles cast on 179 (183) (187) (191) (195) (199) sts.

1st row: K.1, * p.1, k.1; repeat from * to end.

Next (increase) row: K.1 and p.1 all into first st., rib until 1st. remains, p.1 and k.1 all into last st.

Repeat the last row, 9 times more – 199 (203) (207) (211) (215) (219) sts.

Next row: K.2, * p.1, k.1; repeat from * until 1 st. remains, k.1 more.

Next row: K.1, * p.1, k.1; repeat from * to end.

Repeat the last 2 rows, 4 times more.

To shape the neck edge of collar: Keeping continuity of the rib, cast off 3 sts. at the beginning of each of the next 42 rows – 73 (77) (81) (85) (89) (93) sts.

Cast off loosely.

TO MAKE UP THE SWEATER: Press with a warm iron over a damp cloth. Join shoulder seams. Set in sleeves between markers on back and front. Join side and sleeve seams. Sew cast off edge of collar into position beginning and ending at centre front.

You can make this lively chimpanzee as a soft toy – or turn him into an acrobat by sewing short strips of furry Velcro touch-and-close fastener to his hands and feet.

The circus chimp will hang from a horizontal bar or ledge – anything to which you can stick strips of hooked Velcro.

For a trapeze like ours, use a piece of thick dowelling, about 40 cm (16 in.) long. Alternatively, use a thick knitting needle or a coathanger with a bar. Glue a strip of hooked Velcro round the trapeze and suspend it from thick cord or rope.

For the chimp you will need: A man's brown or fawn stretch towelling sock (to fit shoe size 6 - 11); small pieces of thin woven cotton fabric for arms and legs (any colour, as it will not be seen); small pieces of felt – cream for face, ears and hands, coloured for shoes, hat and bobbles, black and brown for facial features; 50 cm (⅝ yd.) of 91 cm (36 in.) wide fabric for suit and neck frill; 30 cm (⅜ yd.) of 91 cm (36 in.) wide fabric for contrasting neck, wrist and ankle frills; small piece of ric-rac braid for trimming hat; a small amount of stuffing; a 6 cm (2 ⅜ in.) long strip of furry Velcro to match shoes, and same amount to match hands (omit these if you're making a soft toy only); UHU glue.

Seams: 1 cm (⅜ in.) seams and turnings are allowed on all pieces unless otherwise stated.

The patterns: All patterns are printed full-size on page 94, some in black outline and some in grey. The suit pattern is the only one not shown full size. This is given as a simple diagram with measurements, on page 95. Draw this out on paper to the sizes given and mark on all lettering.

Trace the head pattern off page 94 (the inner grey lines). The pattern is shown in the position in which it should be placed on the sock (but remember that different makes of sock may vary slightly across the width). If the sock is wider than the one shown, simply carry on sewing the top head stitching line to edge of sock (see following instructions).

Trace all other patterns off the page – both black and grey outlines – and mark on all details.

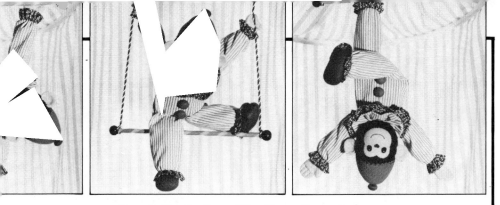

Specially designed by Jean Greenhowe

SIMPLE CHIMP

He's the most lovable of toys, about 18 inches tall . . . and
you can sew him from our trace-off patterns shown overleaf.
We picture a pair in colour on page 74.

HEAD AND BODY

Turn sock inside out then pin head pattern to the sock as shown on page 94. Stitch top head stitching line level with top edge of pattern. Now use a coloured pencil to mark neck line on sock, level with lower edge of pattern. Remove pattern and pin it to reverse side of sock to mark neck line here also. Remove pattern again and trim off sock just above top head stitching line. Run a very loose contrast-coloured tacking thread round sock at the marked neck line. Turn right side out.

Stuff head firmly as far as tacking thread, taking care to push out heel of sock to shape front of face. Run a strong gathering thread round sock at position of coloured tacking thread. Pull up gathers very tightly and knot thread ends, then sew ends into head.

Continue stuffing rest of sock for the body, until it measures about 15 cm (6 in.) from neck to lower edge. Turn in rest of sock if necessary and oversew edges together across lower edge of body.

LEGS, SHOES AND ANKLE FRILLS

For each leg cut two pieces of cotton fabric 9 by 18 cm (3½ by 7 in.). Join pieces at long edges then turn right side out.

Pin shoe pattern onto two layers of felt. Stitch all round close to edge of pattern. Now mark the small dots shown on pattern onto the felt, pushing a pencil point through dots. Remove pattern and cut out shoe close to stitching line. Pull apart the two felt layers and cut a slit in one piece, from one dot to the other as shown on •

pattern. Turn shoe right side out through slit and stuff firmly.

Turn in one end of leg and pin it to shoe to cover slit (see dotted line on shoe pattern), with leg seams facing centre front and back. Slipstitch leg to shoe as pinned. Stuff leg lightly but evenly. Turn in top raw edge of leg then bring seams together and oversew, pulling stitches tightly to gather. Sew legs to lower edge of body. Sew a 3 cm (1¼ in.) strip of furry Velcro to top of each shoe.

For each ankle frill cut a strip of contrast fabric 7 by 36 cm (2¾ by 14 in.). Join short edges of each strip. Now fold strip in half, with right side outside and bringing raw edges together. Run a gathering thread round 1 cm (⅜ in.) from raw edges. Slip frill over shoe and pull up gathering thread round ankle. Fasten off thread then space out gathers evenly. Sew raw edges of frill to leg, then catch frill to leg through gathers.

SUIT AND NECK FRILLS

Cut two pairs of suit pieces. Join pairs at centre edges then clip curves in seams. Join pairs to each other at side edges then inside leg edges. Turn suit right side out and put it on the chimp. Turn in neck edge and run a strong gathering thread round. Pull up gathers tightly round neck and fasten off. Make sure side seams are at sides and centre seams at centre front and back. ·

Let head fall forward onto chest. Sew it securely in this position, where head touches chest under chin, taking stitches through suit and into body.

Continued overleaf

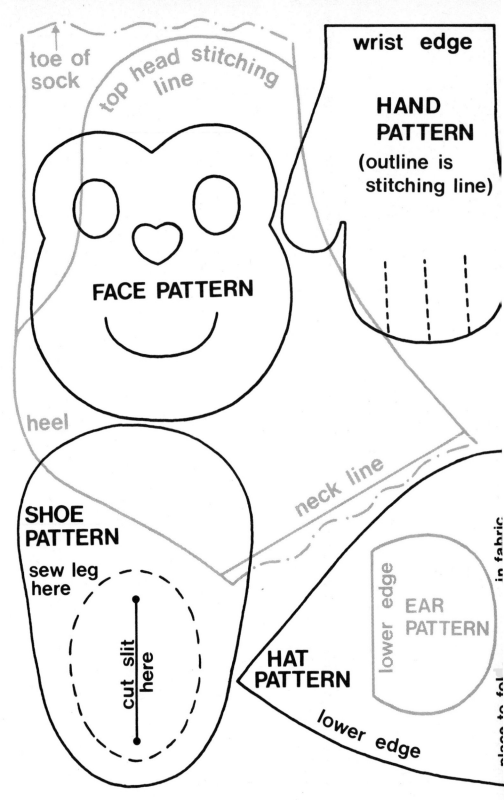

toe of sock

top head stitching line

wrist edge

HAND PATTERN
(outline is stitching line)

FACE PATTERN

heel

neck line

SHOE PATTERN

sew leg here

cut slit here

HAT PATTERN

lower edge

EAR PATTERN

lower edge

in fabric

Run a gathering thread round each ankle edge of suit, 1 cm (³/₈ in.) from raw edge, turn in raw edge and pull up gathers round frill gathers, then fasten off. Space out gathers evenly, then sew to frill gathers.

Cut three 5 cm (2 in.) diameter circles of felt for bobbles down front of suit. Gather round edge of each circle and stuff the centre, pulling gathers up tightly. Fasten off thread and sew bobbles in place.

For contrast neck frill cut a strip of fabric 14 by 70 cm (5½ by 27½ in.). For frill to match suit, cut a strip 12 by 60 cm (4¾ by 23½ in.), joining pieces to make up the length if necessary. Make neck frills as for ankle frills. Gather round raw edges of each frill, slip over head then pull up gathers tightly round neck and fasten off thread.

ARMS, HANDS, WRIST FRILLS AND SLEEVES

For each arm cut two pieces of cotton fabric 8 by 17 cm (3 ¹/₈ by 6¾ in.). Join pieces at long edges and turn right side out.

Pin hand pattern to two layers of cream felt and cut felt level with wrist edge of pattern. Stitch all round close to edge of pattern, leaving wrist edges open. Remove pattern and cut out hand close to stitching line. Turn hand right side and stuff lightly. Machine stitch through hands at positions of dotted lines to divide into fingers. Pull thread ends through to one side and knot, then sew ends into hands.

Turn in one raw edge of arm and slip it 1 cm (³/₈ in.) over wrist edge of hand, with arm seams level with hand seams. Slipstitch arm to hand, easing in the arm fabric to fit hand. Stuff arm lightly but evenly.

Turn in top raw edge of arm and oversew, pulling stitches to gather tightly. Pin an arm to each side of body, about 3 cm (1¼ in.) down from neck, with thumbs pointing towards front. Sew arms in place, taking stitches through suit and into body. Now sew a 3 cm (1¼ in.) strip of furry Velcro to palm of each hand. Make and sew on wrist frills as for ankle frills.

For each sleeve cut a piece of suit fabric 18 by 20 cm (7 by 8 in.). Join short edges of each piece. Turn right side out, then slip a sleeve over each arm, with sleeve seams underneath arms., Gather, turn in and sew wrist edges to wrist frills as for ankle edges of suit. run a gathering thread round top of each sleeve, 1 cm (³/₈ in.) from raw edge. Turn in raw edges then pull up gathers round tops of arms and fasten off. Sew gathered edges of sleeves to the suit.

FACE AND EARS

Cut the face piece from cream felt and mark on the mouth. Stretch face piece at the centre of the mouth area, pushing it out to a rounded shape so that it will fit over the rounded towelling face. Using black thread, machine stitch along mouth line a few times, or backstitch by hand.

Slipstitch the face piece in place as shown in our picture.

Cut nose from brown felt and glue it in place. Cut eyes from black felt and work a small highlight on each one using white thread. Glue eyes in place.

Pin ear pattern onto two layers of cream felt and cut felt level with lower edge of pattern. Stitch, cut out and turn ears as for hands. Now oversew lower edges of each ear together, pulling stitches to gather. Sew ears to each side of head as shown in our picture.

THE HAT

Cut two hat pieces from felt, placing edge of pattern indicated to fold in the felt each time. Join pieces, taking a 3 mm (¹/₈ in.) seam, leaving lower edges open. Turn hat right side out and push a little stuffing in top. Place hat on head as shown in our picture, and pin lower edge in place. Slipstitch lower edge to head, pushing in more stuffing a little at a time to make a firm, rounded shape. Sew ric-rac round lower edge of hat and add a felt bobble to top, made as for the suit bobbles.

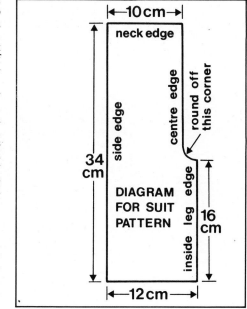

DIAGRAM FOR SUIT PATTERN

←10 cm→
neck edge
side edge
centre edge
round off this corner
34 cm
inside leg edge
16 cm
←12 cm→

A SUMMER WEDDING

"I think you should stay well clear of that young man, Hester," Aunt Bella hissed disapprovingly. "There are rumours that he's rather a scoundrel."

WE honestly hadn't wanted to come, but, as Sophy said, when Aunt Bella sends out an invitation, only the hardiest soul would dare to refuse. For once, my little sister was right. Aunt Bella is a very forceful lady.

A summer wedding: my cousin Celia's wedding. We did not really get on with our McGregor cousins. Celia was a quiet little thing who never entered a conversation unless forced into it. Lindsay, her sister and chief bridesmaid, had once, when we were children, made us take the blame for sending a ball through the cucumber frame. There are some things you never forget!

"My shoes are pinching," Sophy grumbled, trying to ease one off under cover of the crowd. "How long before we can leave? I don't seem to know anyone. I wish I was back in my jeans."

"You'd look a trifle out of place among all this splendour," I told her. There were hats like herbaceous borders, huge masses of flowers on either side of the Adam mantelpiece, and a marquee trimmed with fresh garlands just outside on the lawn.

"I don't care, I'm fed up." Sophy has not yet learned to control her finer feelings. "Couldn't we just slip off for a walk or something?"

"And miss the wedding breakfast? Don't be silly, I'm ravenous." We had dashed out in a rush that morning and I'd missed my two slices of toast. "Perhaps we could squeeze our way out on to the lawn. It's a terrible crush in here."

It was a foolish move. In trying to manoeuvre a way out, I found myself suddenly being jostled up against a broad, masculine shoulder encased in dark green velvet. "Oh, dear, Sophy — your glass!"

The green velvet shoulder turned just in time to prevent the wine from cascading down over my blue silk jacket. "Sorry. That was terribly clumsy of me." A pair of fine brown eyes were regarding me. I ought not to have let them linger so, but they held a long, slow, increasingly delighted smile. "It's you!" the young man said disconcertingly.

"Me?" I knew we hadn't met. He was not the kind of man you could easily forget.

"Umm." The brown eyes rested pensively on the top of my head. "The girl in the blue hat. You took it off, though." He sounded disappointed. "I was admiring it in church." His eyes twinkled. "An enormous blue straw hat, with gorgeous silk poppies all over it. I wanted to ask . . . "

I NEVER found out what he wanted to ask, for Aunt Bella chose that moment to come charging up from behind. "Hester, dear, I want you to come and talk to old Uncle Francis. He's all on his own. You, too, Sophy." You could always tell from Aunt Bella's tone what she was thinking. I heard her say it once: "Such old-fashioned names. I don't know what my brother James was thinking of."

As we were towed away, I cast one quick glance over my shoulder. The young man looked suitably disappointed. I even felt a twinge of regret myself, but Aunt Bella's next words soon dispelled that. "I think you should stay well clear of that young man, Hester," she hissed disapprovingly. "There are rumours that he's rather a scoundrel."

"Who is he?" Sophy was round-eyed. She never minded asking the blunt question. "And what kind of scoundrel?"

"His name's Jon Kendall." Aunt Bella's mouth pursed. "His father's a partner in Kendall and Simons, the estate agents. And perhaps you ought to ask poor Fiona Simons why he's a scoundrel. He broke her heart, poor child!"

"What's he doing here, then?" Sophy asked innocently. "I mean, why did you invite him, if you don't like him?"

Aunt Bella glared. 'Wayward child!' she was thinking. 'Should have been curbed years ago!' "He's a friend of the groom," she said abruptly. "Though I can't think why."

I watched Jon Kendall surreptitiously while the reception continued. He had what my mother called "presence". Heads turned as he moved around the room, female ones in particular. I could

Continued overleaf

I could imagine him — ruthlessly breaking a girl's heart . . .
Odd how that thought caused me a faint sigh of envy.
Surely I was glad to be heart whole . . .

imagine him ruthlessly breaking a girl's heart, I reflected, a little regretfully, as we moved into the dining-room for lunch. He had obvious elegance and charm and was easily the best-looking man in the room.

Sophy must have been observing him, too. "He does look rather wicked," she said, leaning across Uncle Francis to whisper in my ear. "Aunt Bella's right. I think he's what's known as a wolf."

Sophy wouldn't have known a real wolf if she'd met one, being fresh out of school and pretty wet behind the ears. I said, "Don't be silly, Sophy, and do stop staring at him. More ham, Uncle Francis?"

But Sophy was rarely to be cowed. We were standing in the hall later, when she gave me a hard nudge. "He keeps looking at us, Hester," she hissed. "Isn't it exciting? I think he's going to come over."

H E did, brown eyes bright with fun. "We didn't finish our conversation," he said. "It was a hat to inspire sonnets. Won't you put it back on? It's a crime just to hide it away."

"Aunt Bella didn't like it," Sophy said candidly. "She called it a 'charming creation'."

"Aunt Bella?" He looked amazed. "You mean, Mrs. McGregor is your aunt?"

"For our sins," Sophy giggled.

"Sophy!" I shot her a warning frown. This conversation was rapidly getting out of hand. I didn't quite know what to do about the too-charming Mr. Kendall's compliments, and I didn't approve of Sophy's indiscretion.

"I don't know why you're suddenly being so proper," Sophy replied innocently. "You always agree with me about how awful Aunt Bella is when we're on our own. I wasn't talking loudly."

"I think I'd better run and fetch the confetti from the car." In an effort to hide my confusion, I buried my head in the huge bowl of sweet peas on the table and promptly wished I hadn't. Their scent was overpowering, and I came up with all my senses swimming.

"Do you have to go?" He gave me a wry, lopsided smile that only served to make me dizzier.

"Yes. Yes, I'm afraid I do." I moved away in a little flutter of activity. "Mother will be wondering where we are. Sophy, meet me in the porch in five minutes. They'll be leaving soon."

I WOKE next morning to the twittering of birds. I just lay there for a while, thinking how good it was to be home. Stowford is a perfect, unspoiled Cotswold village. Ours is the shabby-beautiful Queen Anne house next to the green. It has a handsome oak staircase with shallow treads, and an unrivalled view, over the lawns, of distant blue hills.

My room is at the top of the house. Before I'd gone off to do a course in art and design in London, I'd spent months furnishing it — cluttering it, my mother said — with all the lovely old stuff I'd brought back from auctions. Now it was nearly perfect. I surveyed it all with sleepy eyes. Richly-patterned oriental rugs, rose-painted jugs and vases crammed with wild flowers, Edwardian post-cards pinned up everywhere and a huge, white paper lampshade gladdened my eyes.

It was wonderful to be on holiday and to have time to enjoy it.

We had had a dull, grey spring, but now there was a pale summer sky scattered with wispy clouds, and I resolved at once that, today at least, I was going to be amazingly lazy. I was a little cross, therefore, when that afternoon, about three o'clock, I heard a car drawing up in the road outside the garden.

"Who's that?" I asked, kicking one leg out of the hammock and opening my eyes.

"I don't know, dear." Mother had just brought out the tea-tray. She put it down and peered through the pergola. "Someone for you, I think. It's a young man. He's dark and rather nice-looking."

"It's him!" Sophy hissed ungrammatically from her deck-chair. "Jon what's-his-name, the wolf!"

He was crossing the lawn even before I could gather my wits. Today, he wore yellowish cords and a blue shirt with a sweater flung casually over his shoulders. Incongruously, he carried in one hand a pale silk scarf. I sat up and stared. It was my silk scarf, the one I had worn to the wedding.

"Tea in the garden?" he said, smiling. "Wonderful! I'm terribly sorry to disturb you. I brought your scarf back, Hester. You left it by the sweet peas."

"How very kind." Mother was already giving him her beaming smile. "Hester, isn't that kind? You must have a cup of tea, now that you're here, Mr. . . . "

"Jon," he said simply. "Jon Kendall. Thank you, I'd love some. What a lovely old house you have. Early-eighteenth century, isn't it?" The brown eyes that he turned on me were unreadable. "I wasn't sure if I'd catch you at home," he said.

"How did you know where we lived?" I asked. The afternoon was suddenly beset with all sorts of dangerous possibilities.

"Sophy told me. We were chatting after you'd gone, yesterday."

I threw Sophy a withering look. She had the grace to look slightly guilty. "We were talking about villages," she explained quickly. "And I said we had a fifteenth-century tithe barn in ours, and he asked where. You can have my deck-chair if you like, Jon." She jumped up with an adoring smile. "I'll sit on the grass."

'So that's how it is!' I thought. 'Sophy's smitten. How silly of her.' I said crisply, "Thanks for bringing the scarf, Mr. Kendall. But you really shouldn't have bothered. Aunt Bella would have sent it over."

"It was no trouble." He turned his dark head to give me another of those slow, disturbing glances. "What have you done with the hat?" he asked. "You look quite different with your hair down."

"It's packed away in its box."

"Pity. It was the prettiest thing there." From the glint in his brown eyes, I sensed that he didn't just mean the hat. He certainly had a way with words, I thought indignantly, trying to avoid my mother's amused smile.

"I hate hats," Sophy announced cheerfully. "I hate weddings, too. They're an awful bore, especially when Aunt Bella's in charge."

"Sophy," Mother said sharply, "go into the house and fetch that plate of shortbread for me. And don't be all day about it." She searched hopefully for a new topic. "Hester's on holiday from art school, Jon. For eight long weeks."

"Really?" He sounded interested.

"Yes. She drove us all mad when she was little. She was always turning out the old trunks in the attic and concocting all sorts of weird and wonderful fashions. Hester, do you remember that time you came down dressed for the school dance all in orange satin, like Nell Gwynn?" Mother was almost incoherent with laughter. "Your father and I nearly died!"

"That was a long time ago," I stated with dignity. I was aware that my cheeks were turning scarlet and I could have killed her for bringing it up.

Wrinkles should merely indicate where smiles have been.

Mark Twain

JON Kendall leaned forward with a delighted smile. "You didn't concoct the hat as well, did you?" he asked wickedly.

"No, I did not! I bought it in London."

"Ah." He was still grinning, lazy brown eyes surveying my flushed and shiny cheeks. I avoided his gaze by bending down to put on my sandals.

"Here we are, then. Freshly baked shortbread." Sophy's interruptions could be useful sometimes. "Gosh, I'm starving. How about you, Jon? Would you like to see the tithe barn after tea?"

"Umm?" He seemed distracted for a moment. Then, "What a marvellous idea! Of course I would."

Mother, of course, thought he was delightful. I couldn't tell her that afternoon that the charm was well practised. Jon was amusing her with stories about all the strange houses he had viewed for his father, and steadily helping her top and tail the huge mound of gooseberries she had brought out into the sunshine. As for Sophy, she just hung on his every word. I escaped as soon as I could, with the excuse that I'd got some sketching to do — a holiday task that I'd forgotten until now.

Sophy thought I was quite mad. She told me so when she came flying up the stairs after Jon had gone. "I don't know why you have to keep running away from him," she remarked, plonking herself down on the bed.

"He's a flirt," I replied. "Coming all that way just to bring back a scarf. You'll get to recognise them when you've seen a bit more of the world, Sophy."

"Oh, stop being so pompous!" Sophy jumped up. "Well, I've invited him to my birthday party. He seemed very pleased. You can be stuffy, if you like — I shall have fun."

OF course, there was no logical reason why my heart should have started looping the loop when Jon crossed the floor to greet me at my sister's eighteenth birthday party. I was hovering over the buffet arrangements in a corner of the tithe barn — the usual venue for village occasions — when I heard Sophy's excited voice.

"What are you doing skulking around over there, Hester? Jon's come to say hello."

The music had just changed to a slow, dreamy number and, before I could argue, he had drawn me on to the floor. We danced for a while without speaking. Then he held me away from him a little. "You always seem determined to run away from me," he said, stealing a seemingly shy glance that I knew must be counterfeit. "I wish you'd tell me if I've said something wrong."

Continued overleaf

"Of course you haven't," I said stiffly. I hadn't the courage to tell him the truth. I was ridiculously aware of the feel of his arms around me.

"Shall I tell you what I was thinking when I first saw you in church? When you were wearing that wonderfully romantic hat?"

"If you like." I didn't know what I wanted. It was like standing on the edge of a precipice and trying not to fall off.

"I kept wishing you'd turn around, so that I could see if the face was as lovely as the hat." He waited for a breath-stopping moment. "And it was. Hester — "

"Look, I'm afraid I'm going to have to run away again." I searched desperately for a reason. "Mother looks as if she needs help with the presents. I'll introduce you to Avril Eliot — we were at school together — I'm sure she'll take you around and introduce you to everyone."

I WAS forced to admit that I could have fallen rather heavily for him under any other circumstances. We might have been a second Romeo and Juliet, if my sensible, forewarned half hadn't been so determined to resist him. He had a way of looking at me that made my head spin.

"I like that young man," Mother said next morning, after our late breakfast. "Jon Kendall, I mean. He's got quite a way with him."

"I know. That's what he relies on," I muttered darkly. "Don't be deceived by it." I told her about poor Fiona Simons' broken heart.

"A scoundrel? I wouldn't have believed it," she said, sounding surprised

Mother always saw the very best in people. That was why she welcomed Jon Kendall with all her usual kindness when he turned up a day or two later with tickets for a Mozart concert that evening. He'd been given them unexpectedly, he said, if anyone wanted to come.

"You didn't really think we'd refuse?" Sophy asked, practically climbing into his little red car there and then.

"Hester?" His gaze was steady.

"I don't know."

"If you don't want to come, Hester," Sophy said with a nonchalant air, "it won't really matter. Jon and I won't mind." She flashed him a gooey smile.

"I'll come," I said promptly. The last thing I wanted was to be within range of those teasing brown eyes, but I really couldn't let Sophy go on her own, I argued. She was such a silly little innocent that somebody had to protect her from Jon's obvious charms.

WE didn't say much to each other that night. Jon seemed to have settled for carrying on a ridiculously lunatic conversation with Sophy, and for teasing her unmercifully when he found out that she was actually tone deaf. It was with a mixture of pain and impatience that I watched him drop a seemingly brotherly arm around her shoulders to point out some detail in the programme that she was studying.

Things only got worse, a week or so later, when he insisted on taking us both to lunch at The George after he had driven out to view a house nearby.

We walked across the green and ate by open french windows in the tiny dining-room. Afterwards, we just sat and soaked up the warmth and splendour of the summer garden outside, the sight of which only served to accentuate my own touchiness and pique.

"More coffee, Hester?" Jon asked quietly, throwing me a quick, searching glance.

"No, thank you." I tried not to look at him.

"How about you, Sophy — another slice of gateau?" His dark eyes always assumed a twinkle whenever he addressed her.

"No thanks, Jon." Sophy gave a deep sigh. "I've had two. I don't think I can move! It must be a wonderful life," she went on dreamily, "just wandering about old houses and having scrumptious lunches at country pubs afterwards."

"It isn't all like that," he answered, smiling. "Mostly, I'm sent on the boring jobs. Or else I have to answer the phone. I'm not very good at that, I'm afraid. I forget to pass on vital messages."

Sophy drained her glass. There were times when she got even more extravagant than usual and, after two glasses of wine, this was to be one of them. "I'll come and answer the phone for you, if you like," she announced. "Was it in the office that you met Fiona Simons?"

There was a long, dramatic pause. Sophy propped her chin on her hands and waited. Outside, the leaves rustled. Jon slowly pushed away his coffee cup, his expression suddenly guarded.

"How did you know about Fiona Simons?" he asked quietly.

"Oh, Aunt Bella told us," Sophy said brightly. "Did you really break this Fiona girl's heart? I never really believed it, you know. Well, I mean, I do believe that you're gorgeous enough to break a girl's heart, but not that . . . "

"I really don't think that this is any of our business, Sophy." I rose abruptly to my feet. I'd had just about enough. "Look, I'm sorry, but I've got to go now. I've got things to do. Thanks for the lunch, Jon. It was very nice. Sophy, don't be long." I fled into the sunshine.

MY mother heard me come in. I remember thinking that I didn't want to speak to her at this particular moment, but she seemed quite impervious to my reserve. In the way that life sometimes hurls too many little surprises at you all at once, she had been waiting to tell me her latest snippet of news.

"There you are, Hester! Guess who I've just been chatting to on the telephone? Betty Latimer. You must remember Betty? She rang to ask if we had any more gooseberries for sale — she lives in that big, old timbered house that backs on to Bella's — and I happened just to ask her if she'd heard the gossip about your nice Jon and this Fiona girl and she gave me quite another version. According to Betty, Fiona Simons is rather a young minx who's been chasing that poor boy unmercifully for months and making life in the office pretty embarrassing for him. In the end, he was forced to put her quite harshly in her place, and, of course, 'Hell hath no fury . . . ' "

As I've said before, my Aunt Bella is a very forceful lady. And, of course, I ought to have known better than to believe her, only I'd swallowed her ridiculous story hook, line and sinker on the flimsiest of evidence, and now I deserved to be miserable. Even Sophy's instincts had been truer than mine, I realised suddenly with a streak of honest shame.

I wandered wretchedly out on to the terrace. Of course, he'd never come anywhere near this house again — and I'd probably die of mortification if he did. I'd been so hostile to him, right from the start. I hadn't made the least little effort to find light or shade or detail in his character. All I'd seen, or wanted to see, was an unadulterated flirt. I'd got my just deserts. As for what I'd lost . . .

AT first, when I heard Mother's voice again, calling from the house, I took no notice. I had other things on my mind. Then she called from the doorway, "Hester, here's Jon." She didn't seem to have noticed my sudden panic. "I'm just going down to the farm to fetch the eggs. You two can amuse yourselves for half an hour or so, I expect? I'll make a cup of tea when I get back."

I wasn't so sure about the amusing ourselves bit. Jon didn't look as if he wanted to be amused at all. There was a firm set to his jaw and his dark eyes were quite unreadable. In fact, he was in a strangely determined mood.

"Jon, I don't quite know how to say this, but — Where's Sophy?" I asked desperately.

"I told her to go and ring the office for me. Lord knows what she'll tell them, in her present state. Hester, I want to talk to you."

"Oh." I did not know how else to reply so I stayed silent, hardly daring to breathe.

"Sophy says your Aunt Bella gave you some garbled story about my relationship with Fiona Simons. Hester, this isn't a very pleasant thing to have to say, but Fiona Simons happens to be a silly, spiteful, little girl. You surely didn't believe the story?"

"I'm afraid I did. I should have known better." I explained, as best I could, the substance of what my mother had told me. I pushed a shaky hand through my hair. "I'm so sorry, Jon. I was a fool to take Aunt Bella's word for it."

"So you don't positively dislike me?" The dark gaze was deep and searching.

"Dislike you?" A great longing to prove to him just how wrong he was washed over me, but I had to be decorous. "Don't be silly," I said softly.

"Ever since I saw you in that wonderful hat, I've wanted . . . But you always seemed so hostile! Oh, Hester, I'm making such a hash of this." With long strides, he covered the distance between us. The anguish in his eyes melted into some softer emotion. He reached out for me then, and our kiss seemed to go on for ever. At the end of it, I found myself locked in his arms, being squeezed half to death.

"I even thought you were trying to flirt with Sophy, too," I explained, laughing.

"Sophy?" He held me at arm's length to study my face. "If it hadn't been for dear, tactless little Sophy, I'd never have dared to keep coming back. I wouldn't be here now." He chuckled. "I hope she doesn't have too much of a headache later."

"Was I so terrible to you?"

He laughed shakily. "Hester, I love you to distraction. In time, I might even bring myself to forgive your Aunt Bella."

When he looked at me like that, I felt my heart lurch. "Me, too," I said. "Though I suppose she did invite us both to a summer wedding."

THE END

©*Lizbie Brown, 1982.*

SPECIALISTS AT YOUR SERVICE!

A list of handy specialist fashion firms for you to keep at your fingertips

Need a buckle covered to match your dress?
Want that expensive pigskin coat cleaned?
Do you take size 8 shoe and can't find any to fit?
If you've searched in vain for the solution to these problems, don't
despair, we know just how time-consuming and frustrating it can be trying to find
firms who offer these specialist services. So we have taken the headache
out of it, with our useful list of firms to keep by you

CLEANING

Association of British Launderers and Dry Cleaners, Lancaster Gate House, 319 Pinner Road, Harrow, Middlesex. Will advise you on cleaners, throughout the country, who specialise in all types of varied cleaning, such as suede and leather, eiderdowns, etc.

The Pigskin Cleaning Co., Eagle Works, 144A Royal College Street, London NW1. Tel: 01 267 1332. Specialists in suede and fur cleaning.

Jeeves, 8 Pont Street, London SW1. Specialist dry cleaners – very used to dealing with very expensive and difficult fabrics, beading, etc.

MENDING

The Savoy Tailors Guild, Strand, London WC2. Will replace worn collars on men's shirts.

DRESSMAKING

MacCulloch & Wallis, 25/26 Dering Street, London W1. Tel: 01 629 0311 Dealers in tailor's equipment.

Harlequin Belt and Button Covering Service, Lawling House, Manningtree Road, Stutton, Ipswich, Suffolk. Tel: 0473 328555. Send s.a.e. to Mr. Bull for details of this service.

J.V. Landers, Factory Unit 4, 11 Long Street, London E2. Pleating service — send s.a.e. for details.

Leslie Fogel, 5 South Molton Street, London W1. Paper pattern service — will make up paper patterns to your individual measurements from sketches or photos. Send for his price list.

SHOES

Small & Tall Shoe Shop, 71 York Street, London W1H 2BJ. Specialise in ladies' small shoe sizes 13 to 2½ English, and large sizes 8½ to 11 English. They do mail order and have a brochure of their styles. Send s.a.e.

Magnus, 2 High Street, Northampton NN7 4DH. Specialise in ladies' shoes sizes 8 to 12 in AA and EE fittings, as well as men's extra large shoes. They have a shop at 63 South End Road, Hampstead, London, NW3, but also do mail order. Send s.a.e. for their catalogue.

Over 8's Shoes Ltd., Freepost, Cambridge CB1 1BR. Specialists in ladies' sizes 8 to 10½ in slim, regular and wide fittings. They have a lot of reasonably priced young styles. Send s.a.e. for their brochure.

CLOTHES

Under 5 ft. 2 in. and larger sizes.

Nellie Frock, 42 Chiltern Street, London W1. Caters for the 5' 2"s and under. Send s.a.e. for brochure.

betti E. Shaw, 56 Chiltern Street, London W1. Stocks sizes 6 to 30 and from 4 ft. to 6 ft. 6 in. Send s.a.e. for brochure.

High Style, Thistley Green, Great Leighs, Chelmsford, Essex. Caters for extra tall fittings. Send s.a.e. for brochure.

Dee Dawson, 5 Thayer Street, London W1M 5LE. Specialist in larger sizes 16 to 26. Send s.a.e. for brochure.

Andre de Brett, Brett House, Water Road, Wembley, Middx HA0 1LE. Caters for larger sizes 16 to 34/36. Send for their mail order catalogue.

GOLDEN AUTUMN

While Autumn, nodding o'er the yellow plain, comes jovial on.

James Thomson

*Over the quilted farms
a lazy drift
of woodsmoke rising
in the quiet air.
Like feathers from the wings
of weary birds,
leaves falling,
softly falling,
everywhere.*

R. H. Grenville

A HOUSE CALLED BAYARD

JACQUELINE GILBERT

Little did I know, that day my godmother introduced me to Bayard, that at least one of its inhabitants would occupy my thoughts for years to come....

EACH TIME I returned to Bayard I was filled with excitement and anticipation, for the lovely mellow house, built of old red brick, was the only home I could remember, even though I didn't really belong there. But today the pleasure was tinged with sadness, for the person who had loved and encouraged me for so many years would not be there to greet me. Alicia Wrexham, my godmother, had died four months ago.

Glancing down at the dashboard clock, I yelped quietly and resisted the temptation to put my foot down. I was late, but the next two miles were not ones to be hurried over, especially in the rain, with the last of the daylight disappearing. I switched the headlights of the little car to main beam. The deluge seemed to be easing off, but this next stretch was full of twists and turns that made driving tricky.

Another four minutes brought me to the copse where the Wrexham cousins and myself had played when we were children, and in another five hundred yards I made out the entrance to Bayard. The gates had been left open and I swung in, passing the familiar "*Bayard-Wrexham Stables and Stud*" signboard, and finally pulled up alongside the old coach-house, now used to hold the family cars.

I felt an odd reluctance to move. The silence was broken only by the steady pounding of the rain on the roof of my car. I could see, ahead and to the right, the outline of Bayard through the trees, a soft glow of light showing behind one or two of the curtained windows. I pictured Hannah working in the kitchen, preparing the food for the meal this evening.

I gave a sigh and thought forlornly that nothing ever stayed the same. The future suddenly seemed bleak.

Orphaned at seven, freakishly surviving the hotel fire that had killed my parents, I had spent months of pain in the intensive care unit of a hospital before Alicia, my mother's dearest friend, erupted into my life. I was dismally short of relations and no one seemed anxious to take me on. She brought me to Bayard to live with her own family, husband George and two children, Josh and Mary. She was already giving a home to her nephew, Christopher, who was being educated in England while his parents were abroad. What was one more mouth and body to feed and clothe?

There was some money due to me from my parents' estate, of course, and I joined Mary at a good school as a weekly boarder, going on eventually to train as a nurse. I was twenty-five now, and senior staff nurse for the past ten months at Flixton General Hospital, five miles away. I had never anticipated being a career girl, had always wanted marriage and a family of my own, but sometimes things just don't work out the way we want them to. Godmother's death, and the advent of a woman called Roz, were making me think that I had better start to cut my ties with Bayard.

A particularly violent splatter of rain made me jump, bringing me out of my reverie. I was just thinking of making a move when a large shape loomed up out of the darkness.

"Are you intending to spend the evening out here, Diana, or are you going to join the rest of us inside?" It was Josh, and he didn't sound too pleased.

"I'm sorry, Josh," I apologised meekly, "I was day-dreaming." I allowed him to take the small case

Continued overleaf

from the back while I gathered together the rest of my things from the seat by my side.

"Ready?" he enquired, and murmuring my assent I joined him beneath the protective shelter of a huge waterproof cape that he had thrown over his head. The path through the shrubbery was narrow and slippery and it was necessary to stay awkwardly close as we shared the cape. Once I slipped on a mossy patch and Josh's arm tightened round me, supporting me effortlessly until I regained my footing. I am fairly tall at five feet eight, but Josh tops me by several inches and is broad-shouldered and muscular. It's the riding, of course, that keeps him fit.

A gusty rain-burst coincided with our entry into the conservatory, lifting the cape high into the air and almost whipping it from Josh's grip. I laughed, stumbling up the steps, and turned to watch him struggling to control it. "Thanks, Josh. I would have been drenched. Lucky you saw me arrive."

"I've been looking out for you. Where on earth have you been, Diana?" he replied shortly. "You told Mary you'd be here about five. It's nearly seven now."

I WATCHED HIM, wondering if there would ever be a time when Josh wasn't exasperated with me for some reason or other. As a child he was always getting me out of scrapes, once even rescuing me from a watery grave in the river. He is kind and reliable, gives good advice and generally keeps an eye on me, in a brotherly kind of a way—which is the root of all my problems.

Contritely, I said, "I'm so sorry, Josh. I did try and ring to warn you I'd be late, but the line was engaged and I couldn't get through. The car wouldn't start, the rain had dampened the plugs or something. Anyway, one of the student doctors fixed it for me."

"I told you that car wasn't reliable. Something's always going wrong with it."

"We can't all afford a Lamborghini," I retorted indignantly. "And it passed its M.O.T."

"Heaven knows how! I'll have a look at it tomorrow," Josh said, and I followed him into the house, knowing better than to offer to take the case upstairs myself. I'm as strong as a horse really, you have to be to nurse, but ever since his first introduction to me, still encased in bandages and plaster, he has treated me like a piece of fragile china. I'd loved it once, but no longer.

Preceding him up the stairs, I gave an inward sigh. Just lately, Josh and I seemed to be annoying each other effortlessly.

He had been fifteen when his mother had brought me to Bayard. I remember it was a few days before my eighth birthday. I didn't see a great deal of him, he was away at school, but I think I fell in love with him at first sight. Then he went on to university and got a good law degree. How bitterly disappointed I was when I found he was going to live and work in London! He did come back, on a permanent basis, some six years later when his father died, setting up his own business in Flixton and dividing his time between law and the Bayard Stables, which his father had built up into quite a respectable stud.

Although I worshipped him as a child, my love was tinged with a certain amount of awe, and I had the sense to keep my feelings to myself. Between Chris, Mary and myself there was an easy camaraderie, helped by the closeness of our ages but, for me, there was no one quite like Josh.

"Oh, how lovely it is to be back," I exclaimed involuntarily as we entered the room which had always been mine. The sloping ceiling and tiny windows beneath the eaves, with their pretty floral curtains and matching bedspread, were very dear to me. I knew that lurking in the future was the likelihood that Josh would take a wife. At thirty-two, it was a wonder he hadn't done so already. The future Mrs. Wrexham might well have other plans for my dear little bedroom, especially if she was Roz, who had loomed up on the horizon some three months ago.

Pulling off my gloves, I said in a rush, "I didn't think we'd have the usual get-together this year, Josh."

Coincidentally, Alicia and I had had the same birthday and over the years, whenever possible, shared a double celebration.

Josh raised an eyebrow. "Why not? It's still your birthday, and Mother would certainly not have wished us to ignore it. Anyway, it seems that you need to have an excuse to come here these days."

Although his comment was a fair one, I found myself flushing before his cool gaze. Josh has inherited his mother's tawny-brown hair and grey-green eyes, speaking eyes, which focussed on me now in a direct, uncompromising gaze.

He was obviously waiting for an explanation of my very infrequent visits since the funeral; six in four months, and four of those when Josh was working at the office. He must know I had more spare time than that. As I was unable to tell him the truth, I kept quiet.

"It's more than just family this year," he said at last. "We have three other guests. Roz, David Lloyd, a friend of mine from university days — he's coming in with me as a partner — and I believe Chris is bringing someone."

I hid a smile. Josh had an easy relationship with his cousin but I knew that he deplored the number of girls that Chris always had in tow. But that was Chris — outgoing, fun to be with and extremely good-looking. What could you expect?

I saw Josh look at his watch and then at my uniform, and said quickly: "I shall have to change, of course. How much time have I?"

"As much time as you want — you are the birthday girl, after all. I haven't congratulated you yet, have I?" He came towards me and brushed his lips lightly against my cheek. "Happy birthday, Diana, my dear. Your presents are on the table here. Chris will, no doubt, be bringing his with him."

"He's not here yet?" To my horror, my voice quivered. It was stupid of me to react like that to his touch. Thankfully, we weren't often so close.

He gave me a sharp look. "No. Like you, he's late, but unlike you I'm not at all concerned for his safety. Don't worry. He'll be here. He said on the phone that he needed a spot of legal advice. Chris always likes to have his money's worth." On that rather abrasive note, Josh left the room.

I STOOD FOR A MOMENT, deep in thought, replaying in my head the scene we had just enacted. Only this time Josh's embrace was more than just brotherly. Then, pulling myself together and telling myself sharply that at twenty-five I really should have put such fantasies behind me, I unpacked and hurried to the bathroom.

This floor had originally been the servants' quarters. Godmother had installed a bathroom in one of the tiny bedrooms. Mary and I shared it, and I could tell she had not long vacated it for the place was warm and her perfume lingered on the air. After a quick bath, I wrapped my candlewick dressing-gown round me and padded along to her room.

I love Mary dearly, probably more than if she had been a real sister. Proof of her generous nature was the fact that she had never betrayed the slightest hint of pique over having to share her mother and father with me. Hearing my tap at the door, she bounded across and flung it open.

"Diana! How lovely to see you. Happy birthday, love." She threw herself upon me, hugging me fiercely. She looked lovely in a dress of deep burgundy, her short, dark hair a bubble of curls.

If one love but a single being from the very heart, all the others seem lovable also.
Goethe

Declaring herself ready, she followed me into my room and we chatted while I did my face. As usual, I kept my make-up to a minimum and concentrated on my eyes, which I consider to be my best feature, cornflower blue and thickly-lashed.

When I slipped on the new dress, bought specially for this occasion, it evoked a vulgar wolf whistle from Mary. It was a soft, smoky lavender in colour, and beautifully cut, but I frowned into the mirror, saying dubiously, "Do you think perhaps it's too . . . ?"

"Not at all," Mary interrupted, eyes twinkling. "It's just the dress in which to celebrate a twenty-fifth birthday. By the way, I wondered if you would be bringing anyone special with you." Her voice was casual.

I searched diligently for my ear-rings. "No such luck."

"Oh, dear. I had such high hopes," mourned Mary comically. "I do think one of us should marry, Diana. We can't both be old maids!"

Looking at her, I found it difficult to understand why Mary hadn't been snapped up years ago. True, she was a year younger than myself, and extremely shy. But the warm and loving personality must surely have been apparent behind her public reserve.

"What's this David Lloyd like?" I asked, and if I hadn't been in line with the mirror and watching a tell-tale blush sweep into her cheeks I might not have guessed, for her voice was matter-of-fact.

"Nice. Not very tall. Interesting to talk to. Smokes a pipe."

We both smiled. During one phase of our adolescence we were madly keen on men who smoked a pipe.

I opened my presents and thanked Mary for the lovely pale grey silk scarf and a new autobiography she knew I had wanted to read. Josh's parcel was an intriguing shape and turned out to be a water colour of Bayard from the paddock side of the house, executed by a local artist. He had written on the card: "*So that wherever you are, you will always have Bayard to remember.*"

I felt the foolish tears rush to my eyes and had to blink rapidly. Luckily Mary was hanging my uniform in the wardrobe and didn't notice. Was this, I wondered, a way of letting me know that memories were all that were left to me?

Chris had arrived by the time we came down. His was the first face I saw as we walked into the drawing-room. Taking me in his arms, he kissed me warmly on the mouth then, holding me slightly away from him, announced loudly: "Diana, you look wonderful! Happy birthday, sweetheart, and many more to come."

Chris is two years my senior, tall but not so rangy as Josh, with fair, curly hair and an abundance of

Continued overleaf

charm. He handed me his present and I was delighted with the fine gold chain with the Saint Christopher medallion attached, and allowed him to put it round my neck. I was then introduced to David Lloyd, who gave me a firm handshake and a nice smile.

Roz was next, stunning in a peacock blue number with her jet black hair swept high. We gave each other a polite smile, this being our third meeting, both knowing that our initial impressions would not improve on closer acquaintance. I noticed that Josh had a rather grim look on his face but I had no time to wonder why as Chris immediately introduced me to his latest girl. Paula Wyngard was strikingly pretty and expensively dressed, and it looked to me as if Chris had finally been hooked.

During dinner David Lloyd sat on my left. Mary was right, he was nice, and very easy to talk to. I seemed to be drinking rather a lot of wine, but decided that, after all, it *was* my birthday. Hannah, bless her, brought in a cake, candles aglow, and my health was toasted. Chris then rose and announced his engagement to Paula, and we all drank their health and wished them every happiness. I found out later that Paula was his boss's daughter and Mary and I shared a knowing look. We had decided, long ago, that Chris would be sure to fall in love with the right person.

However, Paula endeared herself to me by asking Josh how the house came to be called Bayard. As a child, I had never tired of hearing the tale of Charlemagne, the first Holy Roman Emperor, who gave the four sons of Aymon a horse called Bayard. This horse was of normal size until the sons mounted him, and then he became big and strong enough to hold all four of them together.

"Of course," Josh went on, "one of our Wrexham ancestors must have had a horse named Bayard in the Stables, and our Bayard at the moment is a particularly fine specimen."

"And he's always a bay," I added. "That's a reddish brown colour, rather like Josh's hair." Josh, who had been looking quite serious during dinner, smiled back at me. Roz merely looked bored.

W E TOOK OUR coffee into the drawing-room, and as I seemed to be the odd man out, I sat down at the piano at the far end of the room and began to play softly. Now and again I glanced at the others. I was pleased to see Mary talking to David Lloyd, a little apart from the other four. Chopin always soothes me but I admit it's not party-ish and I didn't mind when Chris joined me at the piano. We larked about for a bit, playing some blues and jazz, and a popular song or two, and then, to my surprise, Chris persuaded Mary to sing. I didn't think he'd manage it, but he did.

I slipped from the stool and let Chris accompany her.

Mary has a sweet voice, clear and true. It's not very strong, but just right for a drawing-room. She sang some ballads and I saw David watching her and wished with all my heart that things would go well there. Paula was watching Chris, a half-smile on her face. She seemed a very self-assured young lady and strong enough to keep Chris in order. Roz was gazing into the fire, the glow giving her beauty a warmth that was usually lacking. I wondered what had attracted Josh to her first, her looks or her intelligence, for I had been told that she was an astute businesswoman.

Safe in the shadows, I feasted my eyes on Josh, hungrily devouring every contour of his face, which at this moment looked rather sad. It wasn't until I realised that Mary was singing one of her mother's favourite songs that I realised why. My eyes filled and I looked away.

"No sorrow could betide me, with you once more beside me, You along o' me and I along o' you."

There was silence for a moment and then Chris rose and gave Mary a gentle hug. It seemed to mark the end of the evening. Chris and Paula left. Josh went to see Roz to her car and I announced I was going to give Kelly his run, leaving Mary and David on their own. Kelly, the gorgeous Irish Setter, greeted me ecstatically. I opened the back door whereupon he bounded off into the night.

I heard Roz's car drive off and not long after, David's. It wasn't until I had undressed for bed that I remembered the packet. If I left it until tomorrow, Josh would have gone to work and I wouldn't be able to give it to him personally.

I hadn't heard him come up, and when I tip-toed lightly down the stairs I saw that the light was still on in the drawing-room. Josh was sitting in an armchair by the dying fire, a book on his knee. "Hello, Diana, what do you want?"

He didn't sound very encouraging and I suddenly felt rather a fool with my bare feet and faded dressing-gown. I was also overcome by nerves, and my voice came out brusquely. "I haven't thanked you for your present, Josh. It's lovely."

He gave a tired smile. "I'm glad you like it."

I held out the packet. "I've always brought a present with me on this day, Josh. Somehow, this year, I couldn't bear not to, so I've brought something for Bayard."

I thrust the packet into his hand. The expression on his face, when he unwrapped the last of the tissue paper, was worth every penny I had paid for the present.

"Why, he's a beauty," Josh said slowly, as he held the crystal horse in his palm. "A true Bayard, this one." He rose to his feet and looked down at me. "Thank you, Diana."

Feeling that I just couldn't bear another of those token kisses, I babbled something suitable, backed away, and stammered a good night.

THE ROBIN FAMILY

THE NORTH WIND DOTH BLOW

Little Woodlanders hurry home so as not to get blown away!

FRANKE ROGERS

IT WAS the last lesson of the afternoon at Miss Owl's School, and outside in the Woodlands the wind was beginning to blow. Miss Olivia Owl glanced out of the window and saw the clouds scurrying across the sky, and the trees tossing their branches into the air, and decided it would be best if her little pupils went home early.

"Now," she said, when everyone had put away their books and put their coats on. "You are not to dawdle, you are to hurry home as fast as you can—we don't want any of you blown away in the gale!"

And in *their* classrooms, Miss Thrush and Mr. Rook were telling their pupils exactly the same thing.

The wind was whistling through the grasses and rushing fiercely through the trees and bushes as the three little Robins hurried home, and if they had not been together, they would have been quite frightened.

At last, feeling very breathless, they arrived at the gate of Tree Stump House, where Mrs. Rebecca Robin was waiting.

"It is not safe for Richard to go any farther tonight," she said. "This gale is getting worse. I have rung his mother to tell her that he will be staying with us ..."

Safe indoors, the little Robins were warm and cosy, and in the morning they got up to find that the gale had blown itself into nothing and the sun was shining in a clear October sky.

WHEN I WOKE the next morning, the first thing I saw was my picture propped against the dressing table. I wrapped it up and put it in my case, together with everything else I had brought with me, except for my uniform which I would wear to save time at the other end. I pulled on jodhpurs and jacket and made my way to the stables. It was nearly nine o'clock and I was cross with myself for over-sleeping when I'd wanted to say goodbye to Mary — and Josh, of course. I could hear the radio playing in the kitchen as I went by the window and waved to Hannah. I had a word with all the horses, a ritual left over from childhood, and then saddled up Oberon. He was eager to go and we had a wild gallop on the Downs which did us both some good. I did a spot of hard thinking and made a resolution or two. Trotting back into the yard, I was surprised to see Josh waiting for me. He held Oberon's bridle as I slipped to the ground.

"You look as though you've given him a good ride." He gave me a sharp look. "Have you been jumping him, Diana?"

"Oh, come on, Josh. You know I promised I wouldn't jump when I was out alone." I unstrapped the girth, feeling ridiculously ready to cry. "You're always nagging me these days. I wish you'd leave me alone!" Flinging the saddle over a fence, I led Oberon into his stall and began to rub him down. After a while Josh moved away. When I had finished, I walked disconsolately to the kitchen.

HANNAH WAS making bread, and the scene was so familiar and dear to me that I began to feel better — and hungry. I poured out a cup of tea and made some toast and sat eating it, watching Josh through the window as he gave instructions to one of the stable-lads.

"I thought Josh was going into the office today," I murmured.

Hannah grunted as she thumped the dough. "He wouldn't want to go in today, not with you being here, would he?"

It was a nice idea but strictly for my dreams, and I had decided to be realistic.

"More likely one of the horses needs him," I said darkly. "Anyway, what about his clients?"

"Mr. David can see to them, can't he? Now, what shall I do for your lunch? Fancy a nice bit of fish?"

I went in search of Josh and found him bending over the engine of my car. He was wearing a jumper I had knitted him years ago. It was still miles too big, even after repeated attempts to shrink it.

"I'm sorry, Josh."

He looked up and said gently, "You were right, Diana. I have been a bore lately. I'm not surprised you've kept away." *Continued overleaf*

Full of remorse, I burst out, "That's not why. You've had so much worry — and I know you miss Godmother much more than I do. I feel awful, Josh. I'm an unfeeling ninny!"

He straightened, mouth curving. "Oh, I wouldn't go so far as to say that."

"Well, I would," I returned. "I know you feel responsible for me, Josh, but honestly, you needn't. While Godmother was alive it was different." My voice faltered as I saw his face darken. "It's not fair, you see," I finished lamely.

"What ridiculous idea have you got into that head of yours, Diana?" he demanded, abandoning the engine. Kelly, contentedly chewing a stick, bounced up and began to bark excitedly. A stern "Quiet, dog!" cowed him instantly.

"It's not a ridiculous idea, and don't shout at Kelly!" My own voice rose and I dropped to my knees to fondle the setter as he slunk dejectedly towards me. I picked up the stick and hurled it away from me angrily. Kelly bounded joyfully after it. "You're always telling me to be realistic, and when I try to be I get shouted at."

Josh sighed heavily and thrust a hand through his hair. "How is not coming to Bayard being realistic?" he asked angrily, and I swung round on him, fighting the tears.

"Because when you marry, you fathead, your wife won't want me around, will she? At least Mary and Chris are relations, but I'm nothing!" Furious with myself for breaking down like this, I began to walk hurriedly away, making for the stables.

I might have guessed he'd follow me. A handkerchief was pushed into my hand.

"I'm sorry. I almost never cry."

"I know."

"I seem rather prone to tears, these days." I managed a watery smile and Josh said savagely, "I could murder Chris for bringing Paula last night. Look, Diana, I know how you must be feeling about Chris, but quite honestly, he wouldn't have . . ."

I stopped mopping my eyes and gazed at him. "What do you mean?"

Josh gave a bitter smile. "I've always known how you felt about him — and it's worried me desperately. I knew you'd end up being hurt."

Comprehension dawned on me. "Josh! I'm not at all upset about Chris. Surely you didn't think that." I shook my head wonderingly. "Yes, you did. How could you think it was *Chris* I'm in love with, for goodness' sake! He's like a brother to me."

Josh pondered my words, his face curiously still.

"Who are you in love with, Diana?" he asked at last, and I felt a hot wave of colour sweep over my face. Desperately confused, I couldn't find a flippant answer. As I frantically searched for words, I heard Josh say softly: "Am *I* like a brother to you, Diana?"

I found my voice at last. "Why, yes," I stammered, my heart thumping away like mad. I felt his hands on my arms, and although I resisted he made me turn to face him.

"I have never felt like a brother towards you, Diana," he said, and taking my face in his hands, he kissed me.

HOW OFTEN I had dreamed of this moment, but now I couldn't believe it was happening. When our lips parted I could only say, "Oh, Josh." He mimicked a tender "Oh, Diana", and wrapped his arms around me, holding me close. I began to tremble helplessly as his hand gently stroked my hair. He gave a triumphant laugh and held me closer. "Never like a brother," he repeated, his voice fondly reproachful, and to prove it he kissed me again.

It was the mare's insistent nudging that brought us back to earth. Laughingly, we made our way back to the house, heading for the warmth of the sitting-room fire.

"Come and sit down, you must be frozen," ordered Josh. Meekly, I allowed myself to be drawn into his arms in the comfortable haven of the old armchair.

"I don't think I shall ever be cold again," I murmured, laying my head on his shoulder. "I still can't believe it! I was so sure you and Roz . . ."

"Never, my darling girl. I felt sorry for her, new to the town and knowing no one." He lifted my face with his free hand and looked deep into my eyes. "I was so sure you loved Chris. I worried about you. There were times when I could have knocked him down."

I was delighted and allowed myself the liberty of smoothing back a tawny lock from his forehead. This signalled the end of our conversation and we only broke apart when the door burst open and Hannah stood there, watching us with satisfaction. We grinned back idiotically.

"About time you two got together," she observed laconically. Giving a nod of approval, she retreated, pausing to comment: "That nice bit of fish is done. When you're ready, that is."

THE END
© *Jacqueline Gilbert, 1982*

110

THERE are several methods of preserving plant material for use in vase arrangements like our selection on page 114.

GLYCERINE TREATMENT
If you are going to preserve beech leaves in glycerine and water, the leaves should be cut by early August if you want them to retain their natural green colouring, or in September to achieve tannish-brown colouring.

The stems should be split up one or two inches or crushed with a hammer before standing the branches in jars filled 6 inches deep with one part glycerine to two parts tepid water, for about two weeks.

Other foliage suitable for preservation by this method is camellia, magnolia, pittosporum, laurel, rhododendron, mahonia, Chinese hawthorn, eucalyptus, aucuba, forsythia, oak and elaeagnus.

PRESSING
Flat branches of autumn leaves — beech, maple and bracken, in particular — can also be preserved by pressing between thick sheets of blotting paper or newspaper placed under a carpet, mattress or heavy book. Turn them once a week until quite dry.

WATER DRYING
Berried branches and grasses can be dried naturally, simply by standing them in 3-4 inches of water in a vase and not replenishing after that has been absorbed. Paint with shellac (or colourless nail varnish) to keep plump.

AIR DRYING
Many flowers can be dried simply by hanging them in loose bunches, heads downwards, in a dark, dry room or shed. Strip off the leaves and tie the stems loosely together, three to six to a bunch.

Among the best for this method are the strawflowers (helichrysums), the dainty pink, white and lavender immortelle xeranthemum; sea lavender (statice sinuata); anaphalis, bearing heads of pearly-white "everlasting" flowers;

PRESERVING YOUR FLOWERS
By Joy Simmons

Flowers, foliage, ferns and grasses can all be preserved in various ways so that you can enjoy them indoors long after their season is over

honesty for its silvery seed pods; and bells of Ireland (molucella laevis) with greenish-white sheaths. Gather all these on a dry day, just before the flowers are fully open.

Chinese lanterns (physalis franchetii) can be cut in August for green lanterns or in September or October for orange lanterns and hung upside down to dry. Or use the water drying method.

BURYING METHOD
Some of the "more precious" flowers like lilies, roses, dahlias, lily-of-the-valley, delphiniums, zinnias, day lilies, pyrethrum, narcissi, stocks and violets can be preserved in borax, sand, or silica gel. When flowers are dried in these materials, the colour and shape will remain almost intact.

When using fine sand or powdered borax, line a deep carton or box with thick paper covered with 2 inches of the drying material, then place the flowers (stripped of foliage) heads downwards. Draw the sand or borax gently up and over the blooms, adding more until they are completely covered. Drying time varies with the texture, light textured petals drying in two to three weeks, thicker ones in up to five weeks.

BLEACHING
Some large leaves, such as aspidistra, can be easily bleached to a delicate colour.

You can use domestic bleach, making a solution of roughly equal parts of bleach and water. Leave the foliage to soak for about three hours, occasionally giving a gentle stir with a wooden stick. When the desired colour has been achieved, remove the leaves and rinse them immediately, then spread them out to dry. If they tend to curl out of shape, put them between sheets of blotting paper to dry. (Note: when bleaching, wear rubber gloves and keep materials in an inaccessible place away from children and pets.)

Dried flowers are best stored in a jar, in a dry, dark place, or covered in boxes in a dry room.

Holiday Shopping

Well-chosen souvenirs bring back happy memories

SHOPPING for goodies to bring back home is a precious part of the fun of going on holiday. And the world's favourite holiday haunts offer infinite temptation to both serious and frivolous shoppers.

Istanbul's Covered Bazaar, its maze of high-ceilinged, narrow streets packed with shops selling gold and silver jewellery set with precious and semi-precious stones of every hue, leather, alabaster, carpets, hammered brass and copper, meerschaum, pottery, tiles, Islamic prints, icons, small antiques, spices and gorgeous scents blended for you on the spot, is guaranteed to excite even the most lethargic of shoppers. The whole atmosphere of the place assaults the senses, encourages bold bargaining.

The **souks,** the labyrinthine markets of **Tangier, Marrakech** or **Tunis,** offer similar excitement. A myriad different scents waft from the doorways of tiny, crammed shops that line the streets, offering caftans and jewellery, brass, copper and tooled leather, camel stools and pouffes, rugs and carpets, marquetry boxes and little tables, bales of woven cloth in superb colours, decorated weapons, pottery and straw basketware. Panniered donkeys nose their way past you, Arabs in flowing djellabas gossip and bargain, drink tiny cups of mint tea and alternate high-pitched, reedy music with the latest pop hits.

In an atmosphere of total contrast, the shops of **Amsterdam** can please enormously. The long-famous blue Delftware, pewter, small whole cheeses, bulbs, cigars, old maps and reproductions of old masters, gimmicky souvenirs like the Delft lamps that play *Tulips from Amsterdam* every time they light up, liqueurs and liqueur chocolates and, when in extravagant mood, diamonds, are the best buys. Schipol Airport offers some of the world's best duty-free shopping.

Shopping in **Italy** is always a particular delight, with Florence and Venice special favourites. Goldsmiths and silversmiths have made Florence's Ponte Vecchio famous for jewellery of exquisite craftsmanship ever since medieval days. Florentine leather is marvellous — handbags, shoes, sandals, gloves, trinket boxes, wallets, purses all tempt. And the straw market in the Loggia del Porcellino is a fruitful place for souvenir-hunting. In Venice, a stroll along the Mercerie, which leads from St. Mark's Square to the Rialto Bridge, offers shop windows packed with Venetian glass, lace made on the island of Burano in the Lagoon, painted wooden boxes, trays and peppermills, leatherware, old maps and prints, coral, knitwear and pottery. And the Rialto jewellers have been rivalling those of the Ponte Vecchio for many centuries.

The shops of the **Austrian Tyrol** are agreeably inviting also, with the medieval arcades of Innsbruck's Old Town a particularly attractive venue. Worthwhile presents to look for here are hand-carved wood and wrought ironware, porcelain boxes and dishes, often jewel-studded, gold and silver bracelets and pendants, petit-point, embroidered belts and ribbons, dirndls and lederhosen, buckled shoes, excellent walking shoes and boots and silver-buttoned, soft, warm loden-cloth jackets.

In **Spain,** look out for top quality inexpensive leatherware, handmade, embroidered lingerie and table linen, lace mantillas, ironwork, pearls, Toledo jewellery, fans, castanets, basketware, pottery and dolls.

Pottery is a popular buy in **Portugal** also, as well as table linen, lace from **Madeira,** embroidered skirts, wood-carvings and heavy-knit jackets in natural-coloured wool.

Swiss watches and clocks, musical boxes, wood-carvings, fondue sets, embroidered blouses, linen and handkerchiefs, chocolate and Kirsch liqueur all tempt the shopper in **Switzerland.**

In **Scandinavia,** it is easy to covet Danish porcelain and silverware, toys, pewter and contemporary-design fabrics, Norwegian sweaters and embroidered jackets, candles, enamelware and bronze jewellery, pewter, silver and furs from the far north, and Swedish glassware, ceramics, stainless steel and sportswear.

Lingerie, gloves, silk scarves, costume jewellery and scent are top buys in **France,** along with kitchenware, stationery, lace from Brittany and Calais, crystallised fruits from Nice and high-fashion beachware from the Côte d'Azur.

Holiday shoppers in the **States** will find well made leather boots, towels, bed and table linen, casual clothes, cameras, radios, recorders and all electronic goods and intriguing gadgets far cheaper than at home.

And if you're lucky enough to be going to the **Far East,** you will find the shops of Hong Kong, Singapore and Bangkok the ultimate in temptation, with every imaginable, covetable commodity on sale, from clothes to cameras, jewellery to objects d'art, leather goods to the latest in electronic equipment.

Right: Shopping in Florence.

GOLDEN AUTUMN

A spectacular arrangement of dried flowers and leaves. A guide to
preserving your own flowers appears on page 111.
Right: Bright and beautiful stocking stitch jacket has unusual lacy detail on yoke and
round the lower edge. Instructions on page 127.

*I*n Holland's Keukenhof Gardens, autumn-planted bulbs produce a riot of spring colour. Why not follow our hints about bulbs on page 138?
Right: Shining, healthy hair — always a bonus to your looks. But how do you keep it that way? We give some helpful tips on page 136.

*T*here's no taste quite like home-made bread and jams. Turn to page 124 to find out how simple it is to make your own.
Right: Brightly does it — jolly red and white jersey in an effective slipstitch pattern has polo collar and raglan sleeves. Instructions on page 122.

Reflections

Courage, kindness and wisdom — all are mirrored in the faces of older people who have gained that special beauty of experience

THE television set was switched on for viewing, but with the sound turned right down — a kind of alarm clock we use when waiting for a programme we don't want to miss. That was how, glancing up from my book, I saw an unexplained 'still' of a child's face filling the screen. In an instant another photograph was superimposed. The child had become a lovely young girl. Another instant and that face of dreaming innocence had merged and grown into that of a superbly beautiful, mature woman. More years rolled over the proud, dark head in a flash of screen time and the enchanting features went through the middle years, then finally took on bone-spare contours of old, old age.

I had not a notion in the world of what was behind this television trick with photographs. It was just a more than ordinarily effective bit of magic in the silence of my room, making me acutely aware of time's passing, of a woman's life in all its ages and stages of being, compressed into a few seconds, and I felt that ache of the heart we all have when conscious of the evanescence of human loveliness.

But even while I was thinking that, the old face in the final photograph came nearer, became clearer, became a living face, and I saw that it was as beautiful in spirit as those younger faces had been in the flesh.

I had not been curious enough about the child, the young girl, the Edwardian beauty, to leave my book and switch on the sound of the television set. But the fascination of that aged face could not be resisted, and I was out of my chair and turning up the sound in a moment. I had to learn something about the woman who had made that face for herself out of her life.

PRIDE AND LOVE

A face ninety-one years old. A face with rich laughter in it, with courage in every line. A serene, unconfused face, but still lovely with inquiry because of unfading interest in this changing world. The veil of the past did not cloud and blind those old eyes to the present and the future. There was no bitterness in that face. No querulousness. No complaint or self-pity. Just a proud acceptance of the end of personal struggle, yet a trustful humility so true and touching that one felt that in this respect the woman was ninety-one years young instead of old. Perhaps great age is more in touch with eternity and so knows how young the longest lived human life really is.

I felt a surge of pride and love for my human race as I looked at that woman's face. 'Well,' I thought, when the television interview had ended, 'I was wrong. However long the years, beauty need not vanish from a human face as long as the spirit can shine through.'

If a woman can look like that when she is ninety, make one want to know her as I wanted to know that old, old lady, then no woman need feel that the beginning of the end of her power to charm, to be loved, has

been reached when she looks in her mirror and must admit at last that the wrinkles are there to stay.

That cold, clear light of a certain morning comes to every woman, I believe, and I don't suppose there are many who can meet it without a pang. But though time must take away the bloom, those years of living put much into a face.

You, who have arrived at this certain morning, should look closer. See what time has put into your face besides those lines. You have done a lot of living in these passing years. You have loved, married, borne children perhaps. Or you have worked at a career. You have come to grips with life, and made the acquaintance of death. You have worked and struggled. Known success and failure. You have known disappointments and rich rewards. You have known how frustrating life can be. And how marvellous.

What you have made of all this will now be showing in your face. That is the "second face" of a woman — the one which begins to show through when the young face blurs and changes.

Nature may have made that first young face plain or pretty. But it is **you** who will make the second face, which you will have in your later years.

GOOD TO LOOK UPON

Blessedly, now and again, one sees these old, beautiful faces which draw one near, which it does us good to look upon. From their lives — much the same kind of lives as yours and mine in so far as they have been good at times, and bad at times — these people have learned understanding, learned to be gentle with their fellowmen, learned patience and tolerance, found their good truths to live by and the strength and courage to do so, yet can forgive those who are still floundering and weak. They have learned to live by love instead of hate and know that bitterness, envy, spite and self-pity are stupid feelings because they are destructive of happiness. They have learned the healing power of laughter. Above all, they have cast out fear.

This mixture of wisdom, of gentleness and the serenity which comes when one is at last unafraid, shows in a face and makes it beautiful.

There is a story of a great man who refused employment to a certain applicant because he "did not like the man's face". On being told that one could not help one's face he retorted, "Everyone is responsible for his own face, after forty."

And I believe there is indeed that second face, which we make for ourselves.

So when you are looking in your mirror, using all the arts you know to make yourself as pretty as you can, remember that second face you are making too. That other is not a surface face. It is **you**, the real woman. The face which one day, past camouflage, you will be showing to the world. And the world is going to love to look at it — or not. It is for you to choose.

BRIGHTLY DOES IT!

This classic raglan sleeve sweater relies on bold two-colour effect
and an interesting textured stitch for its appeal, plus that cosy polo collar

Instructions in 3 sizes
Colour photo on page 119

MATERIALS: *Allow the following quantities in 50g balls of Emu Superwash Wool 4 ply: 4 white for 61 cm size; 5 white for 66 cm and 71 cm sizes; 1 red for 61 cm size; 2 red for 66 cm and 71 cm sizes. For any one size: a pair each of No.11 (3 mm) and No.9 (3¾) knitting needles.*

TENSION: *Work at a tension of 31 stitches and 57 rows to measure 10 x 10 cm over the two colour pattern, and 29 stitches and 39 rows to measure 10 x 10 cm over the rice stitch using No.9 (3¾ mm) needles, to obtain measurements.*

ABBREVIATIONS: To be read before working: *K., knit plain; p., purl; st., stitch; tog., together; inc., increase (by working twice into next st.); dec., decrease (by working 2 sts. tog.); sl.1p.w., slip 1 p.wise; w., white; r., red; sl., slip; nil, meaning nothing is worked here for this size; single rib is k.1 and p.1 alternately.*

NOTE: *The instructions are given for the 61 cm (24 inch) size. Where they vary, work the figures within the first brackets for the 66 cm (26 inch) size; work the figures within the second brackets for the 71 cm (28 inch) size.*

THE BACK: With No.11 (3 mm) needles and w. cast on 98 (106) (114) sts. and single rib 12 rows.

Change to No.9 (3¾ mm) needles and join in r. Work the 4-row slip st. pattern as follows: **1st and 2nd rows:** With w., all k.

3rd row: With r., * k.1, sl.1 p.w.; repeat from * to end

4th row: With r., * yarn to front, sl. 1p.w., yarn to back, k.1; repeat from * to end.

Pattern a further 96 (108) (120) rows.

Drop r., and continue in rice st. pattern only as set between decreases.

To shape raglan armholes: 1st row: Cast off 2 sts., * p.1, k.1; repeat from * until 1 st. remains, p.1.

2nd row: Cast off 2 sts., k. to end.

3rd row: Dec., * k.1, p.1; repeat from * until 2 sts. remain, dec.

4th row: All k.

5th row: Dec., * p.1, k.1; repeat from * until 2 sts. remain, dec.

6th row: All k. ******

Repeat last 4 rows, 13 (15) (16) times more, then first 2 (nil) (2) rows again — 36 (38) (40) sts.

Leave sts. on a spare needle.

THE FRONT: Work as given for back to ******.

Repeat last 4 rows, 8 (9) (10) times more, then 1st row again — 56 (60) (64) sts.

To divide for neck and continue shaping armholes: Next row: Pattern 18 (20) (22) and leave on a spare needle for right half front, pattern 20 and leave on a st. holder, pattern to end and work on these 18 (20) (22) sts. for left half front.

The left half front: Dec. 1 st. at each end of the next row and the 6 (7) (8) following alternate rows, then at armhole edge only on the following alternate rows — 2 sts.

Work 1 row.

K.2 tog., and fasten off.

The right half front: With right side facing rejoin w. to inner end of sts. on spare needle and work as given for left half front to end.

THE SLEEVES (2 alike): With No.11 (3 mm) needles and w. cast on 52 (54) (56) sts. and work 12 rows in single rib.

Change to No.9 (3¾ mm) needles and work the 2-row pattern as follows:

1st (wrong side) row: All k.

Continued overleaf

MEASUREMENTS	*in centimetres (and inches, in brackets)*					
To fit chest sizes	61	(24)	66	(26)	71	(28)
All round at underarms	63	(24¾)	68	(26¾)	73.5	(29)
Side seam	20.5	(8)	22.5	(8¾)	24.5	(9½)
Length	35.5	(14)	39.5	(15½)	43	(17)
Sleeve seam	23.5	(9¼)	26	(10¼)	28.5	(11¼)

122

Pick the brightest
colours like royal and
claret cup;
tartan green and rocket red;
smokey blue and
coraline and rust and camel.

2nd row: * K.1, p.1; repeat from * to end.
Pattern a further 3 rows.
Keeping continuity of pattern and working extra sts. into pattern as they occur, inc. 1 st. at each end of the next row and the 11 (14) (17) following 6th (5th) (5th) rows — 76 (84) (92) sts.
Pattern a further 9 (15) (10) rows.
To shape raglan sleeve top: Cast off 2 sts. at the beginning of the next 2 rows, then dec. 1 st. at each end of the next row and the 28 (31) (34) following alternate rows — 14 (16) (18) sts.
Work 1 row. Leave sts. on a spare needle.

THE POLO COLLAR: First join right sleeve to back and front, then left sleeve to front only. With right side facing, using No.11 (3 mm) needles and w., k. across 14 (16) (18) sts. of left sleeve, pick up and k. 18 (20) (22) sts. down left side of neck, k. across 20 sts. at centre front, pick up and k.18 (20) (22) sts. up right side of neck, k. across 14 (16) (18) sts. of right sleeve, and finally k. sts. of back neck — 120 (130) (140) sts.
For 1st and 2nd sizes only: Next row: P.50 (56), * inc., p.2 (5); repeat from * 5 (2) times more, p.22 (25), inc., * p.2 (5), inc.; repeat from * 4 (1) time(s), p. to end — 132 (138) sts.
For 3rd size only: Rib 1 row.
For all sizes: Join in r. working in a stripe sequence of 2 rows r., 2 rows w., work 44 (52) (60) rows in single rib. Cast off loosely in rib.

TO MAKE UP THE SWEATER: Press. Join left sleeve to back continuing seam across polo collar. Join side and sleeve seams. Fold polo collar in half to right side.

The Perfec

There's nothing quite like the smell of home made bread or more satisfying than making your own jam. Here we show you the way to the best bread and most mouthwatering preserves you've ever tasted!

BROWN BREAD
½ oz. or 1 level tablespoon dried yeast
1 level teaspoon sugar
½ pint tepid water
½ pint tepid milk
1 lb. wholemeal or wheatmeal flour
14-16 oz. strong white flour
4 level teaspoon salt
2 oz. lard

Sprinkle the yeast and sugar over the tepid water, whisk with a fork and leave in a warm place for 10-15 minutes until there is a good froth on the top. If easy-blend yeast is used add it DRY to the flour.

Sift the wholemeal and 14 oz white flour and salt into a bowl. Rub in the lard until the mixture resembles breadcrumbs. Make a well in the centre and then pour the yeast liquid and the tepid milk into the centre. Stir with a wooden spoon until well mixed then work until the dough comes cleanly away from the sides of the bowl, adding a further 1-2 oz. flour as necessary. This takes about 10 minutes. If preferred work the dough on a floured surface until smooth and elastic. Cover with oiled cling film and leave in a warm place until doubled in size — about hour.

Knead the dough on a floured surface and cut in half if making two loaves. Knead the dough until smooth. Either place in two small loaf tins or shape into a long oval shape 8-9 inches long and place on a greased baking sheet. Cut diamond pattern on the top with either a razor blade or very sharp knife. Cover with oiled cling film and put to prove for about 40 minutes until doubled in size. Set oven to hot, Mark 8 450°F/230°C. Sprinkle flour over bread and bake above centre of oven for 45-50 minutes.

FREEZING NOTE:

Uncooked: make the dough to the stage where it is shaped for the final proving. Place the loaves in the freezer and freeze for 5-6 hours or until solid. Remove from baking sheet, wrap in plastic bags or foil. Label and keep for up to 3 weeks.

To cook the bread: unwrap and leave in a warm place to thaw and prove — this will take about 4 hours. Bake the bread as normal.

Cooked: After baking and cooling wrap in foil or a plastic bag. Label then freeze.

The bread will keep for up to 2 months after which the crust starts to come away.

SUCCESSFUL BREADMAKING TIPS

Do follow the recipe correctly using the right flour and adding the yeast correctly.

Do add all the liquid at once and knead thoroughly. (If you have a dough hook and mixer it will take only 2-3 minutes.)

Do cover the dough when rising or proving to prevent a crust forming.

Do allow the dough to rise properly and double in size before shaping. Do remember the rising time does vary depending on the temperature at which the rising takes place. Be careful of too much heat since this will kill the yeast, so be patient and let the dough double in size however long it takes. One interesting fact is that the covered dough will rise satisfactorily if left in the fridge overnight.

Continued overleaf

WHAT WENT WRONG:

If your bread is not as perfect as you would like here are some of the most common faults and the possible causes.

Poor volume and a close texture:
the flour is too soft or self raising has been used, too much salt; dough not allowed sufficient fermentation time.

Uneven texture and holes:
too much yeast: insufficient kneading after the first rising; over proved; dough not covered during rising, therefore a crust forming which will give streaks when kneaded.
Note: If the dough is overproved and is beginning to collapse, knock back, reshape and prove again.

Strong yeasty flavour:
dried yeast not reconstituted properly; too much yeast.

Bread stales quickly:
too much yeast; flour too soft; the dough rises too quickly in too warm a place.

APPLE GINGER

Makes about 5 lb.

| 3 lb. cooking apples |
| 1 pint water |
| 1 level teaspoon ground ginger |
| Grated rind and juice of 2 lemons |
| 3 lb. granulated sugar |
| 4 oz. crystallised ginger |

Peel, core and cut up the apples. Tie the cores and peel in a muslin bag and hang in the preserving or large pan with the apples, water, ginger and lemon juice and rind.

Bring to the boil then reduce the heat to a simmer and cook gently until the apples are soft.

Remove the muslin bag, squeezing it by pressing it against the side of the pan with a wooden spoon.

Add the sugar and the finely chopped ginger. Stir over a low heat until the sugar has dissolved. Then bring to the boil and boil rapidly until setting point is reached — 10-15 minutes.

Test for setting point after 10 minutes, removing the pan from the heat whilst carrying out test (see Apple and Blackberry Jam).

If still not set return the pan to the heat and boil for a further 5 minutes. Repeat test for setting point.

Pour into clean, warm jars. Immediately cover with waxed disc then cover with Cellophane disc whilst still warm or when cold. Label. Store in a cool, dry place.

SEEDLESS APPLE AND BLACKBERRY JAM

Makes about 5 lb.

| 2 lb. cooking apples |
| 2 lb. blackberries |
| 2 pints water |
| Granulated sugar |
| Good knob of butter |

Wash the apples and cut out any bruises — do not peel or core. Cut the apples into slices and put in a preserving pan or very large saucepan. Add water and bring to the boil; reduce heat and cook until soft.

Pick over the blackberries, add to the apples and cook both fruits to a pulp.

Rub the mixture through a sieve or fine Mouli to get rid of the seeds.

Measure the pulp, return it to the pan and to every pint allow 1 lb. of sugar.

Heat the pulp and sugar gently to dissolve the sugar, adding the butter to lessen the scum. Bring to the boil and boil rapidly to setting point.

To test for setting point remove the pan from the heat and spoon a little of the jam on to a saucer. Allow the jam to become cold and if it 'frills' or wrinkles when the surface is pushed with a finger it is at setting point. If not, boil the jam for another 5 minutes then test again.

Remove any scum then pour into clean, warm jars, filling completely. Immediately put a waxed disc on jam. When cold, cover, label.

FOUR FRUIT JAM

Makes about 3½ lb

| ½ lb. gooseberries, topped and tailed |
| ½ lb. blackcurrants, destalked |
| ¼ pint water |
| ½ lb. strawberries, hulled |
| ½ lb. raspberries, hulled |
| 2 lb. sugar |
| Small knob of butter |

Put the gooseberries and blackcurrants into a large saucepan with the water. Bring to the boil then reduce the heat and simmer gently for 15 minutes or until the fruit is soft and the mixture reduced by a good third. Add the strawberries and raspberries.

Tip in the sugar and the knob of butter and heat gently, stirring, until completely dissolved. Bring to the boil and boil rapidly until setting point is reached — about 5 minutes. (See Apple and Blackberry Jam on setting point test.)

Remove from the heat and, if liked, remove any remaining scum. Pour into clean, warm, dry jars and cover as usual.

MATERIALS: *Allow the following quantities in 50 g balls of Wendy Shetland D.K.: 10 for the 86 cm and the 91 cm sizes; 11 for the 97 cm size. For any one size: a pair each of No.10 (3¼ mm), 9 (3¾ mm) and a pair of long 9 (3¾ mm) knitting needles; 8 buttons.*

TENSION: *Work at a tension of 23 stitches and 30 rows to measure 10 x 10 cm, over the stocking stitch, using No.9 (3¾mm) needles, to obtain measurements given below.*

ABBREVIATIONS: To be read before working: *K., knit plain; p., purl; st., stitch; inc., increase (by working twice into next st.); tog., together; dec., decrease (by working 2 sts. tog.); s.s., stocking stitch (k. on the right side and p. on the wrong side); y.fwd., yarn forward to make a st.; sl., slip; s.k.p.o., (sl. 1, k.1, pass sl. st. over); p.2 s.s.s.o., (pass 2 sl. sts. over); single rib is k.1, and p.1 alternately; upl, pick up loop lying between needles and k. or p. into back of it; nil, meaning nothing is worked here for this size.*

NOTE: *The instructions are given for the 86 cm (34 inch) size. Where they vary, work figures in the first brackets or the 91 cm (36 inch) size; work figures within second brackets for the 97 cm (38 inch) size.*

THE BACK: With No. 10 (3¼ mm) needles cast on 103 (109) (115) sts. and beginning odd-numbered rows with a k.1 and even-numbered rows with a p.1, single rib 10 rows.
** Change to No. 9 (3¾ mm) needles and beginning with a k. row, s.s. 15 rows.
Work the 9-row pattern band as follows: **1st row (wrong side):** All k.
2nd row: All k.
3rd row: P.1, * y.fwd. twice, sl.2, p.3 tog., p.2 s.s.s.o., y.fwd. twice, p.1; repeat from * to end.
4th row: K.1, * then k.1 and p.1 all into double y.fwd. of previous row, k.1, then p.1 and k.1 all into double y.fwd of previous row, k.1; repeat from * to end.
5th and 6th rows: All k.
7th row: P.3 tog., * y.fwd. twice, p.1, y.fwd. twice, sl.2, p.3 tog., p.2 s.s.s.o.; repeat from * until 4 sts. remain, y.fwd. twice, p.1, y.fwd. twice, p.3 tog.
8th row: K.1, * then p.1 and k.1 all into double y.fwd. of previous row, k.1, then k.1 and p.1 all into double y.fwd. of previous row, k.1; repeat from * to end.
9th row: All k.******

Beginning with a k. row, s.s. 5 rows, then work the 9 row pattern band again.
S.s. a further 64 rows.
To shape armholes: 1st and 2nd rows: Cast off 7 (8) (9) sts., work to end.
Dec. 1 st. at each end of next row and then the 2 (4) (4) following alternate rows – 83 (83) (87) sts.
S.s. a further 5 (3) (5) rows.
Break yarn and leave.

THE LEFT FRONT: With No. 10 (3¼ mm) needles cast on 59 (63) (66) sts. and work 9 rows in rib as given on back.
Next row: Rib 11 sts. and leave on a safety pin for button band, rib to end increasing 1 st. at the end of the row for the 86 cm size only – 49 (52) (55) sts.
*** Change to No. 9 (3¾ mm) needles and s.s. 15 rows.
1st row (wrong side): All k. **2nd row:** All k.
3rd row: K.1 (2) (1), * y.fwd. twice, sl.2, p.3 tog., p.2 s.s.s.o., y.fwd. twice, p.1; repeat from * until nil (2) (nil) sts. remain, p. nil (2) (nil).
4th row: K.1 (3) (1), * then k.1 and p.1 all into double y.fwd. of previous row, k.1, then p.1 and k.1 all into double y.fwd. of previous row, k.1; repeat from * until nil (1) (nil) st. remains, k. nil (1) (nil).
5th and 6th row: All k.

Continued overleaf

MEASUREMENTS	in centimetres (and inches, in brackets)					
To fit chest sizes	86	(34)	91	(36)	97	(28)
All round at underarms fastened	90.5	(35¾)	95.5	(39½)	101	(39¾)
Side seam	36	(14¼)	36	(14¼)	36	(14¼)
Length	57	(22¼)	57.5	(22½)	58	(22¾)
Sleeve seam	44.5	(17½)	44.5	(17½)	44.5	(17½)

WARM THOUGHTS

Fashion right, colour bright jacket in stocking stitch with lacy yoke and matching lacy pattern at wrist and lower edge. It's guaranteed to keep you warm and cosy

Instructions in 3 sizes
Colour photo on page 115

7th row: P.nil (1) (nil), p.3 tog., y.fwd. twice, p.1, y.fwd. twice, * sl.2, p.3 tog., y.fwd. twice, p.1, y.fwd. twice; repeat from * until 3 (5) (3) sts. remain, p.3 tog. (p.3 tog., p.2) (p.3 tog.).

8th row: K.1 (3) (1), * then p.1 and k.1 all into double y.fwd., k.1, then k.1 and p.1 all into double y.fwd., k.1; repeat from * until nil (1) (nil) st. remains, k. nil (1) (nil).

9th row: All k.

Beginning with a k. row, s.s. 5 rows, then work 9 row pattern band again.

S.s. a further 64 rows – s.s. 65 rows here when work the right front.

To shape the armhole: 1st row: Cast off 7 (8) (9) sts., work to end.

Work 1 row – omit this row when working the right front.

Dec 1 st. at armhole edge on the next row then on the 2 (4) (4) following alternate rows – 39 (39) (41) sts.

S.s. a further 5 (3) (5) rows.

Leave remaining sts. on a spare needle.

THE RIGHT FRONT: With No. 10 (3¼ mm) needles cast on 59 (63) (66) sts. and work 4 rows in rib as given on back.

1st buttonhole row: Rib 4, cast off 3, rib to end.

2nd buttonhole row: Rib to end, casting on 3 sts. over those cast off on previous row.

Rib a further 3 rows.

Next row: Increasing 1 st. at beginning of row on the 86 cm size only, rib until 11 sts. remain, turn, leave remaining 11 sts. on a safety pin.

Work as given for left front from *** to end.

THE SLEEVES (both alike): With No. 10 (3¼ mm) needles cast on 51 sts. and work 19 rows in rib as given on back.

Next increase row: Rib 3, * up 1, rib 5; repeat from * until 3 sts. remain, up 1, rib 3 – 61 sts.

Work as given for back from ** to **.

S.s. 2 rows.

Continuing s.s. inc. 1 st. at each end of the next row and the 10 (11) (12) following 6th (6th) (5th) rows – 83 (85) (87) sts.

S.s. 17 (11) (17) rows.

To shape armholes: Cast off 7 (8) (9) sts. at the beginning of the next 2 rows, then dec. 1 st. at each end of the next row then on the 4 following alternate rows – 59 sts.

Work 1 (3) (5) row(s).

Leaving remaining sts. on a spare needle.

THE YOKE: With right side of work facing and using long No. 9 (3¾ mm) needles, rejoin yarn and decreasing 1 st. each end on the 97 cm size only, k. across 39 (39) (41) sts. of right front, k. 59 sts. of first sleeve, 83 (83) (87) sts. of back, 59 sts. of second sleeve, then decreasing 1 st. at each end of the 97 cm size only, k. across 39 (39) (41) sts. of left front – 279 (279) (283) sts.

Next (dec.) row: P. 57 (57) (56) sts., * p.2 tog.

(p.2 tog.) (p.2 tog., p.2 tog.), p.19, then p.2 tog. (p.2 tog.) (p.2 tog., p.2 tog.) *, p.119 (119) (117), repeat from * to *, p. to end – 275 sts.

1st row: P.3, * y.fwd., s.k.p.o., k.1, k.2 tog., y.fwd., p.6; repeat from * ending last repeat with p.3 instead of p.6.

2nd row: All p.

3rd row: P.3, * k.1, y.fwd., sl.2 k. wise, k.1, p.2 s.s.o., y.fwd., k.1, p.6; repeat from * ending last repeat with p.3 instead of p.6.

4th row: All p.

Repeat the last 4 rows, twice.

Next (dec.) row: P.1, p.2 tog., * y.fwd., s.k.p.o., k.1, k.2 tog., y.fwd., p.2 tog., p.2, p.2 tog.; repeat from * until 8 sts. remain, y.fwd., s.k.p.o., k.1, k.2 tog., y.fwd., p.2 tog., p.1 – 225 sts.

Keeping continuity of lace panels, pattern a further 23 rows ending with the 4th row.

Next (dec.) row: P.2 tog., * y.fwd., s.k.p.o., k.1, k.2 tog., y.fwd., p.2 tog., p.2 tog.; repeat from * until 7 sts. remain, y.fwd., s.k.p.o., k.1, k.2 tog., y.fwd., p.2 tog. – 175 sts.

Pattern a further 19 rows.

Next (dec.) row: P.1, * y.fwd., s.k.p.o., k.1, k.2 tog., y.fwd., p.2 tog.; repeat from * until 6 sts. remain, y.fwd., s.k.p.o., k.1, k.2 tog., y.fwd., p.1 – 151 sts.

Pattern a further 4 rows.

Next (dec.) row: P.1, * p.2 tog.; repeat from * to end – 75 sts. Cast off.

THE BUTTONHOLE BAND: With wrong side of work facing, rejoin yarn to inner end of 11 sts. of right front, and using No. 10 (3¼ mm) needles, rib 19 (21) (21) rows.

Next (buttonhole) row: Rib 4, cast off 3, rib to end.

Next row: Rib to end casting on 3 sts. over those cast off on previous row.

Rib a further 22 rows.

Repeat the last 24 rows, 5 times more then the 2 buttonhole rows again. Rib 4 (4) (6) rows.

Leave sts. on a safety pin.

THE BUTTON BAND: With right side of work facing, using No. 10 (3¼ mm) needles rejoin yarn to 11 sts. on left front.

Rib 168 (170) (172) rows.

Leave sts. on a safety pin.

THE COLLAR: With right side of work facing using No. 10 (3¼ mm) needles rejoin yarn and rib across the 11 sts. of buttonhole band, pick up and k. 151 sts. evenly round yoke (approximately 2 sts. from every 1 cast off) then rib across 11 sts. of button band – 173 sts.

Rib 7 rows. Change to No. 9 (3¼ mm) needles and rib a further 26 rows, cast off.

TO MAKE UP THE CARDIGAN: Press lightly with a warm iron over a damp cloth. Join underarm seams then join side and sleeve seams. Sew on front bands. Add buttons.

Scarlet tattoo makes an ideal colour choice for this warm jacket, but highland gorse, piper red, Islay rust, Loch Ness green and Aran would look just as good.

THE VISITOR

AUDRIE MANLEY-TUCKER

Up to now, Tina had been the perfect stepdaughter. How could I have guessed that in Greg's absence she would make her first determined bid to cross the frontier into adulthood? Oh, how I needed her father at that moment, until I realised that this was something she and I had to work out together . . .

I T WAS VERY early when Greg left. I surfaced from sleep to meet his farewell kiss, and saw him standing by the bed, very correct in his dark suit, unruly hair disciplined. He looked well-scrubbed and morning-fresh, briefcase in one hand.

"Take care, Lucy," he said, his free arm sliding around my neck as he pulled me close. "Take *good* care, darling. What shall I bring you and Tina back from Rome?"

"A slice of the Catacombs for me," I murmured frivolously, putting my cheek against his which smelled of expensive aftershave. "I don't know what Tina wants; you'll have to ask her."

He kissed me as though he was going to be away for years not days, on business for his firm. Reluctantly, he let go of me. At the door, he turned.

"Isn't it marvellous that you and Tina get along so well together?" he said happily.

I nodded and smiled. I lay there for a long time after he had left, but when I finally got out of bed it was still early. The eastern sky was prettily pink in readiness for sunrise, and the trees stood to attention in the garden. It was going to be a fine, warm day.

I heard Tina go downstairs. She was soon singing in the kitchen to the accompaniment of clattering crockery. Feeling guilty, I showered and put on a shirt and jeans. The mirror was kind to me; the reflection suggesting that I looked a little younger than my thirty-three years.

I thought about my life before I had fallen in love with Greg, when I had been Lucy Halewood, living in an elegant little flat, enjoying an absorbing career and a sprinkling of men friends. When Greg appeared on my horizon, I was already reconciled to the eventual old-maid-with-cats-in-the-country-cottage bit, one day. After I met Greg, everything changed. The predictable had become unpredictable, my pleasant life had turned into wonderful living.

Greg told me he had been married at twenty; too young, he conceded frankly. Tina had been born just before he and his wife, Fran, celebrated their twenty-first birthdays. Three years later, Fran had walked out of his life with a new love in tow. She was a pretty girl, Greg had told me, feckless and light-hearted. After the divorce she had left Tina with him, and Greg reckoned, with due modesty, that he hadn't made such a bad job of bringing up his daughter. As for Fran, she had been fourteen thousand miles away for a long time now, dutifully sending Tina a card each Christmas, complete with pictures of koala bears and kangaroos on the front.

"*Isn't it marvellous that you and Tina get along so well together?*" Somewhere in my mind, a nerve twitched uneasily. Well, he was right, wasn't he? Tina was uncomplicated, with no hang-ups about a mother who had left her when she was a baby, so I was lucky. Our stepmother/stepdaughter relationship seemed good, and I couldn't find a scrap of resentment in Tina. In fact, she treated me beautifully.

I N THE KITCHEN, breakfast was laid; brown pottery, yellow cloth, a big jug of daisies from what Greg called "the untidy corner of the garden".

"So that's why you had full marks for artistic appreciation," I said to Tina.

She grinned at me over her shoulder. Her pointed, puckish face, with its high cheekbones, reminded me of Greg's. They both had a Slavic look, I had once told him — mysterious and interesting. They had the same brown eyes, too, and mouths which were ready to smile. But Greg's hair was brown and curly, while Tina's hung long and straight and shining to her shoulders.

Continued overleaf

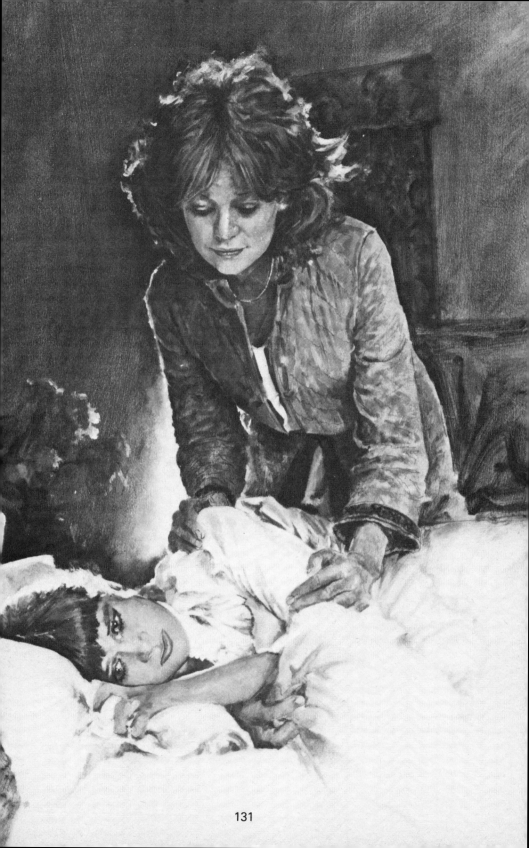

She was also a good cook; Greg's mother had taught her.

I looked at the loaded breakfast plate she put in front of me.

"Tina, what about my figure?" I wailed.

"You're not the sort to get fat," she retorted briskly, pouring coffee for us both. I hadn't the heart to tell her, even after two months of living in the same house, that I'd have settled happily for toast and black coffee.

She flipped bacon and eggs and tomatoes on to her own plate, and said, "Won't it seem quiet without Dad? It's nice that you're here. It means he can go abroad now, sometimes. He couldn't before you came, because of leaving me. I told him to bring me back some of those gorgeous Venetian glass beads. What are you going to do with yourself today?"

She had a solicitous air, as though she was personally responsible for seeing I wasn't bored.

"I'm going to drive into Harstead to choose wallpaper and paint for the spare room," I told her.

"Then I can make a start on it tomorrow."

"We've used it as a junk room for years," she said. "Dad kept saying we should do something about it but, of course, we never did, and we had the other spare room for visitors, anyway. Shall I come to Harstead with you?"

"If you really want to," I said, acutely aware of her grave, polite earnestness.

She hesitated, gave me a long look, and said casually, "Well, actually, I'm going in to have my hair done, and buy a new top to wear tonight."

"Oh, I remember. It's Annie Sand's birthday party, isn't it? Bobbie Clarke is picking you up."

"That's right." She smiled encouragingly. "I'll come in to Harstead with you, we'll both do our shopping then meet for lunch at the Salad Bowl in the Royal Hotel, if that's all right by you?"

"Fine," I agreed.

Tina was used to choosing her own clothes. Anyway, fourteen-year-olds don't take adults with them on a shopping expedition, not if they can help it. So it was illogical to feel that the decisions had been made for me, my morning patted neatly into place by a pair of capable hands. Her attitude was all part of the good, undemanding friendship between us that so delighted Greg.

As I drove us into Harstead, Tina said unexpectedly, "It's great having you around, honestly. And Dad needs someone of his own age."

"Of course," I agreed gravely.

"I'm really glad that my mother went off to Australia before I was old enough to remember her, because now I don't know her, do I? She's a complete stranger, and you can't feel anything for people you don't know."

'All that commonsense and maturity at fourteen,' I marvelled. She was doing well at school, too, getting full marks for a lot of things besides artistic appreciation. I was lucky, I thought.

IN HARSTEAD, we went our separate ways. I chose magnolia paint and a nostalgic wallpaper patterned with cabbage roses. There was a lovely old oak chest in the spare room, crammed with junk. It only needed a good polish and a clear out to make a really attractive feature of my scheme. There was also a chair that would look heavenly re-upholstered in rose velvet, and I knew where I could get hold of a brass bedstead. I had been co-ordinator in Furnishing, Soft Furnishings and Accessories at Brodie's, before I married Greg.

On my way to the Salad Bowl I met Amy Hollis, with whom I'd had a casual friendship for years. She had three teenage daughters and had worked part-time in Brodie's In-Shop Boutique.

"You look blooming," she told me. "I fancy you're putting on a bit of weight. In the old days, they would have blamed that on the contented bliss of the marital state!"

"It's the breakfasts Tina cooks," I told her.

Amy, lean and elegant as a greyhound, looked amused. "Shame on you, working a fourteen-year-old to death! Never mind, all that won't last. Wait until she gets to the difficult stage!"

"You're a cynic," I protested.

"No, dear, I'm the voice of experience. I've survived three teenage daughters, as I often tell Dan. Maureen started being a fiend round about her eleventh birthday, Carla started last year when she was thirteen, and Joanna gave me a break — she was fifteen before all the aggro started."

"What is the aggro like?" I asked curiously.

"It starts off with mother being dim-witted, father not knowing what he's talking about, and everyone over twenty being a crashing bore. Then comes the bit about wanting a lock on the bedroom door, so that privacy and aloneness can be complete. Aloneness means being able to listen to whatever music is 'in' at the moment, or make soulful outpourings into the tape recorder. They have meaningful, in-depth relationships that usually last at least a week, but they don't do the misunderstood bit these days because it's old hat. *We* went through it all, remember? Only our version was less sophisticated."

"I can't imagine Tina. . ." I began.

She smiled gently.

"It will come, dear. When or how, no one knows. Joanna was eighteen yesterday — what a relief! Tina is going to Annie's birthday party tonight, isn't she? So is Carla. I hear that the Sands parents are going out to a hotel for the night, and that Bobbie Clarke is setting up some kind of home-made disco for Annie and friends. Ah well! Carla's father will be there to bring her home at one a.m. and she'll be furious, because I gather the disco is going to be an all-night do. But I told her, in my day it was ten o'clock when you were only fourteen, and if you were lucky, with a bit of pushing, you got an extension to eleven o'clock. Oh, we had a fearful row, with Carla telling me I treat her like a kid and never let her spread her poor little wings! Just the same, she'll be ready when Dan calls."

Amy sounded so matter-of-fact I was shocked. It wouldn't be like that with Tina, I decided, as I went on my way to the Salad Bowl.

TINA WAS WAITING. When I saw her, I stopped dead in my tracks.

She looked at me rather self-consciously, as well she might, I thought, appalled. Her lovely, seal-sleek hair with its fringe and flipped-up ends had been changed into a wild froth of curls and frizzy-looking waves that stuck out around her face. Only the fringe had been spared.

"Well?" she said brightly.

I swallowed the "I-don't-know-what-your-father-will-say" approach and smiled with great determination. "It looks quite different," I told her.

"Of course it does," she retorted, as though I wasn't too bright. "It's meant to be different."

"Did you buy your top?" I enquired, as we sat side by side at the table.

"No, I bought a whole new outfit." She sounded much too casual, I thought uneasily. "You can see it tonight, when I put it on."

She didn't say much on the way home, but she helped me to carry the wallpaper indoors and I unrolled a length to show her.

"Great," she said heartily. "Just the thing the room needs, isn't it?"

I thought her eyes disagreed with her words, but I couldn't be sure. On no account, I reminded myself, must our beautiful friendship be allowed to deteriorate.

"Maybe it's not your kind of paper," I said.

"Oh, that cottagey look is perfect. It goes with the sloping ceiling."

She seemed to be trying hard as she added profoundly, "Anyway, a house has more personality if all the rooms are different."

Upstairs, I set to work. I had already cleared the big cupboard and found a boxful of old toys and books of Tina's. At four o'clock, she brought me a cup of tea in the best china, with a slice of home-made cake on a plate. I sat on the top of the steps and enquired tactfully if she wished to give away the contents of the box?

"Oh, give them to the local Jumble Sale," she cried airily, before she whisked away.

At half-past seven, when I had finished work and was heating coffee in the kitchen, she walked nonchalantly in and stood by the door, looking at me as though to test my reactions.

She was wearing a silky black jumpsuit with thin, glittery shoulder straps that only accentuated her pathetically skinny shoulder-blades. Her black shoes had high heels, and pointed, gold-capped toes. Round her neck she wore a choker of three rows of small pink pearls fastened with a big, brilliant clasp in front. She wore no other jewellery and no make-up except a luminous lipstick that matched the pearls. The effect was bizarre and curiously sad.

I realised suddenly that she had chosen this weekend, when her father was away, to take her first defiant, tottering steps into the adult world. It was good timing. Maybe she thought I'd stand between her and his possible wrath at the kind of debut she was making. If I had been with her throughout her formative years I'd have known how to cope efficiently, the way Amy coped.

"Do you like it?" she demanded.

"Very eye-catching," I said truthfully.

"It cost a bomb. I used all my Christmas and birthday money."

"You look very grown-up," I told her.

She looked pleased. 'Coward,' I told myself wrathfully.

BOBBIE CLARKE called for her. He was a sophisticated nineteen, hard-faced and cool-eyed, and I didn't like him overmuch. I had met him a couple of times before and he had been detached and polite, as though light-years separated us.

Bobbie had his mother's car for the evening. As he and Tina were leaving, I asked the sixty-four-thousand dollar question.

Continued overleaf

133

"What time will you be home, Tina?"

"Oh!" She frowned, glanced uneasily at Bobbie, looked at me and then let her eyes slide away to stare at nothing. "Mm, well, about one. There's no need to wait up, for heaven's sake."

She was gone, with a shrug of her skinny shoulders and an air of having to cope with awkward parents who made her tired and exasperated.

After she had gone, I sat drinking my coffee, feeling that some kind of confrontation was looming up. It was nonsense, of course. Tina, like Carla, was coming home at one a.m. The beautiful friendship wasn't going to get crumpled and frayed around the edges; the nicely balanced relationship wouldn't be damaged for ever. Just the same, I suddenly wished I had met Greg years ago.

The telephone rang at midnight. I thought it was Greg calling from Rome so I flew to answer it. It was Tina, calling from the Sands' house on the other side of town.

"Lucy?" she cried, her voice loud and jerky against a background of frenzied music. "Look, most of them are staying the night, so I said I'd stay, too, instead of breaking up the party. If I don't stay, Bobbie will have to bring me home, you see."

"It's all right," I said swiftly. "I'll fetch you."

"There's no need!" The music was louder; her words seemed staccato and clipped. "We can bed down here. Annie has got loads of sleeping bags and that sort of thing, and we're going out at dawn to cook breakfast in the country."

I thought of Carla's father fetching her, of Bobbie's cool, experienced eyes, of the Sands, uncaring, staying in a hotel. The alarm bells in my head rang and rang. Greg wasn't around, and I had sudden, sobering thoughts about not shelving my responsibilities.

"No," I said firmly. "One o'clock, Tina. I'll fetch you."

"Lucy, you can't! Look, I said, there's sleeping bags and things. This isn't some kind of orgy."

"Maybe not. I'll see you at one." I hung up quickly on her protests, marvelling at the way she managed to make it sound as though I had a head full of very unpleasant thoughts.

T HE SANDS HAD a big house on the edge of the Common: old-fashioned, detached from its neighbours, and enfolded in thick laurels and dense shrubbery. After I had driven through the deserted streets, I came upon it, its every light blazing, music and laughter streaming out into the night. I thought of long-suffering neighbours. Well, once *I* hadn't cared two hoots about those things.

Tina was waiting by the gates, her old jacket pulled tightly across her shoulders against the sharp air. When she saw me, she darted out as though anxious not to be seen, and climbed in beside me, slamming the door resoundingly behind her.

"I feel such a *fool*!" she cried bitterly. "Everyone else is staying."

"Carla Hollis isn't, for a start," I retorted.

"Everyone knows she never has any fun, because her parents think she's still a kid," Tina flung at me.

Then she stared straight ahead, stony-faced, and neither of us spoke again. When we reached home, she jumped out. I garaged the car and, when I went indoors, there was no sign of her.

I went slowly upstairs, pausing to knock uncertainly on her bedroom door. When there was no answer, I turned the handle and went in.

She'd flung off her clothes and got into bed, lying there looking angry and miserable. There was no trace of the breakfast-time Tina. For the first time I marvelled at the speed with which a child crosses the border, passport in hand, ready to enter the new adult world. I wondered if she would ever come back again, however briefly. Amy would know – but then the Amy Hollises of this world knew it all, and I had no experience at all to guide me.

"Look, Tina, I'm sorry," I began.

"*Sorry?*" The cold ferocity of her voice would have stripped the leaves from the trees. "What are you sorry for? Because you dragged me away from a super party, and made me look silly? I was having a fabulous time. No one was planning anything, the way you seem to think. Your generation, Lucy, has got this awful fixed idea that our thoughts run like a tramcar, straight into a terminus marked sex!"

It was a very good line, I thought. Not original, though. I had seen it in a magazine, weeks ago.

I tried to retrieve the situation, saying idiotically, "Well, I suppose if you danced all night, you'd be too tired. I don't know, though, and I don't intend to put it to the test."

She stared at me as though I was mad. The hostility of the young is very potent.

"How stupid can you get?" she said witheringly.

All my good resolutions about how to handle a difficult teenage daughter successfully flew out of the window into the starry night.

"Don't you dare speak to me like that!" I shouted angrily. "You know very well that your father would have brought you home if he had been here, but you didn't want to know what he would have said about your planning to stay all night at the Sands'! Everything that ever happened to anyone in this world began somewhere, but, so far as I'm concerned, your great experience of life isn't going to begin here and now! I don't give a fig if you think fourteen is old enough to start *living* — *I* don't. Only the people who don't care about you let you do as you please, no matter what it is you want to do. I'm your stepmother, remember that. I'm not just a visitor here."

I FELT SUDDENLY that I cared very much what happened to her. It hadn't anything to do with friendship, but it was a rather good feeling. Tina stared at me, open-mouthed. At least I had her attention, I reflected.

"A visitor?" she cried, outraged.

"Yes. I don't need to be entertained, I don't like cooked breakfasts, I don't want it all polite and tidy with neither of us being truthful."

"Oh, that's just great!" Her fury had an outlet at last. "I've been trying to do everything I can to please you, and make you feel comfortable here! Well, I won't get you any more breakfasts, and I think your taste in wallpaper is the end — all those yukky flowers, ugh! — *and* you want to throw all my stuff out for the Jumble Sale. That's all the thanks I get for what I've done for you!"

I fought a wild desire to laugh. Every feature and word delineated depths of her wounded dignity, her pain at the ingratitude of an unworthy stepmother.

Laughter would have been unforgivable. I fled to my room and turned my face into the pillow. In the end the laughter won over the tears. The tears were for Tina, as hurt as only a fourteen-year-old could be. If I had felt like a visitor, it was as much my fault as hers. I had been quite content to come down on the side of friendship, staying uninvolved and detached.

There was no sign of her at breakfast. I laid the table, ate brown toast and drank three cups of black coffee. I carried a tray up to her room and left it beside the bed. The hump beneath the bedclothes acknowledged my presence with only a grunt.

I spent the morning battling with the spare room and my own turned-about feelings. I heard Tina get up just before lunchtime. When the telephone rang, she hurried to answer it. Shamelessly, I opened the door a fraction and listened.

"Oh, did you? I thought it was a pretty grotty do, really. I was bored silly, that's why I asked Lucy to fetch me. Anyway, I couldn't leave her alone in the house all night, not with my father away. Anyway, she's nervous about being on her own. . . Well, she is my stepmother, after all."

I went back to work. I thought about Tina's wonderful gift for face-saving, and gave her top marks for that, too. Lies could be night-black or pale grey, but some were tinted a delicate shade of magnolia, just like the paint in its can, my favourite shade. I had a marvellous stepdaughter.

Some time later she came upstairs, opened the door loudly, and stared over my head.

"I don't know what you'd like for lunch," she said stiffly. "I'm only having a sandwich."

"That'll do for me, too." I concentrated hard on what I was doing. "There's fruit and cheese downstairs, as well. I'll cook for us tonight; maybe a curry. I do them quite well. Do you like curry?"

"Yes," she admitted tonelessly. "I'll do sandwiches, then."

"Thanks," I said, smiling at her.

By the door she bent and unrolled some of the paper, studying it critically and with a professional air.

"It might not look so bad when it's on the wall," she told me.

"You might even get to like it, in time," I said rashly. "I've put your stuff back in the cupboard. There's plenty of room there. No need to give it away. You should have told me how you felt."

Something that might have passed for the ghost of a smile quivered about her lips as she went away to prepare the lunch. I loved her very much, and I was going to have to learn not to show it for a while.

'Okay, Amy, I'm learning,' I thought. 'I can learn fast.' Already I knew about the way they keep crossing the frontiers, back and forth, still clinging grimly to their passports. If you love, you care; when you care, you fight; when you fight, you get hurt — which is what life is all about.

I felt very old and wise. It probably wouldn't last. I might even lose the next round. But I thought happily of telling Greg when he came home: 'Darling, Tina and I have a marvellous relationship. We've begun to argue like mad, and she's going to start being awkward and difficult, and it's all wonderful! Because I'm her stepmother, I'm not a visitor. Dearest Greg, you won't know what I'm talking about, and it doesn't matter a bit.'

THE END

© *Audrie Manley-Tucker, 1982*

THE CONDITION of your hair makes an enormous difference to the way you look, and I think you'll agree, to the way you *feel*. If your hair looks happy, you feel reasonably cheerful about your looks: conversely, if your hair sags and sighs for help, your confidence plummets.

So why not make a real effort, starting *now*, to get your hair into really good shape! Here are some points to bear in mind.

● Get the best cut you can afford. If you're new to an area and don't know who cuts well, don't be afraid to ask people whose hair looks good.

Cut out photographs of styles you like, to take to your hairdresser. If a style is unsuited to your particular type of hair, or to the shape of your face, a good hairdresser will tell you— but any guidance you can give him or her as to what you have in mind will be all to the good.

● Protect your hair both in cold and scorching hot weather with a scarf or hat —both these extremes can prove very drying for hair.

● Don't overclean your hair. If you wash it more often than twice a week, use only one application of a mild shampoo and then use a conditioner.

And *don't* rub and scrub at your hair: this is the mistake made most often by the very greasy-haired who think that by so doing they'll get their hair super-clean and get it to stay fresh-looking longer. All they do, in fact, is to over-stimulate the oil glands into producing yet more oil. So, go gently with your hair and never wash it until it's 'squeaky clean'. If it squeaks, it's in protest that you're overdoing things!

● Start eating for the sake of your hair. Healthy hair demands a good balanced protein-rich, iron-rich diet, supplemented with extra B vitamins. In everyday language, this means fish, cheese, meat (especially liver), eggs, fresh milk, butter or margarine, fresh and dried fruit, salads, cabbage, spinach, watercress, onions, potatoes, cauliflower, wholemeal bread.

● Give your hair a complete rest for as long as you can from all treatments such as bleaches, dyes, perms. Stop using rollers, whether heated or not. Have your hair cut into a manageable style so that you can, for a time, do without curling aids of any kind. You'll soon see an improvement in the overall condition.

● Don't use shampoos with built-in conditioners, and go very lightly on setting lotions and hairsprays. They all tend to build up in your hair to make it feel gummy and lank. If you do get this sort of build-up, try using a medicated shampoo just once to clear your hair, then go back to your usual shampoo.

● Don't always automatically buy exactly the same shampoo time after time; the condition of one's hair varies, so respond to its changing needs.

● Brush your hair, but do so in moderation, and always go gently. Lower your head down close to your knees, and brush your hair from the nape of the neck down to the very ends of your hair. By brushing in this way, you gently free your hair of dust and encourage natural oils to flow down the entire length of the hair, without stimulating the oil glands in your scalp into overproduction.

● If your hair is very dry, give it and your scalp an oil treatment occasionally before you shampoo. Apply olive oil or almond oil directly on to the scalp by making partings and rubbing in the oil with your fingers. Massage your scalp very gently with the tips of

your fingers, and comb the oil down to the ends of your hair. Wring out a towel in hot water and wrap it round your head; replace it with another hot towel before it's had a chance to cool down. Shampoo as usual.

● Have you got dandruff? Any of a whole variety of factors could be to blame, if you have. It be be the products you've been using on your hair—too harsh, alkaline shampoos, for instance, heavy use of hairspray, or hard water. It could be that your skin is dry generally and that your dry, flaky scalp would benefit from the inclusion

in your diet of a little more fat and more fruit and vegetables, plus the use of a mild shampoo.

It could also be a stress-related problem, in which case you should pay attention to your general health, and try to get more rest and fresh air every day. Or it could simply mean that you're not rinsing your hair properly after shampoos. Try this:

(1) Use any good anti-dandruff shampoo now and then to help clear your scalp (don't use these constantly, as they'll dry out your hair).

(2) Watch your diet; eat lots of fresh green salads, fresh fruit and vegetables; drink lots of mineral water.

(3) Massage your scalp gently with your (clean) fingertips every evening, and before shampooing.

(4) Avoid the use of heavy hairsprays and setting lotions and dry your hair naturally, or on the lowest setting of your hair-dryer.

(5) Be scrupulously careful about keeping hairbrushes and combs clean, and try to keep your hands away from your scalp during the day.

(6) If all else fails and you still have severe persistent dandruff, you would be wise to consult your doctor.

Autumn Planting- Spring Flowering

Autumn is the time to plant bulbs for a spring display, says JOY SIMMONS — daffodils, tulips and crocuses plus some intriguing lesser-known beauties

No garden is complete without at least a few spring-flowering bulbs, and the main planting season for these is from September to November. *Trumpet daffodils* in particular, together with the *large* and *small-cupped narcissi,* seem to herald spring, the bright yellow and orange colourings combining well with the fresh green of new foliage.

You can grow them in tubs on a patio, in drifts around trees, on their own in small beds, or in groups in an herbaceous border. *Miniature narcissi* are lovely for planting in a rockery or window box, to delight us from February to May according to variety.

All narcissi (and this includes daffodils) enjoy sun or partial shade and fertile, well-drained soil. The dwarf varieties should be planted three times the depth of the bulbs, 2-3 in. apart; ordinary varieties 6 in. deep and 6 in. apart.

Hyacinths, those beauties in a range of lovely colours, look magnificent massed in formal beds but they are also splendid for window boxes or tubs on the patio, where their fragrance can be enjoyed to the full. Plant them 6 in. deep and 4-6 in. apart.

Crocuses are very popular, too. Great favourites of mine are the charming little *Golden Bunch (c.ancyrensis),* which produce as many as 15 to 20 flowers to a bulb, and the large-flowered *Pickwick,* a pearly-grey, striped lilac beauty.

Plant crocuses in sun or semi-shade, 2-3 in. deep and the same distance apart, in a rockery or as an edging to a border. Or you can naturalise them in short grass under deciduous trees; that is to say, scatter them haphazardly and plant them where they fall, to form an irregular drift of colour.

Other bulbs good for naturalising are the much-loved *bluebell* (they come in pink and white as well as blue!); *chionodoxa (Glory of the Snow),* the first "true blue" flower of the year; double and single *snowdrops;* golden *winter aconite (eranthis)* with large buttercup-like flowers in early January, and sky-blue *scilla bifolia.*

Bluebells are essentially flowers for a woodland or semi-wild border. Scillas, winter aconite and snowdrops are also attractive in a semi-wild border or rockery. Chionodoxa thrive in a sunny rock garden or in large groups at the front of a border.

Less well known, perhaps, are the *dog's tooth violet (erythronium denscanis)* with tapering pink petals and marbled foliage and the pretty little hardy *cyclamen coum album* (white) and the less expensive variety *c. ibericum* (crimson). The dog's tooth violet does best planted 6 in. deep in rich, free-draining soil, in a shady position. Hardy cyclamen enjoy much the same type of conditions; the corms should be planted 1-2 in. deep.

Anemone blanda, with pink, blue and white daisy flowers, is happy in sun or part shade, planted 2 in. deep in well-drained soil. It is suitable for planting in groups in a rock garden or under trees, where it delights us with its unassuming flowers from February to April.

Another attractive bulb flower is the *grape hyacinth (muscari)* with its minute sweetly scented bells on spikes 6-7 in. high. The brilliant blue variety is best known but the white *m. botryoides album (Pearls of Spain)* is equally

SPRING-FLOWERING BULBS — SEE HOW THEY GROW

26" height
24"
20"
18"
12"
10"
8"
6"
3"
2"
4"
6"
depth

| Minor bulbs | Hyacinths | | Tulips | |
| | Daffodils | early | medium | late |

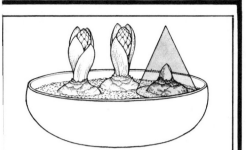

If one bulb in a bowl hangs back, cover it with a paper "dunce's cap" to speed growth.

lovely. All varieties are easily grown. Plant them in clumps about 4 in. deep and 4 in. apart, in sandy loam, in a sunny border or rockery. Once established, they can be left to multiply.

Most spectacular of all are *tulips*, best planted from October to mid-December. If you like something rather different in your rockery, grow some of the species tulips — the multi-flowered *tulipa praestans* with bright orange-red blooms or *t. tarda* with star-shaped flowers tinged green with yellow and white interior. The rosy-lilac, yellow-based *t. saxatilis* is another gem.

A drift of daffodils — so much beauty for so little trouble.

Some of the *parrot* and *fringed tulips* need to be seen to be believed! Outstanding are *Blue Heron*, violet-purple with crystal-white fringed edging; the soft rose variety *Fantasy* with featherings and stripes of apple-green, and *Gay Presto*, a white, feathered and flamed in red.

For more formal planting you cannot beat the *early double tulips* (12 in. high) and the *Darwins* (20-26 in.) in a range of colouring. The *Mendel* and *Triumph Tulips* are also excellent bedders.

Tulips like a sunny position and ordinary light soil enriched with compost. Plant them 4-6 in. deep and 6 in. apart. Normally, the bulbs are lifted immediately the flowers fade, as they tend to deteriorate if left in the ground. If you decide not to lift the bulbs, however, fallen petals should be removed and burnt to prevent spread of disease. *Species tulips* may be left undisturbed from year to year.

BOWLS OF BEAUTY

Bulbs for indoor decoration can be grown in good potting soil, in bulb fibre or in some cases in pebbles and water.

Usually bulb fibre is the most convenient for indoor culture. Clean and light to handle, it can be used in ornamental containers without drainage holes, whereas you really need drainage holes in containers filled with soil.

Hyacinths, tulips and narcissi do best in a container around 4 in. deep. Smaller bulbs — crocuses, chionodoxas, snowdrops and scillas — will grow happily in a slightly shallower container or in special crocus pots with holes in the side for planting.

You should be able to buy sufficient bulb fibre to fill four or five medium-sized bowls for a pound or so. Soak it in a bucket of water and squeeze out the surplus moisture before use.

If you prefer to use soil, John Innes Potting Compost No. 2 or Levington Potting Compost would be a good choice. With these composts you should have containers with drainage holes, and place some pieces of broken crock over the holes before filling up with soil.

Start by part-filling the container with damp fibre or compost, pressing it firmly into position. You can judge the depth of soil or fibre by the size of the bulbs; that is, when planted the tips of the bulbs should be just above the rim of the container. Next, place the bulbs on the prepared "bed", 1 to 2 in. apart, not touching the sides of the container, and pack them round with more growing material until only their tips remain showing.

Now comes the most important part. All the bulbs mentioned *must* have a cool, dark start. "Plunging" the bowls outdoors at the foot of a north wall, by covering them with 4-6 in. of horticultural peat, is ideal. Failing this, a cool, dark cellar, shed or frame will do, providing the rooting temperature is around 5 to 7°C (40 to 45°F). If light is a problem, wrap the bowls in newspaper or black polythene.

How long should they remain in these conditions? Roughly eight to ten weeks, the longer period sometimes being necessary for tulips and narcissi. In about eight weeks, hyacinths should be ready for moving indoors to a dark, warm place — temperature 18 to 21°C (65 to 70°F) — until the flower buds show well out of the neck of the bulbs, when they can stand in the light.

Tulips need to remain in the plunge until they have made at least 3 to 4 in. of top growth. They can then be brought inside and placed in the dark in a temperature of 18°C (65°F) for another ten days.

Warning: Never allow the compost to dry out or the bulb roots will suffer. On the other hand, don't overwater or the roots will rot! Once the bulbs have been moved into the light, turn the bowl occasionally to ensure even growth.

CHARLIE

by Sarah Woodhouse

Jenny had made the decision and that was that. Whatever
the dictates of her aching heart, whatever the children or Jonathan said,
she had decided, positivel and irrevocably, to sell Charlie

"**A** horse?" exclaimed Mr. Jenkins, looking completely astonished.

"A horse," Jenny repeated, watching his grey head bobbing into a dark corner of little village shop. "You see, I'd much prefer to sell him locally. I'd like to know wl he was going, what sort of home he'd have."

Mr. Jenkins looked decidedly unsympathetic. But then, thought Jenny miserably, he had no i how she was really feeling. He saw only a slight, brown-haired young woman, perfectly compo and calm, dark eyes very serious, small hands thrust deep into the pockets of her coat. Broken he were invisible, of course, she reflected, with a sad little smile.

There was a long pause while Mr. Jenkins dipped up and down mysteriously between the sw biscuits and the boot laces, and then he said gruffly, "Well, we've never had a horse before, bu suppose it won't do any harm. If you want to write the advertisement now, I'll put it in the window.

Jenny wrote in bold capitals on the card he handed her. She had made the decision and that w that. Whatever the dictates of her aching heart, whatever the children or Jonathan said, she h decided, positively and irrevocably, to sell Charlie.

Jonathan had tried to talk her out of it again only that morning, propped in the kitchen doorwa watching her trying to cram cornflakes down her ten-year-old brother then see her reluctant sister o on the school bus. But eight o'clock on a frosty winter morning was not the best time to discu anything sensibly, Jenny had found from bitter experience, least of all what she was going to do abou

Continued overlea

Charlie. So far this morning she had coped with burnt bacon and eggs, disgruntled hens, a flood in the bathroom, and the retyping of a chaotic manuscript whose author was already two weeks over his deadline. Jonathan offering brotherly advice, while surveying the chaos serenely from the doorstep, was just too much.

"I'll make a decision in my own good time," Jenny had said furiously, pushing Midge's bulging schoolbag into her arms and shooing her out into the cold, dark morning.

"You've been saying that for months," Jon objected quietly.

"I can't think what you're doing here so early," Jenny remarked rather ungraciously, pushing a stray wisp of hair from her hot forehead. "I've got enough to cope with in the mornings without visitors as well."

Jonathan smiled his slow, lazy smile, not in the least offended.

"I thought I'd drop in after milking, give Adam this." He pulled a book from the pocket of his shabby old jacket and put it on the table.

"Is it the one about butterflies? Oh, thanks, Jon!" Adam cried, diving for it impulsively.

"Adam, look out!" Jenny wailed, catching his mug of tea as it was about to topple over, and hunting feverishly for a cloth to mop up the spillage.

Glancing up, she saw that Jonathan was looking at her with fond amusement as if she was an exasperating younger sister. Well, that was probably how he thought of her, she suspected. After all, they had known each other all their lives. Jonathan was a farmer and owned the farm next door. He had only to walk across two fields to reach the cottage. Sometimes, recently, Jenny confessed ruefully to herself, she had wished he lived further away.

"Don't do anything silly about Charlie," he was saying now. "It's what *you* want that matters, Jenny. He's your horse. It's *your* decision."

"And you're doing your best to make it for me!" she had snapped. Then, feeling ashamed, she had offered to cook him breakfast as a peace-offering. But Jonathan had shaken his head, saying that his housekeeper, Mrs. Flower, would have prepared something for him and that he must get back. Adam, bundling his school things together, had given Jenny a quick peck on the cheek and had run out after him, the butterfly book under his arm.

A LONE AT LAST, Jenny surveyed the mess weekday breakfast-times always seemed to leave behind and quite suddenly felt as if she could sit down at the kitchen table and put her head in her

---

Put one small boy in a bath, add water, and what have you got?
Instant trouble.

Anon

---

arms and cry.

From outside had come a plaintive bleat and then another. The goat! She *couldn't* have forgotten to milk the goat! She rushed for Wellingtons and a coat, remembering at the same time the shopping she had to do, and the dress she had said she would alter for Midge, and that manuscript she must post back to its author.

She cycled into the village later in the morning — and wrote the advertisement about Charlie for Mr. Jenkins' window.

As she stepped out of the shop she met Mrs. Peasgood who, bright little eyes twinkling with curiosity, stopped to ask her if she was all right.

"You're doing too much, dear," she said in her 'I know what's best for everybody' voice, "running the house and seeing to the kiddies and all."

After that Jenny pedalled home in a cloud of gloom, feeling more tired and dispirited than ever.

Perhaps she *was* doing too much, she thought. But then, there was always so much to do. Since their parents had been killed in a car crash two years before, she hadn't had a moment to herself — or so it seemed.

In the beginning, it had been a question of keeping the family together, of proving she could support and care for Midge and Adam, could shoulder the responsibilities, pay the bills. She had been just twenty-two when the accident happened and had had to contend with a bevy of kind-hearted relations, well-meaning friends, and anxious bureaucrats. Even now, life didn't seem much easier. She was always so busy: clacking away at her old machine, typing manuscripts and correspondence for people who couldn't do their own, feeding the hens, milking the goat, hoeing the vegetables, struggling with Midge's algebra.

And that was why Charlie was a problem. Charlie was a luxury they could ill afford.

C HARLIE WAS two years old, conker brown, gangling, invariably covered with mud. He had been born just after the accident and his mother, Jenny's lovely old mare, had died shortly after his birth. It had seemed a cruel twist of fate. For a day or two, Jenny wondered whether she would be able to cope. But then, brushing aside all offers of help, she had begun the long struggle to rear Charlie on the bottle, making up milk substitute, feeding him every two hours, willing him to live and grow. Looking after him had dulled her grief, given her a new purpose. When, six months later, Robert had ended their engagement, it was only to Charlie she had shown the extent of her misery, not wanting anyone — least of all the children — to see her crying.

But Charlie needed time and money. And there didn't seem to be either any more.

In the week after Jenny had put her advertisement in Mr. Jenkins' window, she had three phone calls. She told all the callers firmly that Charlie was sold.

"You're just being silly," Midge told her scathingly at Sunday lunch.

"I can't bear to think of him ending up with people who might neglect him through ignorance," Jenny protested.

"Well, *you* won't know anything about it," was Midge's comforting reply.

Jenny sighed unhappily and thought that Midge was probably right. She was being ridiculously sentimental. She glanced at Midge's oval face, framed in soft fair hair. She was thirteen now and promised to be pretty, perhaps more than pretty. 'She's not like me at all,' Jenny thought with a wry

---

One of the best ways of persuading others is with your ears —
by listening to them.

Dean Rusk

---

smile. 'She's bright and lively and never, ever sentimental! We're about as different as sisters can be.'

"You've got to sell him," Midge was saying. "If he's too much trouble now, what's he going to be like next year when he ought to be broken in and everything? You won't have time, will you?"

"I suppose I won't," Jenny replied quietly, and got up to make some coffee.

Jonathan, squealing up to the back door in his disreputable old Land-Rover then leaving muddy bootmarks all over Jenny's clean kitchen, was equally hard-headed — not to say hard-hearted.

"I told you it had to be your decision," he told her bluntly, sitting down with her for a cup of coffee after the children had rushed outside to race each other across Charlie's meadow. "It mustn't be Midge's, or the bank manager's. You love that horse. If you sell him, you'll regret it, Jenny."

Jenny said nothing but sipped carefully at her scalding coffee. She knew everything Jon said was true and she longed to tell him so, but somehow she didn't feel she could explain, or perhaps she was too tired to try. Midge and Adam — and the bank manager — would have to come first from now on. However much she hated parting from Charlie, it was definitely and unquestionably the sensible thing to do. Until Midge and Adam grew up and became independent, she would always have to do the sensible thing. Their well-being came before Charlie, before her own hopes and needs and wants.

"Jenny, are you listening?" Jon was leaning forward, looking concerned, his blue eyes searching her face. "You look worn out. You ought to have a holiday."

"So Mrs. Peasgood told me this morning, for the twentieth time," Jenny said, her soft mouth curving gently at the memory. "She said I looked as if *I* needed some mothering."

J ON PUT a large, warm hand over hers. "And so you do. You really ought to take a break now and then. You've plenty of relations who'd love to look after Midge and Adam for a while. Come on, Jenny, you've proved you can take care of them. You've done a splendid job. Why not relax, get out and about, meet people?"

"You think I'm a hermit?"

"No, but a girl your age ought to . . . Well, there must be scores of young men waiting to take you out."

Jenny removed her hand from under his and stared down into the dregs of her coffee.

"There's no one — and well you know it, Jon Rowlands," she said with a grin.

Jon gave an answering smile but looked thoughtful. Often in the past it had been such a comfort to know that he was there, to give her sound advice, to cheer her up, to help her clear a blocked gutter or mend a broken fence. But now? 'I can't go on relying on Jon,' she thought suddenly. 'I must learn to manage completely by myself.'

They had always been good friends, having grown up together. Jonathan, four years older than Jenny, had left for agricultural college some time before she had gone up to art school in London.

Jenny had been in two minds about going to London, but city life seemed to offer exciting possibilities to an eighteen-year-old, and she had truly loved her art studies. She had left Thornbury full of optimism, determined to enjoy herself — and so she had.

Continued overleaf

When she was twenty, she had met an economics student called Robert Finch, and after that art had taken a back seat. They were engaged when she was twenty-one and Jenny had brought him home shyly to the safe, kind world of Thornbury in the heart of rolling farmland. Her parents had expressed guarded approval, afraid he might not be the right man for their quiet elder daughter. He had been dark, handsome, a little wild, impossibly charming. Jenny, who had never been in love before, was very, very much in love with him.

The pile-up on the motorway on that terrible foggy night changed everything. Adam had been only eight, and Midge eleven. Robert, who drove Jenny home the day after it happened, was the first to suggest she would be mad to try to keep the family together. He had pointed out how difficult and expensive it would be for them to live in London, how coping with the demands of two growing children would distract her from pursuing her own career in art. When Jenny, dazed with grief, had told him that she had no intention of letting Midge and Adam go to relatives, or of taking them to London, and that she would have to rethink her own position, he had called her a fool and had returned to London in a frosty and unforgiving mood.

He had stayed in London, telephoning infrequently, while Jenny had installed herself in the cottage at Thornbury and had begun the first of several battles to keep the family intact. Three months later Robert ended their engagement; his terse letter had been cruelly to the point. He had no intention, he said, of finding himself responsible for Midge and Adam.

Jenny had chucked his ring into a drawer, and burnt his letter, and had cried a great deal into Charlie's bottle-brush of a mane.

T HAT WAS ALL in the past, she thought now, as Jon helped her clear the lunch dishes, then walked with her across the little orchard to Charlie's meadow.

"About Charlie," Jenny said hesitantly as they reached the gate, "I wondered if you knew anyone who might give him a home?"

It was a gloomy, chilly January day. Their breath curled into the cold air. Jon, as usual, was dressed in his old tweed jacket. Jenny glanced up at him suddenly and it was as if she was seeing him for the first time: he was tall and powerfully built, with thick fair hair. He was only twenty-seven, but he looked older. His father had died several years ago and the farm, Jenny knew, had been a constant worry. He was doing well now but it had been a long struggle.

Charlie came snorting to the fence, leggy and unbrushed, pushing a soft nose into Jenny's hands.

"You know what I think about Charlie," Jon said softly. "Charlie's yours. Charlie's special. That's what I meant when I said it had to be your decision — not Midge's, not anyone else's."

"I haven't time to do him justice," she said reasonably. "It would be selfish to keep him."

"Make time," Jonathan replied bluntly. "Tell you what, get out your sketch book and draw him. You haven't touched your paints for months."

'Since the accident,' Jenny thought bleakly, 'or since Robert, or since I started typing every spare moment I had.'

"I've forgotten how," she confessed lamely.

"You can't have. You spent three years being taught by experts. I hate to see you wasting your talent like this."

She twisted her fingers into Charlie's mane, and because he was Charlie he just stood there patiently. Then Jon's strong brown hand closed over hers and he said: "Look, I'll ask around. There must be someone who'd give Charlie a good home, somewhere where you could visit him."

For a moment, Jenny left her hand in his. He was such a comfortable person, calm and reassuring. They had always been such good friends, and no one, not even old Mrs. Peasgood, had ever read anything romantic into their relationship.

Jenny took her hand away from his rather suddenly. Strange how clearly she suddenly remembered a harvest dance, years before, and Jon's first shy kiss.

"Come back inside," Jon said abruptly, taking her arm. "You look cold."

On the following day, Adam answered the phone to a woman who sounded quite suitable for the position as Charlie's new owner, and Jenny, having wrenched the receiver from her gabbling brother, made an appointment for her to call later in the week.

Adam promptly sat down by the phone and brushed crossly at the tears in his eyes.

"I don't know why you have to sell him. We all love him. And Jon says . . . "

"Midge doesn't care for him much," Jenny reminded him, "and I'd rather not know what Jon says. He's said quite enough already."

Of course, unknown to Jenny, Providence was about to take a hand. That same afternoon, as she staggered down to the stable with a bucket of water — the stable tap having frozen solid again — she slipped and fell. She lay on the ground and moaned theatrically but as usual nobody came so she had to grit her teeth and hop back to the cottage where Midge, just in from school, was waiting for her tea.

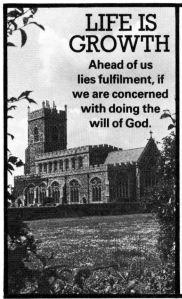

LIFE IS GROWTH

Ahead of us lies fulfilment, if we are concerned with doing the will of God.

HOW MUCH MORE interesting is a "lively" child than a rather phlegmatic and stolid one! And there is this same quality of "liveliness" in the teaching of Christ, which is part of its special appeal.

He made religion attractive, not only by stressing the need to be joyful and to be thankful for God's blessings, but also by the manner in which He presented it as the motive-power of our true development. The way to enjoy life and to preserve one's mental health and vigour is always to be looking forward.

Jesus never thought of human life as static, and always regarded religion as something dynamic. He sought to recreate human personality by opening a window on to the splendour which awaits the children of God. He gave people a vision of the joy that is waiting round the next corner. Ahead of us, if we are concerned with doing the will of God, is fulfilment.

As John the Baptist prepared a way in the wilderness for Christ, so Christ himself prepares the way into the future and eternity. We "press towards the mark," taking with us into the next stage what is good, certain that, as we have now the "first instalment" of God's promises, one day we shall see their full reality.

Jenny persuaded her to begin cutting bread and butter while she sat down for a moment and tried to get her boot off. As soon as she stood up again she nearly passed out, and Midge, throwing down the bread knife dramatically, rushed off in a panic to ring Dr. Cartwright.

Dr. Cartwright was reassuring, saying that it was just a very bad sprain and that all it needed was rest. He looked Jenny in the eye and said firmly that it wasn't only her ankle that needed rest, by the look of things. She had been overdoing it, trying to do four jobs at once. As a parting shot he suggested she take a holiday as far away from the children and Thornbury as it was possible to go. He laughed at her look of surprise and disbelief and told her roundly it would be the best thing for her. After he had gone Jenny went straight to bed, supported by a gleeful Adam and a grumpy Midge. She felt rather light-headed, but that was probably due more to the shock and pain than the thimbleful of brandy Midge had made her drink. Later, seeing her light still on, Adam came in to read her a story, the way she had read him a story every night for years. He had chosen something about pirates, one or more of whom had wooden legs. Very appropriate, Jenny thought with a smile, sliding into sleep.

The morning brought chaos and more chaos. Her leg was worse, having stiffened up and begun to turn blue. Midge brought her up super-crisp bacon and bread and butter, complaining that the toaster had broken and that Adam had given his boiled egg to the cat.

When Jonathan dropped in about ten o'clock, he found Jenny hobbling about the kitchen.

"You look terrible," he said. "You should be in bed. That ankle's twice as big as the other one."

"I had to get up," she wailed, clutching at the table for support.

Jonathan scowled, and, taking hold of her shoulders, made her sit down. "Why didn't you keep Midge home from school for a day?"

She subsided limply on to a chair. She felt exhausted suddenly, and absurdly shaky. Jonathan looked formidable and very, very angry.

"What did Dr. Cartwright say?"

"That I needed a holiday."

"So I keep telling you. Stay there until I get back. I'm going to see to the animals."

When he came in at last, boots caked in mud, streaks of wet and smears of floury bran down his jacket, hair on end, he said: "Charlie kept looking to see where you were."

"There's someone coming to see him tomorrow," Jenny said in a queer voice. "She sounded very nice."

"You'd better ring up and put her off then," Jon replied, shovelling coffee into two mugs. "You're in no state to parade horses for prospective purchasers."

"One horse," Jenny corrected miserably, "and one Very Suitable Lady."

Jon made no answer to this, and as soon as they had finished the coffee he ordered Jenny to bed, saying he was going to send Mrs. Flower to take over at the cottage for a day or two while Jenny was out of action.

"I'm sure we can manage," she told him frostily, as they reached the foot of the stairs.

Continued overleaf

145

"Well I'm not. You need a complete break — and you're going to get it."

Before she could protest, he had swung her into his arms and was carrying her upstairs, stooping to avoid the low beam on the landing.

"Jon, I can't sit in bed all day. There's so much to do," Jenny cried as he deposited her in her bedroom chair.

"Just don't do it. If I find you downstairs again, I'll take you and the children back to the farm and keep you there. Mrs. F. would make a good gaoler."

She certainly would, Jenny conceded gloomily by eight o'clock that night. Mrs. F. had moved in within an hour of Jon's leaving the cottage, and she had everything well under her thumb by the time Midge and Adam burst in from school — including Jenny. She brought her up a very nice supper on a tray, fixed her with a basilisk stare, and said that Mr. Jonathan had left instructions and nothing on earth would make her disobey them.

"You can beg on bended knees," she said cheerfully, "but I won't let you downstairs. Mr. Jonathan says you've been overdoing it and you need a rest."

After she had bustled out to organize the children's bedtime, Jenny pulled herself out of bed and struggled to the mirror. Perhaps she *had* been working too hard, or worrying too much about Charlie. There were shadows under her eyes and her hair looked lank and tired. Brown eyes, mid-brown hair, nothing special. Jenny sighed and hopped back into bed.

When Mrs. Flower came in again with a late-night cup of cocoa and asked suspiciously if Jenny had been crying she denied it, but not very convincingly.

"What you need is a man about the place. I told Mr. Jonathan so, and Mr. Jonathan said you were determined to live like a nun and were getting to the stage where you wouldn't recognise a man when you saw one!"

Jenny blushed a little. How dare Jon discuss her like that! She raised furious eyes to Mrs. Flower's round and amiable face with its shrewd little black eyes and firm, smiling mouth.

"It's none of his business," was the only rather half-hearted protest she managed.

Mrs. Flower considered her for a long moment and then shook her head sadly, turning to sweep out of the door in a flurry of candlewick dressing-gown.

"Perhaps you should ask yourself *why* he worries so," was her parting shot.

I N THE MORNING, after a restless and unhappy night, Jenny remembered Charlie.

"That woman's coming to see him this afternoon," she told an indifferent Midge, who had come up to say goodbye before leaving to catch the school bus. "I forgot to ring her. Have you time, Midge love?"

But Midge had already made her escape, clattering down the stairs and yelling a cheeky farewell to Mrs. Flower in the kitchen.

When Adam came in to collect Jenny's breakfast tray, he informed her that Mrs. Flower had already left for her weekly battle with Mr. Jenkins, armed with a shopping list two yards long. Jenny sighed and pulled back the bedclothes to inspect her ankle; it had returned to its normal size but was a horrifying dark blue in colour.

The sound of a car hooting urgently outside made Adam give her a hasty kiss and gallop down the stairs. Jenny could hear him running at top speed down the long drive to the gate where his lift to school was waiting. It was no good, she thought, she would just have to telephone herself.

It took far longer than she had expected to reach the hall. The only time she put her injured foot on the floor she cried out with pain. With slightly shaking fingers she dialled the number of the Very Suitable Lady and, of course, there was no reply. She rang and rang and then, beginning to panic, made for the kitchen. There she shrugged an anorak over her nightdress, pulled Adam's bush hat down over her eyes, rammed her good foot into a Wellington boot, and using a broom as a crutch, swung herself out of the back door.

The day was cold and wet. The rain fell heavily out of a leaden sky. She managed to reach the stable, peg-legging through the puddles, and Charlie pushed up to her, large, warm and inquisitive. Jenny grasped at his mane to keep herself upright and missed, sliding into an undignified heap in the straw at his feet.

The pain in her ankle made her double up for a moment, biting her lip. Charlie nosed at her curiously and did not seem to mind when she tried to use his leg to hoist herself upright again. Then, from outside, came the noise of a car. Charlie moved to investigate, and Jenny fell back clumsily with a little cry. At least it couldn't be Jonathan, she thought, because Mrs. Flower had told her that he had gone to Stow-on-the-Wold.

"Polishing his hooves?" a sarcastic voice enquired, as Jonathan's familiar figure loomed at the half-door.

"I can't get up," she gasped.

Jon said nothing but came in at once, pushing Charlie out of the way and bending to lift her. For a second she leaned helplessly against the comfortable old tweed jacket that smelled of cattle and tobacco. Briefly, dizzily, she thought he was going to kiss her. But he straightened abruptly, his face grim, and carried her out into the rain.

I N THE KITCHEN, he lowered her roughly on to a chair and lifted the damp bush hat so that he could look deeply into her eyes.

"Don't tell me Mrs. F. has driven you to sleep in the stable?"

"It's that woman," Jenny wailed. "I can't get in touch to put her off. She's coming to see Charlie this afternoon and he looks so awful."

"I do wish you'd stop being so idiotic! Midge could have brushed him before school, couldn't she? It wouldn't hurt her to help you a bit more. And you know perfectly well that you could have asked me."

"There wasn't time!" Jenny shouted. She really shouted, and as soon as she had, she felt terrible and her eyes filled with tears. She shut them quickly in case any spilled over and Jonathan noticed.

But his arm slid round her shoulders, and he spoke gently, his cheek against her hair. "You haven't slowed up since the accident, have you? You've filled your life with so many things to do, you don't even leave yourself time to think."

There was a little pause and when he spoke again his voice was even softer. "No time to think, Jenny. Is that really what you want?"

She was saved by the sudden arrival of Mrs. Flower, breathless and red-faced from her encounter with the dour Mr. Jenkins. Jon helped Jenny carefully upstairs, leaving her sitting wanly on the edge of her bed.

An egg is always an adventure: it may be different.

Oscar Wilde

After a while a thin ray of sunshine pierced the gloom of the day outside and she stood up and hopped to the window, leaning on the sill to look out across the wet green fields. Then she reached out to the little chest and opened the top drawer slowly, groping at the back of it for something.

It lay on her palm, winking and glittering, green and ice-white: Robert's ring. She put it gently on the top of the chest and then brought out the other treasures she had pushed into this dark corner over the years: a plait of grey hair from the tail of her first pony, a dog-eared picture of her father and mother, a few letters, two ears of barley, and a Valentine.

It was the only Valentine she had ever had, and she knew Jon had sent it. She had been eighteen, at the beginning of her new life at art school. She could remember that the pleasure of the Valentine had been dimmed a little because she had known it had come from Jon — dear, safe, predictable Jon.

And the ring? She turned it between her fingers so that the pale sun dazzled on its beautiful stones. It had once promised so much.

The memory of Robert no longer hurt, she realised. The ache she had come to expect was no longer there. She dropped the ring into the drawer and closed it. Jon had been right to say that she had become nun-like in her deliberate seclusion.

Jon knew far too much about her. He had even sensed her disappointment all those years ago when he had called that Valentine's morning.

Jenny left the window and hobbled to the bed. She sat there for the rest of the morning, thinking of all the things she had refused to think about for so long: the accident and what it had really meant to them all; her broken engagement, doomed anyway, she suspected, from the start; the battle to be breadwinner, mother, father and big sister rolled into one. When Mrs. Flower brought up her lunch she hardly tasted it, her mind straying backwards and forwards, facing the past now as much as the uncertain future.

At two o'clock, Jon came up to say that he had smartened Charlie up as best he could and that he would stay long enough to show him off. As he moved to leave, Jenny reached out and touched his hand.

"You were right," she said simply. "You always were. But then, you always knew what you wanted."

He looked at her strangely for a moment, and then smiled gently. "Well, my future was so predictable, wasn't it? I knew by the time I was five that I was going to be a farmer." His smile was tender and warm. "Yes, I always knew what I wanted."

He went out, without looking back.

Jenny sat down again and did some more thinking about Mrs. Flower's cryptic remark the night before; about that brief moment in the stable when she had been so sure Jon was going to kiss her.

Continued overleaf

About Charlie, who had also been constant and true. Charlie, who had helped her through the worst days, and had somehow symbolised a new start, a new life. She turned her head slightly and saw the coloured patchwork of fields and woods beyond the little garden, saw the winter sun shimmer on the window panes.

What would Charlie be like in the spring? she wondered. He would be three then, bursting with energy, his summer coat coming through, bright and glossy as conkers. A terrible ache inside her that had been there for weeks suddenly twinged.

M RS. FLOWER'S heavy tread approached the door. "It's that sister of yours on the phone," she announced disapprovingly. "She sounds hysterical to me. She says she must speak to you or die. I'd better help you downstairs."

They struggled down together. Mrs. Flower's arm was strong but not as comforting as Jonathan's. Had he wanted to kiss her out there in the stable? "Well?" she asked Midge crossly.

"Am I in time?" Midge demanded breathlessly.

"Time for what? You're not ill, are you?"

"Jen, you haven't sold Charlie yet, have you?"

Jenny's heart gave a lurch, as if someone had just hit her in the chest. "Jon's out there now," she said quietly.

"Oh, Jenny, go and stop him! He doesn't want you to sell Charlie at all. He told us so."

"But you were all for it," Jenny protested. "You said — "

"Oh, I know what I said. And I don't really like horses, but I do like Charlie, and you love him, and he means everything to you, and I know that because Jon told us . . ."

"Jon shouldn't interfere!" Jenny yelled, and hurled the receiver back into its cradle. And as she said it, she knew how wretched life would be without Jon to interfere, and worry about her, and nag her to take a holiday, and send her Mrs. Flower when she was in distress, and warn her about selling Charlie.

Charlie!

She did a hop, skip and jump towards the kitchen door. It opened before she reached it and Jon stood there, looking grim, with his hair damp from the rain that was starting to fall again.

"I'm sorry, Jenny. I didn't like her. She said Charlie had big ears."

Jenny let go of the kitchen table and half fell against him. His arms closed round her satisfyingly. "Charlie has got big ears," she said, her voice muffled by his jacket.

"I don't think I could have sold him to anyone, knowing how you loved him."

"But you were the one who kept trying to make me decide whether to sell him or not."

"I was trying to make you stop and think, I suppose, not just about Charlie, but about all those other things. You see, I did hope once that maybe, when you'd got over things . . . "

He tipped her face between his hands so that she had to look at him. "I love you. I always have done. I was going to ask you to marry me when you came home from London. I didn't think you'd settle there, you see. I thought you were too much of a country girl."

Jenny reached up and put her arms around his neck. "Do you remember," she asked softly, "how you kissed me at the harvest dance?"

Jon frowned. "Not very clearly. But I don't think it was much of a success."

"Well, try doing it again."

She was not sure that how he kissed her then was anything like the way he had kissed her by the barn door at the harvest supper. She was leaning against him, eyes closed, the pain in her ankle quite forgotten, when Mrs. Flower burst in.

"That horse of yours," she exclaimed. "It's loose, careering all over the flowerbeds, jumping about on the lawn."

"Bother," Jon said mildly, "I can't have shut the gate properly."

They looked out of the window. Charlie was cavorting about with his tail in the air, giving loud neighs of excitement and gouging great lumps of turf out of the tiny lawn. He was covered in mud and had half a rose bush dangling from his mane.

"You never brushed him at all," Jenny cried. "You let her see him at his worst deliberately, to put her off!"

Jon's arm tightened about her. "Marry me," he said.

Jenny began to laugh, her head against his shoulder.

"Oh, Charlie!" she spluttered.

"I take it that means yes," said Jon.

THE END

©Sarah Woodhouse, 1982.

IN WINTER

**In seed time learn,
in harvest teach, in winter enjoy.**

William Blake

*Urged by the female five-year-old,
(Whose rose-red garb defies the cold),
I postpone all those household chores
To join in snowplay out-of-doors.*

Lorna Bryan

PLAIN AND FANCY

A super asset to your wardrobe is this very wearable
sweater in simple stocking stitch with subtle use of colour
for the contrasting pattern across the yoke

Instructions in 6 sizes
Colour photo on page 154

MATERIALS: *Allow the following quantities in
50 g balls of Patons Fiona:* 6 *loch blue for* 81 *cm,* 86
cm and 91 *cm sizes;* 7 *loch blue for* 97 *cm,* 102 *cm
and* 107 *cm sizes. For any one size:* 1 *ball of the
above yarn in honey, nut brown, heather and
oatmeal; a pair each of No.* 8 *(4 mm) and No.* 10
(3¼ mm) knitting needles.

TENSION: *Work at a tension of 23 stitches and 29
rows to measure 10 x 10 cm, over the stocking stitch,
using No. 8 (4 mm) needles, to obtain measurements
given below.*

**ABBREVIATIONS: To be read before
working:** *K., knit plain; p., purl; st., stitch; tog.,
together; inc., increase (by working twice into same
st.); dec., decrease (by working 2 sts. tog.); up 1,
pick up loop lying between needles and k. or p. into
back of it; s.s., stocking st. (k. on right side and p. on
wrong side); k. or p. 2 tog. b., k. or p. 2 tog. through
back of sts.; m., main (loch blue); h., heather; b.,
nut brown; n., natural (oatmeal); y., yellow
(honey); double rib is k. 2 and p. 2 alternately; nil,
meaning nothing is worked here for this size.*

NOTE: *The instructions are given for the 81 cm (32
inch) size. Where they vary, work figures within first
brackets for 86 cm (34 inch) size; work the figures
within second brackets for 91 cm (36 inch) size, and
so on.*

THE BACK: With No. 10 (3¼ mm) needles and
m. cast on 90 (98) (102) (110) (114) (122) sts. and
beginning odd-numbered rows with k. 2 and
even-numbered rows with p. 2, work 25 rows in
double rib.
 Increase row: Rib 5 (7) (7) (7) (9) (10), up 1, *
rib 10 (14) (11) (16) (12) (17), up 1; repeat from *
until 5 (7) (7) (7) (9) (10) sts. remain, rib to end
— 99 (105) (111) (117) (123) (129) sts.
 Change to No. 8 (4 mm) needles, and
beginning with a k. row, s.s. 94 rows.

To shape the armholes: Cast off 4 sts. at
beginning of next 2 rows.
 Next row: K. 2, k. 2 tog., k. until 4 sts.
remain, k. 2 tog. b., k. 2.
 Next row: P. 2, p. 2 tog.b., p. until 4 sts.
remain, p. 2 tog., p. 2.
 Repeat the last 2 rows nil (nil) (3) (3) (5) (6)
times — 87 (93) (87) (93) (91) (93) sts.
 Next row: K. 2, k. 2 tog., k. until 4 sts.
remain, k. 2 tog.b., k. 2.
 Next row: All p.
 Repeat the last 2 rows 3 (4) (1) (2) (1) (nil)
time(s), then the first of these rows again – 77
(81) (81) (85) (85) (91) sts.
 Next (increase) row: P. 7 (4) (4) (4) (4) (7), up
1, * p. 9 (8) (8) (7) (7) (7), up 1; repeat from *
until 7 (5) (5) (4) (4) (7) sts. remain, p. to end —
85 (91) (91) (97) (97) (103) sts.
 Joining and breaking off colours as required
work the 19-row pattern as follows, which is
worked entirely in s.s., beginning with a k. row,
so only the colour details are given.
 1st and 2nd rows: All h.
 3rd row: 1 b., * 5 h., 1 b.; repeat from * to
end.
 4th row: 2 b., * 3 h., 3 b.; repeat from * until 5
sts. remain, 3 h., 2 b. •
 5th row: 3 b., * 1 h., 5 b.; repeat from * until 4
sts. remain, 1 h., 3 b.
 6th row: All b.
 7th row: 1 b., * 5 n., 1 b.; repeat from * to
end.
 8th row: 3 n., * 1 b., 5 n.; repeat from * until 4
sts. remain, 1 b., 3 n.
 9th row: 1 n., * 2 b., 1 n.; repeat from * to
end.
 10th row: 2 b., * 3 n., 3 b.; repeat from * until
5 sts. remain, 3 n., 2 b.
 11th to 14th rows: As 9th row back to 6th row
in that reverse order.
 15th to 19th rows: As 5th row back to 1st row
in that reverse order, but working y. instead of

MEASUREMENTS	*in centimetres (and inches, in brackets)*					
To fit bust sizes	81 (32)	86 (34)	91 (36)	97 (38)	102 (40)	107 (42)
All round underarms	86 (34)	91 (36)	97 (38)	102 (40)	107 (42)	112 (44)
Side seam	39·5 (15½)	39·5 (15½)	39·5 (15½)	39·5 (15½)	39·5 (15½)	39·5 (15½)
Length	60 (23½)	61·5 (24¼)	61·5 (24¼)	63 (24¾)	63 (24¾)	63·5 (25)
Sleeve seam	40·5 (16)	40·5 (16)	40·5 (16)	40·5 (16)	40·5 (16)	40·5 (16)

h. Break off h., b., n. and y. and continue in m. only.

Next row: All p.

Next (decrease) row: K. 6 (4) (4) (3) (3) (5), dec., * k. 8 (7) (7) (6) (6) (5), dec.; repeat from * until 7 (4) (4) (4) (4) (5) sts. remain, k. to end — 77 (81) (81) (85) (85) (89) sts. **

S.s. 19 (21) (21) (23) (21) (25) rows.

To slope the shoulders: Cast off 7 (8) (8) (8) (8) (8) sts. at beginning of next 4 rows, then 8 (7) (7) (8) (8) (9) sts. on the following 2 rows — 33 (35) (35) (37) (37) (39) sts.

Leave sts. on a spare needle.

THE FRONT: Work as back to **.

S.s. 4 (6) (6) (8) (6) (10) rows.

To divide for neck: Next row: P. 30 (31) (31) (32) (32) (33) and leave these sts. on a spare needle, for right half neck, p. 17 (19) (19) (21) (21) (23) and leave these sts. on a st.holder, p. to end and work on these 30 (31) (31) (32) (32) (33) sts. for left half neck.

The left half neck: Dec. 1 st. at neck edge on next 8 rows — 22 (23) (23) (24) (24) (25) sts.

S.s. 6 rows — s.s. 7 rows here when working right half neck.

To slope the shoulder: Cast off 7 (8) (8) (8) (8) (8) sts. at beginning of next row and following alternate row – 8 (7) (7) (8) (8) (9) sts.

Work 1 row, then cast off.

The right half neck: With right side of work facing, rejoin m. to inner end of sts. and work as given for left half neck, noting variation.

THE SLEEVES (both alike): With No. 10 (3¼ mm) needles and m. cast on 46 (50) (50) (54) (54) (58) sts. and work 25 rows in double rib as given on back.

Increase row: Rib 5 (5) (5) (2) (2) (2), up 1, * rib 12 (8) (8) (7) (7) (6), up 1; repeat from * until 5 (5) (5) (3) (3) (2) sts. remain, rib to end – 50 (56) (56) (62) (62) (68) sts.

Change to No. 8 (4 mm) needles and, beginning with a k. row, s.s. 4 rows, then inc. 1 st. each end of next row, then on the 14 following 6th rows — 80 (86) (86) (92) (92) (98) sts.

S.s. 9 rows.

To shape the sleeve top: Cast off 4 sts. at beginning of next 2 rows.

Next row: K. 2, k. 2 tog., k. until 4 sts. remain, k. 2 tog.b., k. 2.

Next row: All p.

Repeat the last 2 rows 5 (6) (6) (7) (7) (8) times — 60 (64) (64) (68) (68) (72) sts.

Cast off.

THE POLO COLLAR: First join right shoulder seam. With right side of work facing and using No. 10 (3¼ mm) needles, rejoin m. and pick up and k. 22 sts. down left half neck, 17 (19) (19) (21) (21) (23) sts. across front increasing 2 sts. evenly, pick up and k. 22 sts. up right half neck, then k. 33 (35) (35) (37) (37) (39)

Other pretty colourways in this lovely yarn include skye mixture, heather, fine wine, willow green, fawn beige, mosaic pink and tinderbox coral

sts. across back neck, increasing 4 sts. evenly — 100 (104) (104) (108) (108) (112) sts.

Work 59 rows in double rib. Cast off.

TO MAKE UP THE SWEATER: Press with a warm iron over a dry cloth. Join left shoulder seam, continuing seam across polo collar. Set in sleeves, then join sleeve and side seams.

Favourite Festivals and Customs

Pageantry and tradition to look out for on your travels

EPIPHANY-TIME in Austria sees the enacting of the delightful custom of the **Visit of the Three Kings,** Caspar (Kaspar to the Austrians), Melchior and Balthasar, to every village house. Starting a few days before 6th January, so that they have time to get round to everyone, the three robed figures, one carrying a star-topped stick, emerge from the darkness of the night to rap on each door and chalk K & M & B, plus the year, above the lintel, thus bringing a blessing on the house for the coming year. Watch out for them if you find yourself winter holidaymaking in the Austrian Alps at that time of year.

Seville's April Fair, held annually a fortnight after the city's solemn celebration of Holy Week, is Spain's most important festival. Brightly decorated little pavilions are set up in the streets and the people entertain themselves and their visitors with songs, guitar music and flamenco dancing. The morning parades of horses and carriages, with the women dressed in magnificent costume, are a splendid sight.

The two-day **Gipsy Pilgrimage at Les-Saintes-Maries-de-la-Mer,** not far from Marseilles, takes place on 24th and 25th May. Gipsies from all over Europe gather to honour their patron saint, St. Sarah. Escorted by the cowboys of the Camargue, mounted on their white ponies, statues of the saints are carried down to the sea for blessing.

Trooping the Colour, one of London's favourite historic occasions, takes place once a year on the Saturday nearest to 11th June, in celebration of the Queen's official birthday. It provides royal pageantry at its best. The ceremony dates from 1750, when troops about to go into action had their colours paraded before them so that they would recognise their banner in battle.

The Palio, held in the medieval Italian town of Siena on 2nd July and 16th August every year since the 15th century. is a spectacular sight. The participants, dressed in colourful medieval costume, race champion horses from different districts of the town round the picturesque main square, amid an unforgettable atmosphere of excitement.

The lively **Moreska Sword-dance,** performed for more than three hundred years on the Yugoslav holiday island of Korcula, can be seen each year on 27th July. It is a traditional folk-dance, representing the islanders' defence of their home against the plundering Moorish pirates who sailed the Adriatic in bygone days.

Every year, on the last Sunday but one in August, the picturesque **Fête des Filets Bleus,** the Feast of the Blue Fishing Nets, is celebrated at the fishing-port of Concarneau, on Brittany's Atlantic coast. Blue is the traditional colour of the nets used to catch sardine and tunny, the fish on which much of the fishermen's livelihood depends.

The impressive **Military Tattoo,** held nightly on the floodlit esplanade of Edinburgh Castle, is one of the highlights of the Edinburgh International Festival, which takes place each year for three weeks from towards the end of August to mid-September. The city plays host to the world's finest artistes and arts-lovers during this time.

For more than six centuries now, the **Historical Regatta** has brought spectacle to Venice's Grand Canal on the first Sunday in September. Preceded by a procession of historic boats, dressed overall, three gondola races are rowed amid scenes of intense excitement. Set against the gorgeous Venetian background of ancient palaces, domes and spires, the regatta is a superb sight.

Few spectators can fail to be thrilled by the *fantasias* performed by the tribal horsemen of Morocco during national holidays and religious festivals. Across a huge field, lined with colourful Arab tents, the horsemen charge at full tilt, firing their long rifles into the air. One of the biggest *fantasias* can be seen at the annual festival at Moulay Idriss, the city of Idriss, founder of Moroccan Islam, on a variable date in August or September (dates for all main festivals at which *fantasias* take place can be checked with the Moroccan Tourist Office).

The *Ceremony of the Keys*, the ceremonial locking-up of the Tower of London for the night, is a centuries-old tradition still faithfully performed — and precision-timed. It starts at 9.35 p.m. Tickets must be applied for, in writing, from the Resident Governor at the Tower.

Right: Oberau village, Austria.

152

IN WINTER

A touch of inspiration about this polo-neck sweater with its attractive band of
patterning across the yoke. Instructions on page 150.
Right: Victoria the Rag Doll is one of Jean Greenhowe's most popular toy
designs. Instructions start on page 182.

*A*n upper-crust Beef Sausage Pie — a topping of crisp, delicious pastry for a meaty, mouth-watering filling. Recipe on page 172.
Right: A corner collection to gladden the heart of every lover of antiques. For more information see page 163.

*I*n true tradition — family Arans in 10 good sizes with a choice of crew or polo necks.
Instructions on page 170.

A handsome group of foliage plants can brighten the home when flowers are scarce. In front, Pleomele and Maranta, with Crotons and Dieffenbachia in the centre, Ivies and variegated Pineapple behind.

Sure Ways To Succeed With House Plants

The secret is to give each plant a happy home in surroundings that suit it — plus that little extra care

HOUSE plants come into their own in winter when there is less to occupy garden lovers out of doors. But attractively situated plants can add a lot to the home décor at any time of the year.

Plants, like people, are happiest in the surroundings that suit them, So the secret of success with house plants is to provide just the right conditions for each particular plant — or, in other words, choose the right plant for each spot. If you long to acquire a reputation for having green fingers, you might try asking yourself the following questions.

DOES THE PLANT NEED MORE LIGHT?

Only Geraniums, cacti and some succulents enjoy really strong sunlight, say, a south-facing window-sill. The Shrimp Plant (Beloperone) also needs sunlight to produce brightly coloured flower heads. Other plants may suffer rapidly from leaf scorching and drying out.

A reasonably light position is required by most flowering plants, including the popular African Violet (Saintpaulia), and also plants with variegated foliage, such as Chlorophytum, Tradescantia, Coleus and Codiaeum. A variegated plant will lose its attractive white or yellow markings if kept in a dark position; stand it on a not-too-sunny window-sill.

DOES THE PLANT NEED A SHADIER SPOT?

Plants with glossy green leaves, grown for their foliage, do better in a shady position. These include all-green Ivies, Philodendron, Rhoicissus and Cissus antarctica. Also shade-tolerant are the Rubber Plant (Ficus), Aspidistra, the Prayer Plant (Maranta), the Swiss Cheese Plant (Monstera), Peperomias, and Begonia Rex with distinctively marked leaves. Ferns must be kept in the shade and never allowed to dry out.

IS THE PLANT BEING OVERWATERED?

More plants are killed by overwatering than by anything else. In waterlogged soil the roots are unable to function and eventually rot. Do not give daily dribbles of water, but instead give a thorough soaking when the soil is dry on top. In general, never leave plants with their pots standing in a saucer of water. Exceptions to this rule are the moisture-loving Umbrella Plant (Cyperus) and Venus's Flytrap — these two should stand in a saucer of water in summer. The Busy Lizzie, too, needs plenty of water or it will quickly flag.

To maintain a moist atmosphere, pack damp peat around the plant.

As a pick-me-up, stand plant on block of wood and pour round boiling water.

IS THE ATMOSPHERE TOO DRY?

Leaves will go brown at the edges if the air is too dry and extra care is needed in centrally heated rooms. Stand each pot in an outer container, packed round with moist peat, or stand it on a layer of pebbles kept well watered. Grouping several plants together in an attractive large container also creates a moist mini-climate.

Some plants, like African Violet or Begonia Rex, may be happier if transferred to the kitchen or bathroom, where they thrive in the steam. Lots of little leafy plants love the mini-greenhouse atmosphere of a bottle garden.

IS THE ROOM TEMPERATURE RIGHT?

Again, central heating could be a problem, and few of our normal house plants, except cacti and some succulents, appreciate being baked at a really high room temperature. However, rather tender leafy plants such as Codiaeum, Coleus, Monstera and Maranta like it comfortably warm at about 15°C (60°F).

On the other hand, most winter-flowering pot plants — Cyclamen, Cineraria, Azalea, Kalanchoe, Camellia and Gardenia — do best at around 10°C (50°F) and will drop their buds if the temperature is too high. Remember, though, not to leave them on the window-sill at night to freeze behind drawn curtains.

CAN YOU COPE WITH PESTS?

Greenfly occasionally attack the young shoots of indoor plants. So do red spider mites — look for a white webbing on the underside of leaves. White flies are tiny, moth-like insects which suck the sap.

If the attack is slight, remove all affected foliage and wash the plant well with soapy water. Spray with a house plant aerosol insecticide containing liquid derris or malathion, or one of the systemic insecticides which enter the plant's sap. Always follow the manufacturers' instructions carefully and do not overdose.

Consider moving the plant permanently to another room, as certain conditions, such as a hot, dry atmosphere, favour particular kinds of pest.

AFFECTED BY FUNGUS?

The most common fungus diseases of house plants are mildew, a white felt-like mould on the stems and leaves, and botrytis, a grey fur-like mould. The cause of these is usually overwatering, overcrowding or poor ventilation.

Remove and destroy all infected growth and improve the growing conditions. Spray plant with a systemic fungicide such as Benlate and repeat 14 days later.

DOES THE ANSWER LIE IN THE SOIL?

Moss on the soil surface could indicate that the compost has turned sour through over-watering. Scrape off the top inch or two of compost and replace it with fresh.

If a plant has outgrown its pot and roots are protruding through the drainage holes, put it into a slightly larger pot, using John Innes compost or a soil-less (peat-based) compost.

ARE YOU FEEDING THEM RIGHT?

Foliage plants should be given a little liquid fertiliser once a fortnight during the growing season, and flowering plants fed weekly once buds show. Add a few drops of a proprietary plant food to your can when watering, or spray the leaves with a foliar feed.

Do not feed a sick plant or one that is resting during winter or after flowering.

DO YOU TALK TO YOUR PLANTS?

Well, no, it's not actually essential — but if you do, the chances are you've got the right "caring" attitude! Set aside half an hour each week to give them that little extra attention. Take them to the kitchen, spray them with lukewarm water and sponge the leaves. Pick off dead leaves and inspect the foliage for minute pests. Note if incipient buds mean it's time to start feeding.

Pottering with plants can be a very tranquillising occupation, so it could be that they are giving you back something in return.

Water the plant thoroughly then (far left) gently insert a cane up through the drainage hole and push the root ball free.
(Left) Prepare the next-sized pot with crocks over the base, covered by a layer of compost. Set the plant in the middle and fill in with fresh compost, pressed firm.

THIS fine early Georgian pine corner cupboard *(shown in colour on page 157)* makes an attractive setting for a collection of Victoriana.

The two pink jugs known as Cranberry glass are English. This type of glass was very successfully copied by the Americans, hence the name, as it was supposed to resemble the colour of the juice of cranberries, much loved by them. Many different domestic articles were produced such as sweetmeat dishes, drinking glasses, bells, reservoirs to contain paraffin-oil and even the glass shades for the lamps. Most pieces are plain red but many have additions in clear glass such as the handles shown on the jugs. Large, perfect specimens are now much sought after and command very good prices.

In the 18th century, clear glass decanters replaced the rough green bottles that were filled from the barrels in the cellar and brought to the dining-room. Much later, glass jugs, often with silver mounted lids and spouts, were introduced and wine, particularly old claret, would be carefully decanted into them, leaving the sediment in the bottle.

Ribbon Plates were given this name because coloured ribbon, toning with the room's colour scheme, would be threaded through the slots and hung on the wall. They were manufactured in Germany, Austria and Bohemia for the English market. The scenes vary considerably. Boating, fishing, sport and picnicking perhaps, also fruit and flowers. But the most popular were the ones with a view of a well known landmark with "A Present From ...." written underneath the view. These would have been bought either as mementos or for friends while on holiday. This would also apply to five of the teapots as they, too, have scenes; both plates and teapots come under the title of Pictorial Souvenirs.

The pair of Spill Vases, shown on the third shelf, would have graced nearly every Victorian mantelpiece as the spills, made from thin strips of wood, would have been ignited from the fire and used to light the candles or oil lamps and later, the gas mantles. Poorer or more provident households would make their own spills from twisted strips of paper, usually old newspapers. Safety matches were, by comparison, very expensive in those days.

RENÉ CAIRON

163

THE SMALL JOYS OF CHRISTMAS

Being so well-organised for Christmas made me feel vaguely uneasy. But wasn't this what I'd always wanted?

I CAN hear Alex moving around the kitchen, whistling "The Holly and the Ivy" whilst he makes tea for us both.

This year, Christmas was different. To begin with, both the children were away from home for the first time.

Mia sounded anxious when she telephoned, a month before Christmas. "Mother, you *could* both come to us, you know."

"Yes darling — lovely of you to think of inviting us, but you and Mike should have your first married Christmas on you own."

"You're wonderful," she murmured. "So understanding."

Sandy, tall and loose-limbed, with his father's good looks, mentioned the Spanish villa with a lack of concern that fooled no one. The villa belonged to the father of one of his college friends, and half a dozen of them were going, young people around his own age.

"You go, dear," I said blithely.

"Christmas is a family affair," he reminded me sternly, with a hopeful gleam in his eye.

Alex pointed out: "Your Aunt Julia isn't coming this year because she's on duty at the hospital, and Mia and Mike are staying put. A quiet time will suit us both. We're not feeling rejected, so don't look so agonised."

"Do you mind that we'll be on our own?" I asked Alex.

"No!" he said emphatically. "Much as I love the kids, I'll settle happily for a pile of books from the library. What about you?"

I HEAVED a great, contented sigh, mentally planning my small joys of Christmas, a list of long-overdue pleasures.

"On Christmas afternoon I shall listen to Dylan Thomas reciting 'A Welsh Child's Christmas' in that lovely, fruit-cake voice of his. Then I shall hear the Nutcracker Suite, *right through*, without interruption. I've never yet managed to play either of those records on Christmas Day. We *won't* lay tea properly, either; we'll make coffee instead, and roast chestnuts by the fire. Oh, yes, and we'll go to church all leisurely and relaxed on Christmas Eve, instead of in a mad rush at the last minute because I've been busy."

"Do you good," he told me.

"And you," I reminded him.

I had plenty of time to do my shopping and there was no one to "borrow" my wrapping paper and leave me with odd-shaped pieces. I even had time to decorate my parcels with ribbon bows. The cake was iced in good time; the tree ordered early. By Christmas Eve, the holly and the ivy made green crowns on the old dresser and the grandfather clock.

The day before Christmas dawned fine and clear. The air crackled at the edges; the sun diffused soft, lemon-coloured light.

"I shall walk to the library," Alex announced, after breakfast.

"We're having a candlelit supper for two this evening," I told him. "Home-made soup, home-

Continued overleaf

baked ham and fresh fruit salad — all your favourite things. Now I'm going to have my hair done."

"All on your own for Christmas?" said the girl at 'Delia Hair Fashions'. "Oh, you poor things! My parents are coming, and some cousins and a friend of Bill's. I'll be exhausted, but I don't care."

"You and Alex on your own!" cried Anne Manville, when I met her in the Coffee Shop. "We're having Sam's parents this year, and the girls will be home. Why don't you join us?"

I thanked her, and told her we were looking forward to our first ever quiet Christmas. She didn't believe me.

WHEN I reached home, the house was peaceful; though it didn't feel right, it looked beautiful and orderly. I scooped up the cards on the mat and put them with the others.

After lunch, Alex went down to the bottom of the garden to saw logs. He made a bonfire of the rubbish and blue smoke plumes wavered prettily on the still air. I fed the robin, hung up a half-coconut for the bluetits, and scattered seed lavishly all over the bird-table. Then I laid the dining-room table, still feeling vaguely surprised that I could do it slowly, unfussed by a dozen problems.

Our dining-room is at the front of the house overlooking the rest of the garden. I put a damask cloth on the table, then red candles in silver holders. I polished the best glasses. The table looked both elegant and Christmassy; I had just finished arranging it when the telephone made its peremptory clamour in the hall.

"Mother," said Mia's voice, at the other end of the line, "we're coming to supper this evening."

"It's a thirty-five mile drive each way!" I said.

"So what's thirty-five miles on the motorway? We'll be there about half-past seven and we'll leave in time to get home and wish the cottage a Merry Christmas. I didn't want Christmas to come and go without seeing you both. We were going to surprise you but Mike said we ought to make sure you'd be in. You haven't planned to go anywhere, have you?"

"No," I said.

"See you about half-past seven, then," she told me.

I laid two more places at the table. It was a lovely idea of Mia's, I thought, and so like her. It would make a perfect start to Christmas.

The bonfire burned itself to grey ash. Alex raked it over and came indoors, cold and cheerful.

"Mia and Mike are coming," I said.

"For Christmas?" he asked quickly.

"Just for supper." I sketched the details for him. "You don't mind if it isn't a twosome, Alex?"

"Of course not," he told me.

HE rinsed the earth from his hands, then sat at the breakfast-bar and took the mug of rum-laced tea from me, suddenly looking like a man with something on his mind.

"Cold out there," he said casually. "By the way, I met Tom outside the library this morning. I picked his brains shamelessly."

"You always do. He should charge you for good advice about the garden."

"I asked him how he was spending Christmas. He said he was on his own this year because his sister has gone to some friends, but he didn't want anyone to feel sorry for him, he had a pile of books to prove he was going to enjoy himself. He could have gone to his sister's friends, he said, but he wanted peace and quiet."

"Did his voice lack conviction when he said that?" I asked Alex.

"No." He looked warily at me. "All the same, I've just had a thought. If Mike and Mia are coming for supper tonight, we could ask him to join us. We've known him a long time. No one should spend the whole of Christmas on their own, anyway."

He looked at me the way Sandy had looked when he mentioned the Spanish villa.

"Tell him we're eating at eight o'clock," I said.

I listened to him talking to Tom, who is nudging fifty and could pick up all the Christmas invitations he wants because everyone likes him. His sister keeps an eye on him from five minutes' walk away, but Tom lives alone in a little house in the middle of three acres of grounds. He has classic good looks and prematurely white hair — an irresistible combination, many women think — and the greenest fingers of anyone we know. He grows flowers and shrubs, plants and vegetables, from the humblest species to the most exotic. He writes about the things he grows, and sometimes lectures about them.

Alex came back looking triumphant.

"He'll come!" he said, as though it was a great victory.

"Congratulations!" I said, feeling absurdly pleased.

BACK TO SCHOOL

**The holidays are over and the autumn term
begins for Roley, Rosemary and little Richard**

THE lovely summer holidays had ended and the three little Robins were on their way back to school again.

Rosemary Robin could hardly wait to get there and meet all her school friends again, but Roley was in no hurry at all.

"The longer we keep away from school, the longer the holidays will last," he said and he walked along so slowly that his sister skipped on ahead.

Their little cousin, Richard, would have liked to hurry, too! He had picked out one of the prettiest shells from the collection he had brought home from the seaside and he was longing to give it to his teacher, Miss Thrush. But he didn't like to admit to Roley that he really *wanted* to get to school quickly, so he dawdled along too.

"I don't expect that the teachers will feel much like work, today," said Richard, hoping to spur his cousin on."

Then Roley remembered how they had caught a glimpse of Mr. Rook shrimping and he wondered if his teacher would look any different and he suddenly felt curious and began to hurry.

As they drew near to Miss Owl's School they could see Mr. Rook and Miss Thrush talking together by the staff-room window.

Mr. Rook looked just the same but very cheery, and Roley decided that the first day at school might be fun after all and little Richard was soon happily giving Miss Thrush his lovely, little shell.

I REARRANGED the table to accommodate one more guest. It was dusk by now, and I lit the big candle in the window, leaving the curtains undrawn. When I went outside to assess the welcoming effect, a florist's van, with 'Christine' lettered in gilt on its sides, was just turning into the drive.

Christine climbed out, and reached into the back of the van for a bouquet of flowers. She looked tired, because Christmas and Easter are her busiest times. Six years ago, just when our small village was beginning to grow into a big one, she took over a previously moribund business, and now she employs an assistant and a van driver. She is a quiet woman, small and curvy. Her husband died just before she came to live locally, and her daughter, Jenny, went to secretarial college with Mia.

"One for you, Lisa," she said. "I'm sorry it's so late — you should have had them hours ago, but Lorna went home early with a raging toothache, and as Debbie can't drive I had to leave her to cope with the shop whilst I did the deliveries."

I took the bouquet from her. It was a very big one: roses, carnations, daffodils, chrysanthemums and freesias all making a bright surge of colour behind a cellophane wrapper tied with red ribbon.

I read the tag pinned to the bow.

"Thank you both. Bless you. Have a beautiful Christmas, Love, Sandy."

My nose prickled, my eyes ached — it was no more than tiredness — and I thought about the children: the wonderful, complicated, unexpected creatures.

"He came into the shop and paid for them days ago," Christine said, adding frankly: "They cost him a bomb. He said it didn't matter because you both needed a load of flowers to cheer you up as you were going to be on your own for Christmas."

She stood there, smiling, looking small and vulnerable in her duffel coat and pants, her fair hair screwed into a knot on top of her head. I remembered that Jenny was working in Paris and couldn't get home for the holiday. I thought of Chris all alone in her flat above the shop.

I WAVED goodbye to 'A Welsh Child's Christmas', The Nutcracker Suite, the chestnuts and everything else, as I said: "Come and spend Christmas Day with us."

She shook her head determinedly but I saw her look at the window where the big candle, patterned with its frieze of cherubs, had begun to burn steadily. Behind it, the room glowed, looking like a Christmas card come to life.

"We'd love to have you," I told her.

"Nice of you." She shook her head again. "But I know you don't need cheering up; that you planned a quiet Christmas. Go on, have it. You may never get another. I'll be all right, honestly."

I had a bright idea. I said casually: "At least you can come for a meal this evening. Mike and Mia are driving down to have a candlelit supper. Go home, have a hot bath and get back here by eight o'clock. That gives you two hours."

"If it's a family party . . . " she began warily.

Continued overleaf

167

"It isn't. Alex invited Tom Jewell as well."

"Tom?" She looked only mildly interested. They had met on a few occasions and I knew she had asked his advice more than once, but the friendship had never really got under way, because they were both rather reserved people.

"See you at eight," I insisted. "Home cooking. How does that sound?"

"Wonderful. You're really tempting me." She capitulated.

The flowers filled the house, hinting at spring just around the corner. I put a bowl of freesias on the supper table between the candles. I found a box of crackers. They looked festive on the table and six people pulling crackers on Christmas Eve added up to more fun than two people doing the same thing on Christmas Day.

I was ready — just — when Mia whirled into the house with Mike. She held out her arms and put her cold cheek against mine, hugging me fiercely. They had brought gifts: wine, expensive chocolates, a tiny silver tree in a china pot as big as a thimble.

T OM came in almost on their heels. I told him that Christine was coming and his eyes looked suddenly wary.

When Chris came, she was wearing a pretty dress under her fur jacket; she looked relaxed, the tiredness ironed out. I noticed Tom getting off to a fair start with her after the 'hello' bit.

It was wonderful to have half a dozen people in the house. The tree was a pyramid of lights at the far end of the lounge; the flames between the piled logs burned gold and crimson; the candle flames dipped and wavered, and as I served the meal, I listened contentedly to the stream of talk flowing around me.

"I thought I might grow Christmas trees," Tom was saying to Chris.

"The cottage has a personality all its own," Mia was saying to Alex. "It doesn't always see eye to eye with what we plan, but we usually reach a compromise."

Mike smiled at me, and said softly: "You'll have a lovely quiet day tomorrow."

The wine sparkled in the glasses, the freesias smelled sweet, and I felt a sharp pang of regret at Sandy's absence which was quickly lost in thoughts of his having a wonderful time in Spain.

We pulled the crackers. Tom had a necklace of plastic beads that he gave to Christine, and he jammed a tissue paper crown on his hair with a look of amused resignation. Christine fastened the beads around her neck, and Mia said to me reprovingly, "You are naughty, Mother. You should really have kept the crackers until tomorrow. You never let *us* have them on Christmas Eve."

"There will only be two of us tomorrow," I pointed out.

"That's crazy!" Mia exclaimed. "Sandy won't be home, and I won't be here and this house will *rattle* with just two people inside it."

"Of course it will!" I cried. "Do stay for Christmas — Tom — Chris."

"That's kind of you," Tom replied firmly, "but I have my Christmas planned. A pile of books and a stack of records that I never have time to listen to as a rule."

"I shall be lazy." Chris managed to make it sound like her idea of paradise. "I shall cook a late lunch and take a walk in Tarley Woods afterwards. Next year there's going to be a row of houses there, instead of trees."

Alex never looked at me. He told them emphatically that we'd be delighted to have them both. They were as polite as two children who have been warned not to ask for second helpings. Mia shook her head at their refusals and said they had the wrong idea of Christmas. I looked at them and thought: 'I don't need to feel guilty — they really do want to spend Christmas alone.'

"Sorry I dropped a clanger," Mia murmured repentantly to me as we cleared away the dishes.

Mike and Mia left just before eleven o'clock. Tom, who had walked up from the village, accepted the offer of a lift home from them. Mia hugged me and whispered: "What a shame you couldn't persuade them to stay. Don't be too lonely tomorrow."

A LEX and I walked to Church in the chill of a starry, frosty night. The church was full. There were daffodils by the pulpit, holly and ivy wreathed around the manger scene. The carols were all the old ones, our favourites. Alex held my hand coming home, and we shouted Christmas greetings to the sky. It was Christmas Day and the warm, quiet house waited patiently for our return.

It was nearly nine o' clock when I awoke in the morning. The bed beside me was empty. I pulled on pants and a sweater and ran downstairs.

Alex had laid breakfast for one, on a tray.

"I was going to bring it upstairs, as a surprise," he told me dolefully.

"That's a lovely present, darling," I told him.

"You haven't had it — and now you won't get it, will you?" he pointed out.

We exchanged presents over toast and coffee. He had bought everything on my list: a new frying-pan, a chiffon nightie, a set of pottery mugs with the four seasons painted on them, and a pair of tiny gold earrings. "A neat balance between the sublime and the ridiculous," he called it. My presents to him were all sensible ones.

The telephone began to ring.

"Sandy, I'll bet!" I cried. "All the way from Spain!"

I ran to answer it. Tom was at the other end; he sounded vaguely embarrassed.

"I've been thinking," he said hesitantly, "it seems a bit unkind to leave you two on your own at Christmas when you've been used to having a family around you. Mia and I talked it over, driving back here last night. She's worried about you, so I thought if you'd still like me to come to lunch . . ."

"And tea!" I cried recklessly. "Of course, Tom. That would be fun!"

"Is Chris really going to be on her own, too?" Tom asked casually.

"Yes, Jenny can't get home this year."

"Tough luck. She's being very good about it, the way you are about Sandy and Mia. She said she didn't mind being alone, but people don't always say what they mean, do they?"

"As a matter of fact, I was about to phone Chris when you rang," I assured him.

A H well, it was the snowiest of white lies. I rang Chris and pointed out that a threesome was a trifle lopsided, and the turkey seemed very large somehow.

I was surprised to find that she needed very little persuasion.

When I went back to the kitchen, Alex was staring out of the window, apparently absorbed in the activity on the bird-table. Only when I looked closely did I see how his shoulder shook.

"Dinner will be late," I said, with dignity, "on account of the fact that I overslept."

"What does it matter if dinner is late, when there's only two of us?" he said, in a voice that wobbled. He turned then, and I saw how hard he was trying not to laugh.

"All right!" I cried furiously. "What else could I do? What about all those books you brought from the library?"

Nothing great was ever achieved without enthusiasm.

Ralph Waldo Emerson

"What about The Nutcracker Suite, and all that?" he countered.

"Same as last year," I said resignedly. "I'll play my special records on a summer afternoon and pretend that it's Christmas. I forgot to buy the chestnuts, anyway. And you will have to find the Angel Chimes and fix them together because we're going to have tea laid properly, with all the trimmings. I suppose we could play Scrabble this evening."

"We'll make another list next year. We'll probably be on our own then."

"I doubt it. Mia is going to have a baby in July. She'll want us to go to her, or they'll come here, I expect."

"Mia? You should have told me!" he protested.

"She only told *me* as she was leaving last night. I was going to choose a beautiful moment in which to pass the news on to you; perhaps when we were sitting by the fire, roasting chestnuts. The year after next, Sandy will probably be married, and then there will be another baby. Goodbye, quiet Christmas, for ever."

We had a lovely Christmas this year. It's already half an hour in the past. Two of our three spare rooms are occupied, because it would be all wrong to send people home on Christmas night and, anyway, we've all made plans for today. Mind you, I'm unsentimental. I don't have any ridiculous ideas about Tom and Chris getting together, but it does look as though, this time, the friendship is getting off the ground to a flying start.

Lunch was late, and we all sat around talking, so no one walked in Tarley Woods. The tea-table looked just as it has always done, and we didn't play Scrabble afterwards because we sat around and talked all over again. Sandy telephoned at teatime, and Mia soon afterwards. She said she was so glad that Alex and I had been sensible and insisted upon having company because we just aren't the kind to enjoy a quiet Christmas.

So I have put my list of the small joys of Christmas on the fire and I'm watching it burn. It doesn't seem all that important. I think the important thing is to have a wonderful Christmas Day, and I've certainly had that; so has Alex. We're not really exhaused — at least, no more so than usual.

I mean — who wants a quiet Christmas, anyway?

THE END

©*Audrie Manley-Tucker, 1982*

IN TRUE TRADITION

A family of Aran-style sweaters — the
all-time favourites
Instructions in 10 sizes
Colour photo on page 158

MATERIALS: *Allow these quantities in 50 g balls of Littlewoods Keynote Type 10 for Aran knitting:* **Crew Neck Version:** 9 *for 66 cm size;* 10 *for 71 cm size;* 12 *for 76 cm size;* 14 *for 81 cm size;* 16 *for 86 cm size;* 17 *for 91 cm size;* 19 *for 97 cm size;* 21 *for 102 cm size;* 23 *for 107 cm size;* 24 *for 112 cm size.* **Polo Neck Version:** *Allow 1 extra ball. For any one size: a pair each of No. 6 (5 mm) and No. 8 (4 mm) knitting needles; a cable needle.*

TENSION: *Work at a tension of 22 stitches and 25 rows to measure 10 × 10 cm, over the rice st. pattern, using No. 6 (5 mm) needles, to obtain measurements.*

ABBREVIATIONS: To be read before working: *K., knit plain; p., purl; st., stitch; tog., together; inc., increase (by working twice into next st.); dec., decrease (by taking 2 sts. tog.); r.st., rice st.; inc.p., increase p. wise; tw. 2 lt., twist 2 left (slip next st. on to cable needle and leave at front of work, k. 1 then k. 1 from cable needle); tw. 2 rt., twist 2 right (as tw. 2 lt. but leave cable needle at back of work); c. 4 or 6 rt., cable 4 or 6 right (slip next 2 or 3 sts. on to cable needle and leave at back of work, k. 2 or 3 then k. 2 or 3 sts. from cable needle); c. 4 or 6 lt., cable 4 or 6 left (as c. 4 or 6 rt. but leave cable needle at front of work); tw. 5, twist 5 (slip next 3 sts. on to cable needle and leave at back of work, k. 2, slip end st. off cable needle, back on to left hand needle and p. this st., then k. 2 from cable needle); tw. 3 rt., twist 3 right (slip next st. on to cable needle and leave at back of work, k. 2, then p. 1 from cable needle); tw. 3 lt., twist 3 left (slip next 2 sts. on to cable needle and leave at front of work, p. 1 then k. 2 from cable needle); M.B., make a bobble (into next st. work k. 1, yarn round needle, k. 1, yarn round needle, k. 1, turn and p. these 5 sts., turn then k. 3, k. 2 tog. and pass the 3 k. sts. over the k. 2 tog. thus finishing with 1 st. on right hand needle); single rib is k. 1 and p. 1 alternately.*

NOTE: *The instructions are given for the 66 cm (26 inch) chest size. Where they vary, work figures within first brackets for 71 cm (28 inch) size; work figures within second brackets for 76 cm (30 inch) size, and so on.*

SPECIAL NOTE: *It is advisable for knitters to first go through instructions and underline in red all figures relating to size to be worked.*

THE BACK: With No. 8 (4 mm) needles cast on 67 (73) (79) (85) (97) (103) (107) (113) (117) (123) sts. and beginning odd-numbered rows with k. 1, and even-numbered rows with p. 1, work 13 (13) (13) (15) (15) (15) (15) (17) (17) (17) rows in single rib.

Inc. row: Rib 7 (7) (7) (7) (11) (11) (11) (14) (14) (14), ★ inc. p., inc. p., rib 4 (4) (4) (4) (5) (5) (5) (5) (5) (5), inc. p., rib 1, inc. p., rib 4 (4) (4) (4) (5) (5) (5) (5) (5) (5), inc. p., inc. p. ★, rib 23 (29) (35) (41) (41) (47) (51) (51) (55) (61), work from ★ to ★ once, rib 7 (7) (7) (7) (11) (11) (11) (14) (14) (14) — 79 (85) (91) (97) (109) (115) (119) (125) (129) (135) sts.

Change to No. 6 (5 mm) needles.

1st pattern row: P. 4 (4) (4) (4) (7) (7) (7) (10) (10) (10), ★★ tw. 2 lt., p. 1, c. 4 (4) (4) (4) (6) (6) (6) (6) (6) (6) rt., p. 4, tw. 5, p. 4, c. 4 (4) (4) (4) (6) (6) (6) (6) (6) (6) lt., p. 1, tw. 2 rt. ★★, for r.st. panel p. 1 (1) (1) (3) (3) (3) (3) (3) (3) (3), tw. 2 lt., p. 1, ★ k. 1, p. 1; repeat from ★ 4 (7) (10) (11) (10) (13) (15) (15) (17) (20) times, tw. 2rt., p. 1 (1) (1) (3) (3) (3) (3) (3) (3) (3), then repeat from ★★ to ★★ once, p. 4 (4) (4) (4) (7) (7) (7) (10) (10) (10).

2nd row: K. 4 (4) (4) (4) (7) (7) (7) (10) (10) (10), ★★ p. 2, k. 1, p. 4 (4) (4) (4) (6) (6) (6) (6) (6) (6), k. 4, p. 2, k. 1, p. 2, k. 4, p. 4 (4) (4) (4) (6) (6) (6) (6) (6) (6), k. 1, p. 2 ★★, for r.st. panel k. 1 (1) (1) (3) (3) (3) (3) (3) (3) (3), p. 2, k. 11 (17) (23) (25) (23) (29) (33) (33) (37) (43), p. 2, k. 1 (1) (1) (3) (3) (3) (3) (3) (3) (3), then repeat from ★★ to ★★ once, k. 4 (4) (4) (4) (7) (7) (7) (10) (10) (10).

These 2 rows form the r.st. panel in centre. Keeping continuity of r.st. panel, continue diamond panels as follows: **3rd row:** P. 4 (4) (4

MEASUREMENTS													*in centimetres (and inches, in brackets)*
To fit sizes	66	(26)	71	(28)	76	(30)	81	(32)	86	(34)	91	(36)	97
Side seam	25	(9¾)	29	(11½)	33	(13)	36·5	(14¼)	39·5	(15½)	39·5	(15½)	39·5
Length	42·5	(16¾)	47·5	(18¾)	52	(20½)	56·5	(22¼)	61	(24)	61	(24)	63
Sleeve seam	31·5	(12¼)	34	(13¼)	37	(14)	41	(16¼)	43·5	(17¼)	43·5	(17¼)	43·5

(4) (7) (7) (7) (10) (10) (10), ** tw. 2 lt., p. 1, k. 4 (4) (4) (4) (6) (6) (6) (6) (6) (6), p. 3, tw. 3 rt., p. 1, tw. 3 lt., p. 3, k. 4 (4) (4) (4) (6) (6) (6) (6) (6) (6), p. 1, tw. 2 rt. **, r.st. panel 17 (23) (29) (35) (33) (39) (43) (43) (47) (53), repeat from ** to **, once, p. to end.

4th row: K. 4 (4) (4) (4) (7) (7) (7) (10) (10) (10), ** p. 2, k. 1, p. 4 (4) (4) (4) (6) (6) (6) (6) (6), k. 3, p. 2, k. 3, p. 2, k. 3, p. 4 (4) (4) (4) (6) (6) (6) (6) (6), k. 1, p. 2 **, r.st. panel 17 (23) (29) (35) (33) (39) (43) (43) (47) (53), repeat from ** to **, once, k. to end.

5th row: P. 4 (4) (4) (4) (7) (7) (7) (10) (10) (10), **tw. 2 lt., p. 1, c. 4 (4) (4) (4) (6) (6) (6) (6) (6)rt., p.2, tw. 3rt., p.3, tw. 3 lt.,p.2, c. 4 (4) (4) (4) (6) (6) (6) (6) (6)lt., p. 1, tw. 2 rt. **, r.st. panel 17 (23) (29) (35) (33) (39) (43) (43) (47) (53), repeat from ** to **, once, p. to end.

6th row: K. 4 (4) (4) (4) (7) (7) (7) (10) (10) (10), ** p. 2, k. 1, p. 4 (4) (4) (4) (6) (6) (6) (6) (6), k. 2, p. 2, k. 5, p. 2, k. 2, p. 4 (4) (4) (4) (6) (6) (6) (6) (6), k. 1, p. 2 **, r.st. panel 17 (23) (29) (35) (33) (39) (43) (43) (47) (53), repeat from ** to **, once, k. to end.

7th row: P. 4 (4) (4) (4) (7) (7) (7) (10) (10) (10), ** tw. 2 lt., p. 1, k. 4 (4) (4) (4) (6) (6) (6) (6) (6), p.1, tw. 3rt., p. 5, tw. 3 lt., p.1, k. 4 (4) (4) (4) (6) (6) (6) (6) (6), p. 1, tw. 2 rt. **, r.st. panel 17 (23) (29) (35) (33) (39) (43) (43) (47) (53), repeat from ** to **, once, p. to end.

8th row: K. 4 (4) (4) (4) (7) (7) (7) (10) (10) (10), ** p. 2, k. 1, p. 4 (4) (4) (4) (6) (6) (6) (6) (6), k. 1, p. 2, k. 7, p. 2, k. 1, p. 4 (4) (4) (4) (6) (6) (6) (6) (6), k. 1, p. 2 **, r.st. panel 17 (23) (29) (35) (33) (39) (43) (43) (47) (53), repeat from ** to **, once, k. to end.

9th row: P. 4 (4) (4) (4) (7) (7) (7) (10) (10) (10), ** tw. 2 lt., p. 1, c. 4 (4) (4) (4) (6) (6) (6) (6) (6) rt., p. 1, tw. 2rt., p. 3, M.B., p.3, tw. 2 lt., p. 1, c. 4 (4) (4) (4) (6) (6) (6) (6) (6) lt., p. 1, tw. 2 rt. **, r.st. panel 17 (23) (29) (35) (33) (39) (43) (43) (47) (53), repeat from ** to **, once, p. to end.

10th to 16th rows: Work 8th row back to 2nd row in that reverse order, but reading tw. 3 lt. in place of tw. 3 rt. and tw. 3 rt. in place of tw. 3 lt.

These 16 rows form the pattern. Pattern a further 34 (44) (54) (60) (68) (68) (68) (72) (72) (72) rows.

To shape armholes: Cast off 3 (3) (3) (3) (6) (6) (6) (9) (9) (9) sts. at beginning of next 2 rows—73 (79) (85) (91) (97) (103) (107) (107) (111) (117) sts. ***

Pattern a further 36 (38) (40) (42) (46) (46) (50) (54) (54) (56) rows.

(38)	102	(40)	107	(42)	112	(44)
(15½)	42	(16½)	42	(16½)	42	(16½)
(24¾)	67	(26¼)	67	(26¼)	68	(26¾)
(17¼)	49·5	(19½)	49·5	(19½)	49·5	(19½)

To slope shoulders: Cast off 8 (9) (9) (10) (11) (11) (12) (12) (13) (14) sts. at beginning of next 4 rows, then 8 (9) (10) (11) (11) (13) (13) (12) (13) sts. on the following 2 rows.

Break yarn and leave 25 (25) (29) (29) (31) (33) (33) (33) (35) (35) sts. on a spare needle.

THE FRONT: Work as back to ***.

Pattern a further 27 (29) (29) (31) (35) (33) (37) (41) (39) (41) rows.

To divide for neck: Next row: Pattern 31 (34) (36) (39) (42) (44) (46) (46) (47) (50) sts. and leave on a spare needle for right front neck, pattern 11 (11) (13) (13) (13) (15) (15) (15) (17) (17) and leave on a st. holder, pattern to end and work on these last 31 (34) (36) (39) (42) (44) (46) (46) (47) (50) sts. for left front neck.

The left front neck: Dec. 1 st. at neck edge on each of the next 7 (7) (8) (8) (9) (9) (9) (9) (9) (9) rows—24 (27) (28) (31) (33) (35) (37) (37) (38) (41) sts.

Pattern 1 (1) (2) (2) (1) (3) (3) (3) (5) (5) row(s)—pattern 2 (2) (3) (3) (2) (4) (4) (4) (6) (6) rows here when working right front neck.

To slope shoulder: Cast off 8 (9) (9) (10) (11) (11) (12) (12) (13) (14) sts. at beginning of next row and following alternate row.

Work 1 row.

Cast off 8 (9) (10) (11) (11) (13) (13) (12) (13) sts.

The right front neck: With right side facing, rejoin yarn to inner end of sts. on spare needle, and work as left front neck, noting variation.

THE SLEEVES (both alike): With No. 8 (4 mm) needles cast on 39 (39) (43) (43) (47) (47) (51) (51) (55) (55) sts. and work 13 (13) (13) (15) (15) (15) (15) (17) (17) (17) rows in single rib as given on back.

Inc. row: Inc. in first st., rib 11 (11) (13) (13) (14) (14) (16) (16) (18) (18), inc. p., inc. p., rib 4 (4) (4) (4) (5) (5) (5) (5) (5) (5), inc. p., rib 1, inc. p., rib 4 (4) (4) (4) (5) (5) (5) (5) (5) (5), inc. p., inc. p., rib 11 (11) (13) (13) (14) (14) (16) (16) (18) (18), inc. in last st—47 (47) (51) (51) (55)

Continued overleaf

Aran-style sweaters: continued

(55) (59) (59) (63) (63) sts.

Change to No. 6 (5 mm) needles.

1st pattern row: For r.st. panel p. 1, * k. 1, p. 1 *; repeat from * to * 2 (2) (3) (2) (2) (2) (3) (3) (4) (4) times, tw. 2 rt., p. 1 (1) (1) (3) (3) (3) (3) (3) (3) (3), for pattern panel repeat from ** to ** given on 1st pattern row of back, p. 1 (1) (1) (3) (3) (3) (3) (3) (3) (3), tw. 2 lt., for r.st. panel, p. 1, repeat from * to * 3 (3) (4) (3) (3) (3) (4) (4) (5) (5) times.

2nd row: For r.st. panel k. 7 (7) (9) (7) (7) (7) (9) (9) (11) (11), p. 2, k. 1 (1) (1) (3) (3) (3) (3) (3) (3) (3), for pattern panel repeat from ** to ** given on 2nd pattern row of back, k. 1 (1) (1) (3) (3) (3) (3) (3) (3) (3), p. 2, for r.st. panel k. 7 (7) (9) (7) (7) (7) (9) (9) (11) (11).

These 2 rows form the r.st. pattern each end and set the position of the panel in centre.

Keeping continuity of pattern panel to match back and working extra sts. into r.st. as they occur, inc. 1 st. each end of next row and the 4 (6) (3) (4) (11) (11) (11) (16) (10) (16) following 4th rows.

Work 5 rows, then inc. 1 st. each end of next row and the 4 (4) (7) (8) (5) (5) (5) (4) (8) (4) following 6th rows—67 (71) (75) (79) (91) (91) (95) (103) (103) (107) sts.

Pattern 17 (15) (17) (15) (11) (11) (11) (9) (9) (9) rows—mark each end of last row to denote end of sleeve seam.

Pattern a further 4 (4) (4) (4) (8) (8) (8) (12) (12) (12) rows. Cast off.

THE NECK RIBBING: First join right shoulder seam. With right side facing, rejoin yarn. Using No. 8 (4 mm) needles, pick up and k. 20 (20) (21) (21) (21) (22) (22) (22) (23) (23) sts. from row ends of left front neck shaping, k. across 11 (11) (13) (13) (13) (15) (15) (15) (17) (17) sts. at front neck, pick up and k. 20 (20) (21) (21) (21) (22) (22) (22) (23) (23) sts. from row ends of right front neck shaping, and finally, k. across 25 (25) (29) (29) (31) (33) (33) (33) (35) (35) sts. at back neck—76 (76) (84) (84) (86) (92) (92) (92) (98) (98) sts.

Work 11 (11) (11) (13) (15) (15) (15) (17) (17) (17) rows in single rib—for polo neck version, change to No. 6 (5 mm) needles and rib a further 11 (11) (11) (13) (15) (15) (15) (17) (17) (17) rows.

For either version, cast off loosely in rib.

TO MAKE UP THE SWEATER: Press lightly on wrong side with a warm iron over a dry cloth, taking care not to flatten the pattern. Join left shoulder seam, continuing with a flat seam across neck ribbing. Set sleeves into armholes, setting rows above markers to sts. cast off at underarms. Join side and sleeve seams. Fold crew neck ribbing in half to inside and catch in place. Fold polo neck ribbing in half to outside.

BEEF SAUSAGE PIE

Serves 4-6

1 lb. British beef sausages
1 tablespoon oil
¾ lb. leeks, cleaned and sliced
½ lb. mushrooms, sliced
2 level teaspoons cornflour
4 tablespoons double cream
2 tablespoons horseradish cream
Pepper and ½ level teaspoon salt
7½ oz. packet frozen puff pastry, thawed
1½ pint pie dish

Set the oven to fairly hot, Gas Mark 6 or 400°F, 200°C.

Fry the sausages in the oil for 5 minutes until well browned. Add the leeks and mushrooms and fry gently for a further 5 minutes, stir in the cornflour.

Remove the pan from the heat and stir in the cream, horseradish and salt and pepper to taste. Turn the sausage mixture into the pie dish.

Roll out the pastry a little larger then the top of the pie dish. Stand the dish on the pastry and cut around it, allowing half an inch pastry border. Grease the rim of the dish and arrange the pastry trimmings cut side inwards, on it. Damp the pastry rim with water and place the pastry lid on top. Press the edges together, trim then knock the edges up with the back of a knife and scallop them.

Roll out the trimmings and use to decorate the top of the pie.

Bake above the centre of the oven for 40 minutes, until golden brown.

Colour photo of Beef Sausage Pie on page 156 by courtesy of British Meat.

Pies and Casseroles

Some of the character of British cooking rests on its rich variety of pies and casseroles. Handed on and revised from generation to generation, these dishes have established themselves as firm family favourites

Right: Tasty Cheese and Onion Pie.

CHEESE AND ONION PIE

Serves 4-5

1¼ lb. onions, peeled and sliced

Good pinch nutmeg

½ oz. margarine

6 oz. mature British cheese

1 level teaspoon dry mustard

2 large eggs, size 2

Salt and pepper

For the pastry:

5 oz. margarine and lard mixed

10 oz. plain flour

½ teaspoon salt

Water to mix

9 inch round ovenproof plate

Place onions, nutmeg and margarine in a covered pan. Cook gently over a low heat for 15 minutes until onions are soft but not coloured. Shake the pan occasionally to prevent sticking. Transfer to a bowl when cooked and leave to cool.

Set the oven to hot, Gas Mark 6 or 400°F/200°C.

Next make your pastry. Rub margarine and lard into flour and salt until the mixture resembles fine breadcrumbs then add enough water to form a soft, not sticky dough. Knead gently until pastry is smooth. Cut off 3 oz. for decoration and leave covered.

Divide remaining pastry in two. On a floured surface roll out one half into approximately a 10 inch round and line the base of the plate. Roll out the other half to the same size for the lid.

Add the grated cheese, mustard and beaten eggs to the cooled onions and mix well together. Season. Spoon mixture into pastry-lined plate.

Dampen the edges with a little water and place on the lid. Trim off excess pastry and combine with the reserved pastry. Roll out and cut 10 ¼ inch wide strips of appropriate length. Arrange in a lattice design. Pinch edges to decorate and secure the pastry strip ends. Brush with milk.

Bake just above the centre of the oven for about 30 minutes, until pastry is golden brown.

APPLE PIE

Serves 6

For the pastry:

3 oz. lard

3 oz. margarine

12 oz. plain flour

½ teaspoon salt

For the filling:

1 oz. butter

2 oz. light brown sugar

2 lb. cooking apples, peeled, cored and sliced

1 level tablespoon cornflour

1 level teaspoon cinnamon

1 level tablespoon caster sugar

8-9 inch pie plate

Set oven to fairly hot, Gas Mark 6 or 400°F/200°C. Put a baking sheet in the oven to heat up.

Rub the fats into the flour and salt until it resembles breadcrumbs. Add enough water to make a soft, not sticky dough.

Melt the butter and brown sugar together in a pan. Stir in the apples, cornflour and cinnamon, and cook for about 4 minutes, until apples begin to break up and sauce thickens. Let cool.

Meanwhile cut off 12 oz. of pastry and roll out to line the pie plate. Roll out remaining pastry for lid. Place apple in centre. Dampen edges with water, cover with lid. Press edges together to seal, trim and discard. Pinch edges together for decoration and cut three slits in the top. Brush with milk; sprinkle with caster sugar.

Place pie on baking sheet and bake in the centre of the oven for 35-40 minutes.

Continued overleaf

PEAR PUDDING PIE

Serves 6

For the pastry:

4 oz. plain flour

A pinch of salt

1 oz. margarine

1 oz. lard

Cold water to mix

For the sponge: :

2 oz. margarine

2 oz. caster sugar

2 oz. semolina

2 oz. self-raising flour

1 level teaspoon ground ginger

1 large egg (size 2)

1 tablespoon milk

For the topping:

3 pears

The juice of ½ a lemon

6 walnut halves

½ oz. butter, melted

A 7½ inch round sandwich tin

Mix the flour with the salt. Add the margarine and lard cut into small pieces, and rub them in until the mixture resembles breadcrumbs. Stir in enough water to give a soft, but not sticky, dough. Knead the pastry lightly on a lightly floured board, then roll out and line the sandwich tin. Trim and decorate the edges, prick the base with a fork and put the pastry in the fridge or a cold place to chill.

Pre-heat the oven to moderately hot, Gas Mark 5 or 375°F/190°C.

Meanwhile, make the sponge. Cream the margarine and sugar together until light and fluffy, then beat in the egg. Sift the flour, ginger and semolina together and fold them into the creamed mixture, with the milk. Leave on one side while preparing the pears.

Peel the pears, cut them in half then carefully remove the core with a teaspoon and cut out the stalky bit. Turn each pear half in the lemon juice in a small basin to prevent discolouration.

Spread the sponge mixture over the pastry in the tin, then press the pear halves, cut-side uppermost, into it. Put a walnut half in each pear 'core', then brush the pear and walnuts with the melted butter. Bake in the oven for 35 to 40 minutes, until the cake is golden brown, well risen and cooked through. Leave the flan to cool in the tin for about 15 minutes, then run a round-bladed knife round between the tin and pastry.

Turn the flan out on to a plate, then reverse it on to a wire rack to cool completely.

It's very simple to make delicious pies with perfect, light shortcrust pastry once you've learnt the basic rules of working quickly and keeping everything cool.

A good shortcrust pastry is light and crumbly when eaten and one of the best pastries to make is with a mixture of fats, half margarine and half lard or white fat and using plain flour.

Make sure the fat is cut into small pieces before stirring into the flour. Coat the fat with flour then rub it in quickly with the fingertips — warm hands spell disaster to pastry.

Add the cold liquid quickly and lightly add jus

SYRUP TART

Makes two plate tarts

Shortcrust pastry, made with 6oz. flour, etc.

6 oz. plain flour

2 oz. demerara sugar

The grated rind of 1 lemon

1 level teaspoon nutmeg

4 oz. margarine

4 tablespoons golden syrup

Two 8½ inch plates

Make the pastry and roll out half to a size roughly ½ inch larger than the plate. Lift pastry on rolling pin, unroll over plate, and press gently into place. Trim edges with a knife then prick the base with a fork to prevent pastry rising.

Make cuts the depth of the plate rim and about 1 inch apart all round the edge. Lift one corner of each pastry flap and fold it over to form a triangle. Line the second plate in the same way with the rest of the pastry.

Mix the flour with the sugar, lemon and nutmeg. Melt the margarine and pour it gradually into the flour, blending with a fork until the mixture resembles crumbs.

Spread two tablespoons of golden syrup over each pastry base and spoon half the lemon

GUID

Most casserole recipes freeze well and no special freezer recipe is needed. As it takes not much more effort and time to make two, three or more times the recipe, it is well worth preparing as large a quantity as possible so that you've one for immediate eating and the rest can be frozen for use in a week or so.

Do remember:

That you will need to cook the casserole for three quarters of the usual cooking time; the reheating will complete the cooking.

Make sure there is plenty of liquid to cover the meat or it may dry out.

Ordinary flour in a recipe may result in curdling during reheating and cornflour should be substituted. Sauces and gravies tend to thicken during freezer storage so it may be necessary to thin them down during reheating.

enough to hold the ingredients together to be pliable and damp. Too much water makes the crust tough, shrinking when baked.

As a general guide you need 1 teaspoon water to 1 oz. flour, although it may be necessary to sprinkle a teaspoonful more water over.

Wrap the pastry in cling film or greaseproof and leave to rest for half an hour in the fridge; this rest period allows the moisture to distribute itself more evenly through the pastry and the gluten in the flour to become more elastic and pliable. The pastry will roll out more easily and will shrink less when baked.

---

mixture over the top of each. Brush pastry with milk.

Place on a baking sheet and bake above the centre of a hot oven, Gas Mark 6 or 400°F/200°C, for 25 to 30 minutes until the pastry is crisp and golden brown.

CASSEROLE OF OXTAIL

Serves 4

| 1 large or 2 small oxtails, weighing about 3 lb. in all |
| 2 tablespoons oil |
| 2 large onions, peeled and sliced |
| 1 lb. carrots, peeled and sliced |
| 1 oz. flour |
| 2 level tablespoons mild paprika |
| 14 oz. can tomatoes |
| ½ pint water |
| 1 beef stock cube |
| 1 level teaspoon caraway seeds |
| Salt and pepper |
| *A 4½ pint casserole dish* |

Set the oven to warm, Gas Mark 3 or 325°F/ 160°C.

ZING CASSEROLES

Add the minimum amount of seasoning; add garlic during reheating — this particular flavouring tends to develop an 'off' flavour very quickly during freezing.

Before freezing remove any surplus fat from the surface to prevent rancidity.

Casserole mixtures can be packed in the freezer in ovenware dishes, in cartons, in foil or plastic-lined casseroles from which the wrapped mixture can be removed for storage.

Do not pack casserole mixtures in very large quantities as reheating will take too long — 2-2½ pint size is about the best.

To use: reheat from frozen; it may be necessary to thaw slightly to get the food out of the package or container.

Add seasoning and extra liquid, such as water or stock, as required.

Fry the oxtail pieces, a few at a time, in the oil until brown all over, then transfer to the casserole dish. Turn the onions and carrots in the remaining fat for a minute or two, then add to the oxtail. Stir the flour into the fat in the pan, then add the paprika, tomatoes, water, stock cube, caraway seeds, salt and pepper.

Cover the casserole with the lid or foil and cook in the centre of the oven for 3 hours. Skim the surface to remove excess fat if to be eaten immediately, and serve with boiled potatoes.

Note: This hotpot is best prepared and cooked the day before, then cooled and refrigerated overnight. The excess fat can be scraped off before the hotpot is reheated for 45 minutes in a moderately hot oven, gas mark 5 or 375°F/ 190°C; or turn the oxtail into a pan, bring slowly to the boil and simmer for 10 minutes.

To freeze: After cooling, skim, pack and freeze. Thaw overnight at cool room temperature, then re-heat in a covered dish in the oven, as above.

HOTPOT

Serves 6

| 1½ lb. stewing steak |
| ½ lb. leeks or onions |
| 2 sticks celery |
| ½ lb. carrots |
| 1 oz. dripping |
| 1 level teaspoon sugar |
| 2 level tablespoons flour |
| ½ pint stock or water |
| 1 large bay leaf |
| A good pinch of ground nutmeg |
| 1½ lb. potatoes, peeled |
| 1 oz. butter |
| Salt and pepper |
| *A 4 to 5 pint casserole dish* |

Cut the steak into 1 inch cubes. Wash and slice the leeks (or peel and slice the onions), celery and carrots.

Melt the dripping, stir in the sugar and fry the meat, a few pieces at a time, until brown all over, then transfer to a plate.

Fry the vegetables in the fat in the pan for 1 to 2 minutes. Stir in the flour and cook gently, stirring all the time, until the flour starts to brown. Pour in the stock or water and bring to the boil, stirring continuously, and boil for 1 minute. Remove from the heat, add the meat, plenty of seasoning, nutmeg and a bay leaf, then spoon the meat mixture into the dish.

Thinly slice the potatoes and arrange them in overlapping circles on top of the meat. Dot them with butter and bake in the centre of a moderate oven, Gas Mark 4 or 350°F/180°C for 3 hours.

To prevent over-browning, cover with foil.

BETTER THAN A CHRISTMAS PRESENT

Sheila was too accustomed to the species
Small Boy to be taken in by tumbled fair hair and innocent-looking
blue eyes. And yet there was something about
Geoffrey that would tug at the strings of the stoniest heart. . .

RED, orange and silver, the fish jerked temptingly, invitingly, on near invisible threads. They swooped in circles, catching now the cold red of the winter sun, now the warm lights already glowing in the bungalow.

Sheila turned the mobile on its cord. After three frustrating weeks puzzling over dubious instructions, she had finally constructed the coloured thing.

By the time she had one-handedly manoeuvred the kitchen stool into position in the lounge, her self-satisfied expression had changed into one of acute agony. The effort of keeping the mobile hanging untangled was giving her arm pins and needles. She climbed precariously on to the stool, looped the mobile over its hook, and stepped back.

The mobile was certainly eye-catching. She considered throwing a small party to celebrate. She preened herself, conveniently forgetting the advice on the side of the kit: "*Suitable for ten to twelve year olds.*"

The door bell rang which meant the usual struggle with the jammed lock. It would have to be someone she didn't know. All her friends were well aware of her problems with her front door. Only several minutes' toil would cause the door to open. Even pronouncing 'Sesame' wouldn't work; Sheila had tried it, often

The stranger had a patient look when she finally saw him. He needed it.

"Miss Nicholls? It's about the playgroup."

The centrally heated air was flowing out into the ungrateful world as fast as the cost of fuel was rising. Sheila invited him in.

By the living-room light she could see that he was thin and pale. His face had a capable look, enhanced by a squarely–chiselled jaw and sensible nose, but the friendly eyes hadn't seen much laughter lately, she thought.

"We've just moved here," he said nervously. "My lad, Geoffrey, is just four. I'd like him to start at your playgroup. If that's possible," he added.

Sheila felt like a dentist, ushering in the next patient. What on earth made him so edgy? "I try to fit children in at once," she explained, aiming at a friendly tone. "People are always arriving or leaving. It isn't worth making a list. Bring him along on Monday. I'm sure he'll enjoy himself."

They stood up together and moved in opposite directions: Sheila, from force of habit, aiming for the kitchen door; Mr. Dawson, a conventional soul, going for the front.

"It's bad luck, you know, using a different door to leave by," he said.

"You need more than good luck to open that door," said Sheila. "Would you care to risk it?"

At the kitchen door, Geoffrey's father found his manners. "I'm Tom Dawson," he said. "Thank you, thank you so much." They shook hands in a formal but friendly manner.

Sheila buttered the hot currant scones while waiting for the kettle to boil. She set the tray precisely – cup, saucer, milk jug, sugar bowl — turned her head to check the kettle and poured the milk carefully on to the work top. 'I need a cat to lick this up,' she thought. 'No I don't. I'd either fall over it or forget to feed it. It'd leave without giving notice.'

Safely settled in the rocking chair, she stared through the mobile into the middle distance and, in planning the next chapter of her new book, forgot all about the Dawsons, father and son.

Continued overleaf

176

G EOFFREY arrived at the playgroup in good time on Monday. His father looked harassed and out of place among the cheerful, gossipy mums. They stood together awkwardly in the entrance.

Sheila straightened her pullover along with her best playgroup-supervisor manner and went to ease them out of the traffic flow into the big playroom. Tom Dawson had shaving cream behind one ear, she noticed, and his shirt collar was all puckered at the points. Probably Geoffrey's mum was in hospital.

"His granny will be collecting him at lunchtime," explained his dad. Ten out of ten.

Geoffrey seemed like many another small boy. He was tidy. 'But not,' thought Sheila, 'for long.' He had the kind of face that invites kindred spirits to join forces in search of mischief. Sheila, being fairly well acquainted with the species Small Boy, was not fooled by the floppy fair hair and virtuous blue eyes, either. She found him a couple of likely companions and started off the morning's activities.

As the days passed, Sheila was increasingly aware of Geoffrey's harassed dad, and began to view the badly ironed shirts and continuing signs of a poorly run home with concern. The leaves from the beeches outside formed a soggy mat underfoot. They put down a carpet of newspaper inside the door, and still Geoffrey came in summer sandals.

"We do have play ouside each morning," she hinted. "Does Geoffrey have wellingtons or lace up shoes? Children's feet get cold so quickly."

Tom Dawson looked horrified. Geoffrey tugged his hand firmly. "I haven't, Dad. Those others I have curl my toes over."

"I'm afraid I've let things get disorganised at home," said his father. "Geoffrey's mother died in February, and we're a bit slow getting back on our feet."

Sheila's toes curled up in embarrassment. "I thought your wife was in . . ." They stared awkwardly at each other.

"He needs a lot of things," said Tom Dawson. "I can slip out tomorrow and fix him up."

"You must take him with you for the shoes," she said urgently. "A good fit is so important."

"That's the trouble. The shop's so busy with Christmas coming, I can't take him shopping."

She felt she owed him something. "I have to go to town tomorrow. Could I take Geoffrey? I'd look after him very carefully."

He looked surprised. "Would you really? Don't you see enough of the children in the mornings?"

"I'd like to," she said. "I'll collect him at two o'clock."

At milk time, Sheila chatted to Simon who ran the banging and sawing group. "Nice kid," Simon nodded. "Not allowed to bang at home. His mum died in February and Granny lives with them."

"You know a lot," said Sheila.

"They live at the end of my road. He's started coming to see me in the afternoons."

Every person has two educations; one which he receives from others and one, more important, which he gives to himself.

Gibbon

N EXT morning, Sheila found Geoffrey in front of the cloakroom mirror. His tongue stuck out sideways in concentration as he squinted down at the zip of a spanking new anorak.

"Did Daddy buy you that?" asked Sheila.

"Mm," managed Geoffrey. The zip negotiated successfully, he took the anorak off with care to stand revealed in all his glory: a royal blue pullover crested with bold white yachts and a pair of neat red cords.

"Wow," she breathed.

He was satisfied. "You're taking me for wellies," he said kindly, "and an ice-cream. I'm going to show Simon."

They found the shoe shop. It was on a corner. Geoffrey looked through one window and Sheila looked through the other, enjoying his face searching for the wellingtons. "I like the red ones," he said, pointing. "Will you have red shoes? Then we'd be the same." He grinned up at her.

After the wellies, Geoffrey decided on black shoes. He stood on a foot measure and wriggled his toe through the sizable hole in one sock. Sheila added to her shopping list. They chose navy lace-ups.

There were too many lights and sparkles in shop windows to hurry over the shopping, but finally they did finish and walked back to the bus stop, hand in hand, firm friends now. Geoffrey had chocolate round his mouth. "Too cold for ice-creams," decreed Sheila. "We'd turn into eskimos."

There was a shop with socks by the bus stop. Geoffrey's taste ran to bright red and yellow diamonds on navy. Three pairs was a good idea, they thought. The counter backs had mirrors in which Geoffrey tried to catch himself sideways. Suddenly, he tugged urgently at Sheila's coat.

"There's ties," he said. "Daddy has to have a new tie, Granny said so." Sheila hesitated. "Granny *said*," insisted Geoffrey.

"Perhaps Daddy likes to choose his own ties." Never fight a losing battle. "Which tie would he like?" They chose a striped one in three shades of blue.

Geoffrey arranged himself comfortably on her lap in the bus, one finger hooked confidingly into her buttonhole. His eyelids drooped, recovered, closed firmly. Sheila watched his face reflected in the window. Tom's chin was like that, and his ears. The eyes must be his mum's, as well as the hair. It tickled against her chin. She kissed the small boy's head and cuddled him closer.

Next morning there was a sticky trail on the floor starting from where Andy spilt the wood glue, and Suzanne flicked red paint over Mary's dress before she had her pinny on. Tom watched Sheila work smoothly through the chaos. An appreciative grin lit his tired eyes, if only she could have seen it.

"We're late because Geoffrey couldn't decide whether he liked the lace-ups or the wellingtons best," he said. "Thank you so much for taking him out. He took ages going to bed for telling me about it."

"He really wants a helicoptor most," she said impulsively. "One that chatters when the blades go round. It suits you," she grinned. "I've never chosen a tie before."

L AST day of term! Sheila arrived early, padding round the playgroup hall, checking the storage heaters, running her fingers over the smooth wood of Simon's manger. The ever present smells of wood and plasticine, powder paint and milk, had an added tang today. Sitting down at the piano, unbuttoning her coat, she considered it. Like very fresh glue and open air and rain. The Christmas tree, of course!

The children were soon bouncing in, excited at the dressing up, nervous when they saw the rows of chairs and imagined their parents in them, watching as they sang and acted.

All the mums came, with their woolly scarves and coughs and boots that left puddles on the floor, and if they sang "Away in a manger" and "O little town" slightly off key, they made enough noise to bring in a few passers-by to join them.

Granny Dawson held Geoffrey's mittened hand. "Have a good Christmas, dear," she said to Sheila. "I'm off to my daughter's on Thursday, so I won't be seeing you until January."

On Thursday morning, still puzzling over Granny Dawson's departure, Sheila was doing careful things with the ingredients for chelsea buns. The dough was rising nicely when Tom rang.

"I — er — bit of a problem," he said. "The district nurse thought I might .. don't know quite ... could you come over? Would you mind?" he asked.

June, the nurse, was one of Sheila's friends. She opened Tom's door ten minutes later, but stood blocking the entrance. "Have you had chicken pox?" she demanded.

Sheila nodded. "Half the children in the area seem to have caught it," June went on. "Lovely Christmas present. Trouble is, Geoffrey's granny has just left to spend Christmas with her daughter, and Tom Dawson has to go to work. Busy time, of course. Come in then," she continued. "Geoffrey's upstairs in bed, and I'm going to trade on our friendship and ask you to look after him. It's either that or hospital, and hospitals are a bit taboo because of his mum being there such a lot."

"Don't break my arm, I need it to write with," murmured Sheila, and wondered how she would finish her Christmas shopping.

Upstairs, Tom looked more distracted than ever. Sheila started organising. "You're both coming to stay with me for Christmas," she said. "You go to work now, Tom. June and I will pack and move Geoffrey and you can collect anything else this evening." With an effort, she left his tie alone.

J UNE packed a case while Sheila collected blankets and pillows. They cleared the fridge and carried Geoffrey to June's car.

In Sheila's kitchen, a towering shape lurked under a cloth, giving off yeasty promises of melt-in-the-mouth deliciousness. Sheila yelped. "My chelsea bun dough!"

June, ever practical, seized a spoon, whipped off the cloth and indulged in some hearty stirring. The dough, ingloriously deflated, lay in the bowl like a burst balloon. "You'll just have to start again," June told it, not unkindly.

They settled Geoffrey and a hot water bottle in the spare bed. June explained the medicine. "Ring me any time. I shall, of course, allay any gossip." She looked prim.

"You horror," laughed Sheila. "You'd better allay *all* gossip. You're the cause of it."

If she could have seen the self-satisfied expression on June's face as she drove away, Sheila might have been less amused and more puzzled. June was quite content with her morning's work. It would not be the first time she had played Cupid in the village.

Simon's mum came in later, part of the conspiracy. "Not sure if he's eating much, but here's his

Continued overleaf

favourite gingerbread men," she said.

"I suppose people will think it a bit odd," Sheila said tentatively, "having them both staying here."

"There's nothing odd about being neighbourly, although some people might try it more often," was the tart comment. "Don't give it another thought. Now, if you need to do any shopping, Simon and I can come in the morning and let you go out."

Geoffrey dozed in the afternoon, allowing Sheila to finish her chapter. She looked earnestly in to the fridge at the left-over chicken casserole. It would be okay, she hoped, with rice and mushrooms.

Tom arrived later than she had expected. He carried, besides a suitcase, a battered and elderly blanket. "It's his comforter," said Tom. "Sometimes he likes to cuddle it. How is he?"

The green pepper and tomato salad was an inspiration. Sheila set a tray with Tom's supper and a small bowl of chicken soup for Geoffrey. In the bedroom, Tom had propped pillows round his son. She saw they were both absorbed in studying a new toy. Leaning the tray against the door, she felt a desperate longing to be invited to share in the game.

"Look, Sheila," said Geoffrey. "Dad's come home."

Later, Tom came to the living-room to watch television with her. "You're so kind," he said. "When I asked June what I should do, she suggested I ring you. I didn't mean you should move us both here."

"I thought I managed rather well. A neat piece of kidnapping, I call it," murmured Sheila.

Very slowly, Tom's worried expression lightened. "Yes, indeed. A really smooth operation."

A T the head of Sheila's shopping list next day was a minimum-iron shirt for Tom, closely followed by a Christmas tree. Three hours, two umbrella jabs and one parking ticket later, she called it a day. "Three French hens, two turtle doves and a partridge in a pear tree," she sang to the red lights.

Holidays were supposed to be leisurely occasions for Sheila. The morning lounging in house-coat, the afternoon researching or writing, the evening entertaining or being entertained. The last person to describe herself as organised, she happily plunged into the bustle that over-worked father and sick child necessitated. "I'll miss them after all this is over," she thought, and knew that even seeing them every day at playgroup wouldn't be good enough.

Fortunately, before Sheila could become utterly depressed, the hurriedly ordered Christmas tree was delivered one morning. Geoffrey, wrapped up fat as a snowman, came to help decorate it with coloured balls and tinsel. There were lights, too, in a lovely tangle of flex, and Tom had brought a bag full of chocolate animals in silver paper and some gold-wrapped chocolate coins.

Then came the serious business of wrapping presents. Sheila was allowed to help wrap Tom's present from Geoffrey.

"What are you giving Daddy?"

"A shirt, look. Will he like it?"

Geoffrey was critical. "It won't go with his tie. It's pink."

Wrapping it was easy. She wrote the label. *"To Tom, Happy Christmas, love from Sheila."* Very conventional, 'Love from Sheila'. Five minutes' brown study later, Sheila decided to send back her diploma in psychology. If she couldn't recognise what was going on in her own mind, she could hardly claim to be able to understand what was going on in anyone else's.

Sheila's Christmas party was always held the day before Christmas Eve. The party paper napkins were white with red and green holly, and robins in the corners. She set out cheese dips, lots of bread and cracker biscuits. There were forks, glasses, salt and pepper, celery in a green jar. She even remembered the chutney.

"Can I come and look?"

"Sorry, Geoffrey, I was miles away. Yes, of course."

"Don't you have plates?"

She squeezed him. "Yes, when I remember them." She gave him an apple and some cheese to munch in bed. "No biscuit crumbs," she said sternly. He giggled.

Tom arrived, looking exhausted. "Only one more day, then you can start thinking about the January sales," consoled Sheila, waiting to help with his raincoat.

Tom groaned. "If I didn't own the shop, I'd resign," he said gloomily. "I was so fed up with the place, I didn't even stop to wash my hands. Look at them."

She held up his hands for inspection. "Disgraceful," she condemned. "Let me see the backs."

"Much too dirty for a schoolmarm," he said. His eyes were grey. "You're very sweet. Did you buy some mistletoe? I feel I'd like some."

"Promises," she murmured.

He liked the way her lips twitched. He discovered a dimple he couldn't resist. Sheila buried her face in his tie, so he had to raise her chin with one grubby hand to kiss her again. When Tom finally went to see Geoffrey, Sheila hugged his raincoat all the way to the cupboard.

Supper was on trays as usual: steak and kidney pie, followed by rice pudding with raisins. Geoffrey had mashed potato and carrots in flower shapes with the gravy.

"Can I get up for the party?" he asked, spooning up carrots in gravy.

"Party?" echoed Tom. "Oh, no! You told me this morning, but I forgot completely. What time does it start?"

"In about half an hour," Sheila responded cheerfully. "And, no, spotty face, you may *not* get up."

W HEN the last of the partygoers had been eased out of the door, Sheila found Tom stacking the dishwasher with plates and glasses."You," he said, "have worked like a Trojan. I should say, 'Sit down, darling, I'll clear this up', but I have to confess that I haven't the remotest idea how this machine works."

"Easy." With both his arms round her, it wasn't that easy.

"I've already made coffee," he said proudly.

He carried the tray into the lounge while Sheila switched on the dishwasher. The menacing grumble followed her until she bravely closed the door on it.

"You're making this a splendid Christmas for Geoffrey," Tom said. "He's happier than he's been for a long time, in spite of the chicken pox. Last year wasn't much fun for him, poor love."

"It's a splendid holiday for me, too," remarked Sheila. She slumped in a chair and watched the mobile. "I haven't written a word all week. Don't tell my publishers."

"I suppose you'll have plenty of material now," Tom said vaguely. "All these people, sick boy, nurses, plenty of drama there."

"Gracious, no. I have to be very careful what I write about. In a village like this, I'd be defending libel suits all the time if people thought I was writing about them. I write what you might call historical detective stories. I do lots of research on things like household accounts and letters, real

---

Silence is not always tact and it is tact that is golden, not silence.

Samuel Butler

'spadework' as the detective novels have it. The publishers like them and they're very interesting to write, but don't let me get on my hobby horse." She reached for her coffee.

"You do everything so efficiently."

"Hardly," she laughed. "You should see the mounds of scribbling I chuck out. It doesn't come easily at all. It's just fun, and even now exciting when I see my name in a bookshop."

He waved a spoon. "I don't really believe you. The first day I came here, you terrified me. Everything in the room was just exactly right. That mobile is, for instance, quite fiendishly clever. What can't you do?"

"Can't hold a cup still," muttered Sheila, in an acute state of nerves. "Anyway, my cousin is an interior designer, though not at *all* exotic, and she 'did' the bungalow for me. The mobile came out of a kit." She stirred her coffee for a long time before remembering the sugar. "I had to train to be a playgroup teacher, of course. That was an uphill struggle, I can tell you." That made him laugh as she had known it would.

"I really thought . . ."

For some reason he held the coffee pot out towards her.

"You've just given me some," she said helpfully. He looked vague. Wisely she rescued the treasured pot.

"I really thought –" he tried again – "when Jo died, well, I couldn't believe I'd find anyone else. You're not like her, not a bit. I can't compare you two at all, but you've come to mean such a lot to me." He fidgeted with the tray. "You'll think I'm just grateful," he said miserably.

She felt deliciously superior. "Try me," she invited.

He looked up suddenly. "You little horror. You know quite well what I want to say. I bet you've got your answer all ready, too."

"You won't know unless you ask," she teased. He took a deep breath.

Geoffrey woke and called out.

"Come on. Unless you want to change your mind," said Tom, hauling Sheila up from her chair. "Got something to tell you, sleepy head," he said to his son. "Want to sit up? Sheila's going to marry me and be Mummy for you. How about that?"

Geoffrey pulled Sheila out of Tom's protective clasp. His hair tickled her chin as he gave her a kiss.

"You're the best Christmas present of all," he whispered.

THE END

Victoria, the Rag Doll

A very special favourite from Jean Greenhowe, our toy designer.
Victoria, the 24-inch doll with a delightful dress sense — see colour
photo on page 155.

Trim, attractive and very lovable is Victoria, a 24-inch rag doll with a complete outfit of clothes. These comprise a dress with full sleeves and a long, flouncy skirt, a frilled over-pinny, a cape and hat for outdoor wear, plus a full-length petticoat and underskirt.

You can make the doll from pink cotton fabric (with printed cotton fabric for body, upper arms and upper legs, to give the look of Victorian-style underclothes).

You will need: 20 cm (¼ yd.) of 91 cm (36 in.) wide pink cotton fabric for head, lower arms and lower legs; the same amount of printed cotton fabric for body, upper arms and upper legs; ½ lb. of kapok, or Terylene stuffing (for a washable doll); 25g of 4-ply wool for hair; two 1 cm (⅜ in.) diameter black or dark blue buttons for eyes (substitute circles of felt if the doll is for a very young child); black and red thread for facial features; pink lipstick for colouring cheeks; 1 m (1⅛ yd.) of frilled lace; metric graph paper marked with 1 cm squares.

Note: 3 mm (⅛ in.) seams are allowed on all doll pattern pieces. Join fabrics with right sides facing unless otherwise stated.

To make your patterns: From our scaled-down patterns on page 184 copy all the outlines on to graph paper, square by square (each square on our patterns =1 cm). Include all lettering and marking on your patterns. Cut out the graph

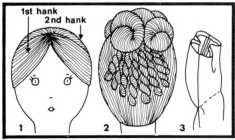

1st hank
2nd hank

1   2   3

paper patterns and use them to cut out fabric pieces as directed below.

To make the head: From the pattern cut out two head pieces in pink cotton, marking dotted line positions on to wrong side of both pieces, and facial features (including topmost dot) on right side of one piece only.

Bring arrow-shaped dotted lines at neck together and stitch to form a dart on each head

piece. Join head pieces all round edges and across neck edges, leaving a gap at top of head for turning and stuffing. Turn right side out and stuff very firmly, then turn in and slip-stitch remaining raw edges together.

Work eyelashes and eyebrows in black thread and mouth in red thread. To sew the buttons in place, thread a darning needle with very strong thread, take it through from back of head to cross which marks eye position on face, thread on button then take needle through to back of head again. Knot thread ends tightly to depress the buttons slightly into face. Colour cheeks with lipstick, then place a paper tissue over cheeks and press gently with a warm iron to seal colour into the fabric.

The hair is made from several hanks of wool. For the first hank, wind the wool 24 times round a piece of card 33 cm (13 in.) long. Pull it off the card and sew centre of hank to forehead to cover the spot marked there. Take each end of the hank down sides of face and sew them together at the back of neck. Make another hank as for the first; sew the centre of hank behind centre of first one (see diagram 1), take ends straight down back of head and sew to neck. Make two more hanks and sew them in place each side at back of head, so it is completely covered.

For ringlets, make small hanks of wool by winding six times round a 15 cm (6 in.) length of card; pull off card and twist ends in opposite directions then bring them together so the wool forms a twist. Make several ringlets and sew ends to back of head, about 10 cm (4 in.) up from neck line of hair. Use remaining wool to make a twisted hank for the bun and sew this to cover top of ringlets (see diagram 2).

The body. Cut two pieces of printed fabric 13.5 by 21.5 cm (5¼ by 8½ in.). Join pieces round edges, rounding off corners and leaving a gap at one short end for turning and stuffing. Trim off corners, turn right side out and stuff firmly, then turn in and join remaining raw edges.

Sew head to one end of body, ladder-stitching dotted line on neck to the body, pulling the stitches tight to make it very firm. Make a waist 7.5 cm (3 in.) up from lower edge by using strong thread and a darning needle and taking a stitch from one side seam of body through to the other side; pull thread up tight and fasten off.

The arms. Use pattern to cut out two lower arm pieces, each from double thickness of pink fabric. From printed fabric cut four pieces 6.5 by 13.5 cm (2½ by 5¼ in.) for upper arms. Join one short edge of each printed piece to upper edge of each lower arm to form complete arm. Join arm pieces in pairs, leaving upper edges open. Turn right side out.

Put a little stuffing in hands and thumbs, then machine stitch through hands, making dividing lines for fingers and thumbs. Pull thread ends through to one side of each hand, knot them and sew ends into hands. Stuff lower arms to within 1 cm (³/₈ in.) of where the fabric joins, then machine stitch through arms at join. Stuff remainder of arms to within 5 cm (2 in.) of top edges. Turn in raw edges 5 mm (¼ in.), bring seams together, then fold and pleat each edge (see diagram 3), and oversew arms securely to body.

The legs. Use pattern to cut out two lower leg pieces, each from double thickness of pink fabric. From printed fabric cut four pieces 7 by 12.5 cm (2¾ by 5 in.) for upper legs. Join upper and lower leg pieces as for arms, then join complete legs in pairs, leaving upper and lower edges open.

Use pattern to cut out sole from double thickness of pink fabric. Place a sole inside each leg at lower edge, A to heel, B to toe, then sew soles in place. Turn legs right side out and stuff firmly to within 1 cm (³/₈ in.) of fabric join at knee; bring seams together and stitch across through legs. Continue stuffing upper legs to within 1 cm (³/₈ in.) of top edges; turn in raw edges 5 mm (¼ in.) and slip-stitch them together, then slip-stitch tops of legs to body at front, 2.5 cm (1 in.) up from lower edge of body.

Trim with lace as shown in the photograph, sewing a strip of frilled lace right round each leg, about 1 cm (³/₈ in.) above the knee.

UNDERSKIRT AND PETTICOAT

You will need: 90 cm (1 yd.) of fine white cotton fabric; 20 cm (¼ yd.) of narrow elastic; 3.30 m (3⅝ yd.) of lace edging; 4 snap fasteners; 70 cm (¾ yd.) bias binding.

Note: 5 mm (¼ in.) seams are allowed on all clothes pieces. Join fabrics with right sides facing.

The underskirt. Cut a strip of fabric 28 by 91 cm (11 by 36 in.). Hem one long edge and sew on lace trim. Hem other long edge and thread through elastic to fit waist. Join short edges of skirt.

The petticoat. Cut strips of fabric as follows: one 15 by 91 cm (6 by 36 in.) for top of skirt, and two 16 by 91 cm (6¼ by 36 in.) for skirt frill.

Use pattern to cut out one bodice front from folded fabric, placing dot-and-dash line to fold in fabric. Use complete pattern to cut out a pair of bodice back pieces. Trim 1 cm (³/₈ in.) off neck edges and 5 mm (¼ in.) off armhole edges of bodice pieces. Sew four rows of lace trimming down front of bodice. Turn in straight edge of each back bodice piece 1 cm (³/₈ in.) twice, and hem. Join front to back bodices at shoulder seams. Bind armhole and neck edges, then join side seams.

Join the short edges of skirt strip for 7.5 cm (3 in.), taking 2 cm (¾ in.) seam. Press seam to one side. Gather upper edge to fit lower edge of bodice and sew in place. Join short edges of skirt frill strips. Hem and sew lace trim to one long edge, then make two 3 mm (¹/₈ in.) tucks, 2.5 and 4 cm (1 and 1½ in.) above hem. Gather remaining raw edge of frill to fit lower edge of skirt and sew in place. Sew snap fasteners to back.

THE DRESS

You will need: 90 cm (1 yd.) of printed cotton fabric 91 cm (36 in.) wide; 4.20 m (4⅝ yd.) of ric-rac braid; 4 snap fasteners.

To make: Use pattern to cut out one bodice front from folded fabric, placing dot-and-dash line to fold in fabric. Use complete pattern to cut out a pair of bodice back pieces in fabric. Use sleeve pattern to cut out two sleeves, placing dot-and-dash line to fold in fabric each time.

Turn in and hem edges of bodice back as for the petticoat. Join front and backs at shoulder seams. Set sleeve tops in armholes, gathering top edges of sleeves between dots to fit; clip underarm curve of seams.

For wristbands, cut two strips of fabric 9 by 14 cm (3½ by 5½ in.). Sew one long edge of each band to lower edge of each sleeve, gathering sleeve edges to fit. Sew two rows of ric-rac to each band, 2.5 cm (1 in.) from seam. Join side, sleeve and wristband seams. Turn raw edges of

Continued overleaf

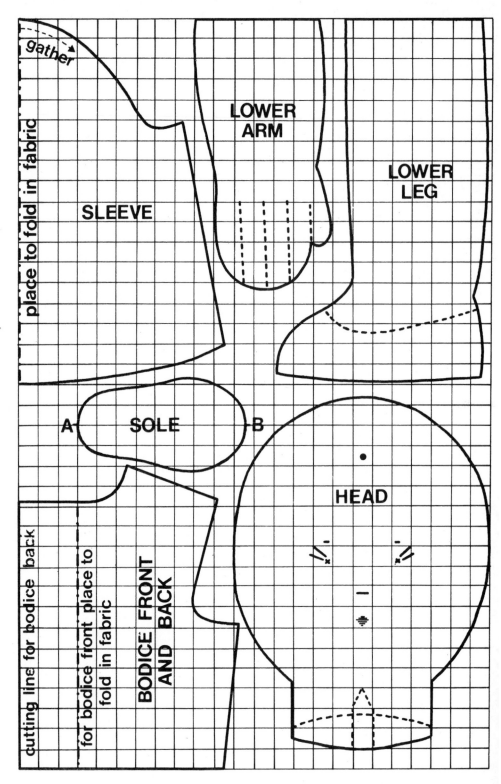

gather

place to fold in fabric

SLEEVE

LOWER ARM

LOWER LEG

A SOLE B

HEAD

cutting line for bodice back

for bodice front place to fold in fabric

BODICE FRONT AND BACK

30.5 cm (2½ by 12 in.). Fold in half down length, right side out, and press. Gather long raw edges to measure 18 cm (7 in.). Cut two strips of fabric 2.5 by 18 cm (1 by 7 in.), bind gathered raw edges of frills with these, then sew on lace edging.

Sew a frill to each side of bib, overlapping raw edges of bib, with the short raw edges of bib and frill ends level. Sew bib and frill ends to inside of waistband at centre front. Sew other ends of frills to inside of waistband at back so that frills fit over shoulders.

The hat. On the interfacing draw then cut out a 25.5 cm (10 in.) diameter circle; from the centre cut out and discard an 11.5 cm (4½ in.) diameter circle. Cut away and discard one quarter of the remaining shape. To cover this brim cut a strip of fabric 15 by 61 cm (6 by 24 in.). Sew lace edging to right side of strip, about 5 cm (2 in.) from one long edge. Fold strip in half down length, right side out, and sew long edges together taking 3 mm ($^1/_8$ in.) seam. Now slide and ease this tube of fabric on to brim shape, with raw edges of fabric at inside edge of brim. Overlap and stitch short edges of brim, then turn in one short raw edge of fabric strip and slip-stitch over other short raw edge.

For crown of hat, cut a 20 cm (8 in.) diameter circle of fabric. Gather edge to fit inner edge of crown and sew in place. Bind raw edges with bias binding. Sew another length of lace edging round hat where crown and brim meet, then sew lace edging round edge of brim.

wristbands 5 mm (¼ in.) to inside and slip-stitch to top of wristband seams.

Clip curve in neck edge, then cut a strip of fabric 19 by 4 cm (7½ by 1½ in.) for neckband. Sew one long edge of band to neck edge, then turn in remaining raw edge and ends and slip-stitch in place over neckband seam.

For the skirt and frill, cut and make as for petticoat but omit the tucks. Instead stitch two rows of ric-rac to lower edge. Sew snap fasteners to back edges of bodice.

PINAFORE AND HAT

You will need: 90 cm (1 yd.) of cotton fabric, 91 cm (36 in.) wide; 4 m (4⅜ yd.) of cotton lace edging; a 25.5 cm (10 in.) square of stiff interfacing or buckram for hat brim; a scrap of bias binding or bias strip of fabric.

The pinafore. For the skirt cut a strip of fabric 20 by 91 cm (8 by 36 in.). For the frill cut two 10 by 91 cm (4 by 36 in.) strips. Join the frill strips along short edges to form one long strip. Hem one long edge and sew on lace edging. Gather other long edge to fit one long edge of skirt strip and sew in place. Gather other long edge of skirt until it measures 30.5 cm (12 in.). Hem remaining short raw edges.

For waistband cut a strip of fabric 6.5 by 91 cm (2½ by 36 in.). Turn in raw edges 5 mm (¼ in.) all round and press; then fold strip in half down length and press. Slip top gathered edge of skirt inside waistband at centre and pin in place — the remainder of the waistband at each side is for tying in a bow at back. Join edges of waistband all round, catching in top of skirt.

For apron bib, cut a strip of fabric 7.5 by 12.5 cm (3 by 5 in.). Fold in half to bring the short edges together; tack them together. For each shoulder frill cut a strip of fabric 6.5 by

CAPE AND SHOES

You will need: 20 cm (¼ yd.) of 91 cm (36 in.) wide fabric; a small piece of felt for shoe soles; 2.20 m (2⅜ yd.) of bias binding; a fabric scrap for interlining shoe uppers; UHU glue.

The cape. For a pattern, cut out a 41 cm (16 in.) diameter circle with a 12.5 cm (5 in.) diameter circle removed from centre. Fold this in half and use semi-circle as pattern to cut fabric cape.

Gather inner neck edge to measure 18 cm (7 in.), then round off lower corners.

For collar cut a strip of fabric 25.5 by 4 cm (10 by 1½ in.). Gather one long edge to measure 18 cm (7 in.), and round off other corners. Bind ungathered edges of collar with bias, then sew gathered edge of collar to gathered edge of cape, with right sides of both uppermost. Bind all remaining raw edges of cape and collar, then sew bias to neck edge at each side for ties.

The shoes. Use pattern to cut out two soles from felt. Use dotted line on lower leg for upper cutting line for shoe pieces. Glue a fabric scrap to wrong side of shoe fabric, then cut two pairs of shoe pieces. Join front seams, bind upper edges, join back seams. Sew on soles as before. Sew bias bows to shoe fronts.

An amusing short story by Constance Hayes

THE WAY TO A MAN'S HEART

The letters fell on her desk thick and fast... letters of complaint from a very angry and frustrated gentleman who was obviously no Cordon Bleu!

The Editor
Practical Help for Everyone

Dear Sir,

I was persuaded to buy the January issue of your magazine by the invitation on the cover: "Learn to cook yourself the perfect meal at home. We can teach you how to produce the tasty, the succulent, the appetising — no previous cooking experience necessary."

As one who eats out whenever he wants anything tasty, succulent and appetising, you can see why I was tempted. And there was another reason. My nearest restaurant is a Chinese establishment and, much as I like Chinese food, I was somewhat alarmed, when shaving the other morning, to discover a distinctly Oriental cast to my eyes.

So tonight I followed the instructions on page sixty-three of your January issue and prepared my first "Complete Meal for One." While it spent its scheduled sixty minutes in the oven I took a shower, set the table attractively as suggested, and indulged myself in the luxury of a pre-dinner drink — all in anticipation of the perfect meal to follow.

Well, I am writing to tell you it was a complete and unmitigated disaster. In fact, it was more dried up than an Egyptian mummy. I don't use that comparison lightly either, as for the past ten years I have been employed by the Museum, where there is an extensive Egyptology Department.

Obviously there is some error in your instructions. Not only did this carelessness cost me £1.02 in wasted ingredients, but it also meant that when I finally arrived at my friendly Chinese restaurant, two hours later than usual, I found myself among complete strangers, all my friends having eaten and gone. I must admit I use the term "friends" rather loosely — nodding acquaintances may be nearer the truth. Nevertheless, there are certain people I look forward to seeing there, and smiling at across the chopsticks, so to speak. It was not the same without them.

I should be pleased to have your comments and the corrected text for page sixty-three at your very earliest convenience.

Yours faithfully,
Henry G. Brown.

February 5th

Dear Mr. Brown,

Your letter has been passed on to me as I am the Cookery Editor of *Practical Help for Everyone*.

I am very sorry to learn that your first attempt at cooking yourself the perfect meal at home was not a success. However, after checking the instructions most carefully, I can confirm that the text is correct in every detail.

I wonder if perhaps your ablutions or pre-meal drink lasted rather longer than you thought, so that you inadvertently exceeded the cooking time?

May I suggest that you follow the old adage "If at first you don't succeed, try, try, again"? After all, Rome was not built in a day — and nor are good cooks.

I do hope you will have more success next time, and that this will restore your faith in *Practical Help for Everyone*.

Yours sincerely,
Charlotte Wright.

February 11th

Dear Ms Wright,

Thank you for your letter. Against my better judgment, I followed your advice and tried again.

I regret to tell you that the result was exactly the same as before, though I can assure you the cooking operation was timed as accurately as an Apollo moon launch.

This experiment cost me a further £1.06 (which is a measure of today's inflation) in wasted ingredients, and another late (and lonely) meal at the Chinese.

I hope that this will now convince you that there is some error on page sixty-three of the January issue of P.H. for E. Kindly re-check and let me have the corrections by return of post.

I feel perfectly justified in asking P.H. for E. to reimburse me with my out-of-pocket expenses, which now amount to £2.08.

Yours faithfully,
Henry G. Brown. *Continued overleaf*

February 14th

Dear Mr. Brown,

Thank you for your letter. I can assure you that I check each recipe scrupulously before it is published in *Practical Help for Everyone*.

To eliminate any possible doubt as to accuracy, I have once again checked every stage, from preparation to the finished product, and I can only reiterate that the instructions published on page sixty-three of the January issue are correct in every detail.

If you are sure your cooking time was as the recipe stated, then either you are not setting the thermostat of your cooker correctly, or it is faulty.May I suggest that you check this latter point with an oven thermometer? Should the thermostat prove to be at fault, you will need to seek expert advice from either your Gas or Electricity Service Centre.

I do hope you will overcome the problem soon. Please don't lose heart.

Yours sincerely,
Charlotte Wright (Miss).

February 19th

Dear Miss Wright,

I have done as you suggested and checked my gas cooker with an oven thermometer (which, incidentally, cost me £3.97).

At the gas setting which you gave for the "Complete Meal for One" in the January issue of P.H. for E. the thermometer registered 425°F or 220°C, whichever you prefer.

As you are the expert, perhaps you would be kind enough to let me know if this is satisfactory.

Yours sincerely,
Henry G. Brown.

February 23rd

Dear Mr. Brown,

Well, it seems we have tracked down the source of your problem. As you will see, the cooking instructions on page sixty-three of the January issue state Gas Mark 5 or 375°F/190°C electric should be used.

As your test gives you a temperature reading in excess of this, it is obvious that your thermostat is defective (assuming, of course, that you used the thermometer correctly).

May I suggest that you ask your local Gas Service Centre to send an engineer to verify this and, hopefully, correct the fault?

Wishing you every success.

Yours sincerely,
Charlotte Wright (Miss).

March 2nd

Dear Miss Wright,

I am writing to let you know that the Gas people sent a Service Engineer last Friday. This took a considerable amount of organisation on my part and even necessitated my taking a half day's leave.

It also cost me some £7.82 for a ten-minute visit. This was the time it took for the Service Engineer to verify my readings, confirm your diagnosis of a faulty thermostat and pronounce his verdict of thumbs down on the cooker.

It seems it's such an old model that spare parts are no longer available. In fact, the engineer said it is as old as he is — if not older.

The only suggestion he offered as an alternative to my buying a new cooker, was that if I could pinpoint the degree of error on the thermostat accurately enough, I might be able to adjust the settings given in the recipes accordingly. But he said that there could be unquantifiable fluctuations as well as unknown variables in the gas supply. To be honest, he didn't sound at all hopeful about it.

What do you advise?Thank you for all your help.

Yours sincerely,
Henry G. Brown.

Dear Mr. Brown,

I was so sorry to learn of the Gas Board's inability to supply a replacement thermostat for your venerable cooker.

Any attempt to allow for the irregularity in your present appliance by adjustment of the gas setting would, I am sure, prove most unwise.

I would most strongly advise you to purchase a new cooker or, if this proves too expensive, at least a good reconditioned one from your Gas Showroom.

I do hope that when you get a replacement model you will have no further problems. Let me know if I can help in any further way.

Every good wish to you.

Yours sincerely,
Charlotte Wright (Miss).

March 8th

Dear Miss Wright,

I have been doing a little research into the overall cost to date of my purchasing the January issue of *Practical Help for Everyone*. I find it amounts to:

	£ p
Cost of magazine	45
Wasted ingredients — 1st attempt	1.02
— 2nd attempt	1.06
Oven thermometer	3.97
Visit of gas service engineer	7.82
Total	£14.32

I am beginning to think that buying your magazine may well prove to be my most costly mistake of the year, especially as I have decided to take your advice and purchase a new gas cooker — which isn't going to leave me much change out of £300.

I hope you will agree with my reasoned view that P.H. for E. is — even if indirectly — involved in this ever-increasing drain on my financial resources. This prompts me to ask whether, as a sort of goodwill gesture, you would assist me in choosing the new cooker?

I do hope you will agree. Thanks again for all your help in the past.

Yours very sincerely,
Henry G. Brown.

P.S. I have bought the March issue of P.H. for E. in anticipation.

March 15th

Dear Charlotte,

It was so nice of you to invite me back to your flat for a meal after our visit to the Gas Showroom on Thursday. I agree that the January recipes from P.H. for E. are delicious. And how strange that we should have known each other, in a manner of speaking, for so long — you at your table for one in the Chinese and I at mine! What a small world.

I must admit that you were the last person I expected to be an "eater-outer" — but then, if you've been involved in cooking and recipes all day, I suppose it's no fun going home to start again at night.

Incidentally, I had a letter from the Gas people yesterday. The cooker we chose is what they term 'temporarily out of stock", and it may be anything up to twelve weeks before it is delivered. I can't wait.

Obviously I can't try out my culinary skills without a cooker, so may I return your hospitality and take you out for a meal? Perhaps we can *share* a table at the Chinese, for a change.

Please say yes.

Henry.   *Continued overleaf*

May 14th

Dearest Charlotte,

Thank you for all the marvellous times we've had together — what wonderful weeks these have been — not to mention all those meals we've cooked together. I feel I've had a preview of all the P.H. for E. recipes for the rest of the year.

And, as you say, it makes all the difference when you've someone to cook for and eat with — especially when that someone is very, very special.

Darling, I'm so happy — so pleased that I bought the January issue of P.H. for E. Though as you pointed out, goodness knows what the resulting expenditure will finally add up to! Tell you what, we'll sit down and work it all out fifty years next Saturday, when we'll be celebrating our Golden Wedding Anniversary.

Darling, I love you.

Henry.

P.S. I went round to the Gas Showroom this afternoon and cancelled the cooker. But I still think we should have let them deliver it and then stored it in the garage. After all, it did bring us together.

THE END

' *Constance Hayes, 1982*

Even on "ordinary" days we can find so much to be thankful for

A THOUGHT FOR EACH NEW DAY

YOU HAVE HAD the experience, I am sure, of certain texts from the Bible staying in your mind and cropping up at various times, perhaps quite unexpectedly, or recalled to help you at a time of need.

One such quotation that I personally like to think over sometimes is a verse from one of the Psalms (118:24): *"This is the day which the Lord hath made; we will rejoice and be glad in it."* It comes from a Psalm of Thanksgiving which was part of the Jewish Hymn of Praise and has a special place in worship at times of national commemoration and on important feast days. This may have been the psalm which was sung by our Lord and his disciples before they left the upper room at the conclusion of the Last Supper.

Originally it was probably composed as a song of thanksgiving for victory over the enemies of Israel, but its relevance to the great acts of God in the ministry of Jesus Christ, and especially to his victory over death, will be obvious. Supposing, however, that we thought over this verse, not only on days which have for us a personal or religious significance, but on "ordinary" days, for I am quite certain that there will be something in the day, by way of opportunities of service or some experience of human goodness, that should make us thankful.

Come to think of it, it might be a very good plan to take these words with us into each New Year, and to begin each day with this simple act of praise.